ADVANCE PRAISE for *Patient*

Patient but no patience describes the personal journey of Victor Levin in the early days of modern oncology and the development of research and treatment of brain tumors. His journey started in the era before CT and MR brain imaging became available, at a time when all established tumor treatments were still to prove their role in the field of brain tumors. The memoir describes the development of the early clinical trials, combinational regimens including the still important PCV schedule, the mathematical modelling of the penetration of compounds into brain tumors using animal models, pharmacokinetics of agents used in brain tumors, the early clinical studies in this field, the development of nitro-sourea's, studies on the interactions between anticonvulsants and alkylating agents, the change from whole brain radiotherapy to involved fields radiotherapy, the concerns about radiotherapy induced cognitive deficits, development of tyrosine kinase inhibitors: it's all there.

There is a vivid description of the first gatherings of brain tumor investigators and the birth of neuro-oncology groups, and of the first early brain tumor centers with many of the names that changed our field. This autobiography is a very personal document, honest, about ambitions, achievements, and disappointments. In many ways Victor Levin was a pioneer and a leading figure in the field of neuro-oncology, many of the topics he worked on and of which he understood the importance of are of relevance and still with us. But the book is also a time capsule; for those who want to understand the history of the early beginnings of the field this is a must read.

—**Martin van dent Bent**, MD, PhD, Professor in Neuro-Oncology, Erasmus University Rotterdam and Head Neuro-Oncology Unit at Erasmus Medical Cancer Center, the Netherlands

This memoir is an insightful commentary of Dr. Levin's personal and professional academic journey that is conveyed with thoughtful reflection and honesty. While highlighting his successes and achievements, he also bravely describes the challenges he faced and his own shortcomings. For anyone in the field of Neuro-Oncology, there are so many lessons to be learned, especially about bringing to reality a vision to improve the care we provide to our patients as well as the importance of education and professional community. In addition to his accomplishments in building programs at UCSF and at MDACC, his contribution to the formation of the Society of Neuro-Oncology is a testament to his incredible passion, dedication, and generosity.

—**Susan Chang**, MD, Professor, Department of Neurosurgery and Co-Program Leader of the Neuro-Oncology Program in the Helen Diller Family Comprehensive Cancer Center, University of California San Francisco

This book offers an intimate portrait of the life, accomplishments, and at times struggles, of a pioneering clinician-scientist who devoted his career to improving outcomes for patients with brain tumors. Interwoven with personal anecdotes and touching patient vignettes, Victor Levin sets out the foundations of the modern-day field of neuro-oncology, chronicling his efforts, as well as those of his many colleagues and trainees, to combat what remains one of the most challenging and complex areas of cancer medicine. In order to know where we are going, we must first understand where we are from, and in *Patients but no Patience*, Dr. Levin offers us a rich historical context upon which future generations of multidisciplinary neuro-oncology cancer researchers can build upon to realize a more hopeful and promising future for patients suffering from devastating CNS tumors.

—**Chas Haynes**, JD, Executive Director of the Society for Neuro-Oncology

This is a remarkable memoir of a man who is arguably the founding father of modern neuro-oncology. The seasoned practitioner will be encouraged by the slow but steady progress Dr. Levin made throughout his half century career, whereas the early career physician will have a role-model to pursue novel therapies driven by science and clinical trials to provide the practice-changing therapies that will eventually cure brain cancer. A must read for clinicians and basic scientists alike who are interested in central nervous system neoplasia.

—**Edward G. Shaw,** MD, MA, Emeritus Professor of Radiation Oncology and Geriatrics, Wake Forest School of Medicine, Winston-Salem, NC, and Past-President, Society for Neuro-Oncology

The seven years I spent with Victor in San Francisco and Houston was the brightest time in my life. Through his targeted remarks and swift actions, I was able to learn from his pragmatic optimism and problem-solving abilities. I joined Victor's UCSF lab in 1988. It was just around the time that he was starting the first in the world effort to try and develop an inhibitor of the c-Src tyrosine kinase and he was putting all his energy into it. The time I spent with Victor in San Francisco and Houston were the brightest time in my life. In retrospect, a multidisciplinary program to develop inhibitors ofc-Src was a tremendously advanced idea at the time. This memoir tells of his motives and inspiration when he started the project. He has always had amazingly advanced and original ideas and the ability to solve difficult problems and learning them from him has changed my life significantly. This memoir describes how the philosophy and capabilities underlying my lifelong mentor's ideas and actions was constructed before we met and what he continued to accomplish until he retired in 2021.

—**Hideyuki Saya,** MD, PhD, Emeritus Professor, Division of Gene Regulation, Institute for Advanced Medical Research, Keio University School of Medicine, and President of Japanese Cancer Association

Patients but no Patience

My Path as a Neuro-oncologist

VICTOR A. LEVIN, MD

Best wishes to David

V. Levin

MADERA CREEK PRESS

ISBN 978-1-7374502-6-9

CoverPhoto/ Illustration:
The cover art is adapted from the painting "Mt. Tamalpais from King
Mountain" by © Kathleen Lipinski. www.emerylipinski.com

Book Design: Jim Shubin, BookAlchemist.net

Disclaimers

I have tried to recreate events and conversations from my memory.
To protect privacy, in some instances I have changed the names of
patients, identifying characteristics, and details such as physical
properties, occupations and places of residence. In other cases, the
patients and/or family have given permission for the name of the
patient to be included.

Although the author has made every effort to ensure that the
information in this book was correct at press time, the author does
not assume and hereby disclaims any liability to any party for any
loss, damage, or disruption caused by errors or omissions, whether
such errors or omissions result from negligence, accident, or any
other cause.

Dedication

This book is dedicated to my wife. Ellen, and our children, Lisa and Jason, who supported and enabled me to pursue my neuro-oncology path for more than fifty years. It is also dedicated to my colleagues and post-graduate trainees who joined me on my neuro-oncology journey and from whom I learned to be a better physician and scientist.

Contents

Preface

"I shall be telling this with a sigh
Somewhere ages and ages hence:
Two roads diverged in a wood, and I
I took the one less traveled by,
And that has made all the difference."

—*The Road Not Taken* by Robert Frost

For more than two decades, many of my colleagues have encouraged me to write a book that describes the history of neuro-oncology, a field that grew from a hyphenated new word four decades ago to become a recognized clinical subspecialty and worldwide clinical and research framework, today. Initially, I resisted writing about this nascent field because the growth and maturation of neuro-oncology so closely paralleled my own academic career that it would be difficult to separate them in my writing. But I decided to take the challenge and while writing a history of neuro-oncology, I decided to tell my story, as well.

A pragmatic optimist! That is how I see myself today and what I have been throughout my life. This approach to life and its challenges has guided me as a physician caring for people with central nervous system (CNS) tumors, as a laboratory and clinical researcher charting new research directions and as a program leader and department chair. Being a pragmatic optimist is not without penalty and frustration—frustration when unsuccessful in achieving my goal and the penalty of not quitting when failure seems reasonable. Frustration has been a driver of my career and the reason I founded a conference for those working in brain tumor research, developed and directed the first National Cooperative Drug Discovery Group grant, guided, and helped organize three CNS

Anticancer Drug Development and Discovery Conferences, a multi-disciplinary neuro-oncology society, and several companies hoping to stimulate advances that would provide better treatment options for patients afflicted with CNS tumors.

Having had the good fortune to help create the important and fascinating field of neuro-oncology, this memoir describes who I am, why I am so driven, how my family helped and encouraged me, how my contributions became a driving force in the field and how my obsession with finding new drugs to treat primary infiltrative CNS tumors led to exploring different avenues for the discovery and development of novel anticancer agents in the field. This memoir is the story of my neuro-oncology journey and the path I continue fifty-four years after starting on it at the National Cancer Institute (NCI) in 1967.

In telling my story, I share relevant recollections of my childhood, my education, initial forays into laboratory research, postdoctoral research at the NCI, my neurology residency at Massachusetts General Hospital, work at The University of California San Francisco (UCSF) and the Brain Tumor Research Center (BTRC), in its early years, and my contributions to The University of Texas, MD Anderson Cancer Center (MDACC), Department of Neuro-Oncology and the Brain Tumor Center. Referring to records that I kept and relying on memories I hold dear, I have included stories of some of my patients and have attempted to document the establishment and first years of the International Brain Tumor Research and Treatment Conference and the founding of the Society for Neuro-Oncology.

In addition, I thought that writing my memoir would help future generations understand the origins of programs like the International Brain Tumor Research and Treatment Conferences, the Society for Neuro-Oncology, and it would provide a context for my contributions to these and the neuro-oncology programs at the UCSF and the MDACC.

Writing about the history of neuro-oncology so late in the trajectory of my life has been fun and enlightening. I see some past events differently through the lens of time. It is a joy and revelation to learn new facts about past events or new insights about myself. I feel that some aspects of the history of neuro-oncology evolved through my strength of purpose and hard work. Conversely, chance and opportunity were also drivers that might deserve more credit than I sometime gave them.

On my life's path, I met and helped train and mentor many neuro-oncology fellows and young faculty. I tried to help treat and diagnosis thousands of adults and children with CNS tumors. I met and befriended many patients, as well, as their families and care-givers; from these experiences on my journey I learned to be a better physician and mentor.

1

Prologue

I have been interested in the nervous system since I was a young teen. Part of my interest came from curiosity and an interest in scientific inquiry. Another part came from family expectations. According to my mother, Gertrude, in 1941, when my grandmother, Rosie Ottenstein, first lifted me out of the bassinet, she proclaimed me to be "Victor Shmictor the surgeon." As a Jewish boy growing up in Milwaukee in the 1940s and 1950s, there were many life options to consider based on people I met and family role models, but early on there was also underlying family pressure and an assumption I would become a physician. I had two uncles who were physicians, one a general practitioner and the other a neurosurgeon. Both served in World War II, one in North Africa and other in Europe. Another uncle, a dentist, also served in the war stateside. Interest in diseases of the nervous system was encouraged by my uncle Jules Levin, a well-regarded neurosurgeon in Milwaukee. He often shared stories of some of his patients and their maladies that he saw during the war and in his Milwaukee practice. In retrospect, family pressures and examples of family members working in medicine, modeled my life's path.

Curiosity drives the scientist and the scholar. I was a reader from an early age. I read comic books, especially *Classics Illustrated*. I read my dad's *Boy Mechanic* series, and other magazines my parents bought or subscribed to, like *Life* magazine, *Readers Digest*, as well as a small encyclopedia we had at home. I read magazines I subscribed to or borrowed from the school or public libraries such as *Popular Science, Mechanics Illustrated* and *Boy's Life*. I also read books that I borrowed from the school and public libraries. I especially liked historical fiction and books about the American West. In my teens, probably because I took Latin, stories about the Roman Empire interested me. I also gravitated to biography and books about explorers, like Ernest Shackleton and Roald Amundsen, and how each made their way over land to Antarctica. My tastes were eclectic and ranged from the Three Musketeers and Swiss Family Robinsons to biographies of Harvey Cushing, Ben Hecht (an unusual Bar Mitzvah present), and Michelangelo novels by Aldous Huxley and Antoine de Saint-Exupery.

Because I liked building things, I read many how-to books. I recall reading one multi-volume set over and over. I went from creating things in wood to making electronic devices. One day I decided to make a crystal radio. My mother agreed to take me downtown to an electronics parts store. There, I found all the parts I needed and paid for them with money I earned cutting grass, shoveling snow for neighbors, and selling greeting cards in my neighborhood. It was great fun to build the radio, tune into a station, and, using headphones, hear the news, music, and even the sound of static, all of it proof that I had been successful building my first crystal radio. Eventually, I became a ham radio operator (K9ELL), fixed family and neighbors' radios and TVs, and built an analog computer for a high school physics class. My parents encouraged me by giving me the freedom and opportunity to try new things. Little did I know how childhood experiences would inform the approach I took in the research I would eventually do.

Reading provided a vision of the greatness of life and what could be accomplished by the willingness and ability to reach for a dream. Dreaming and imagining were a big part of my life. The more I read, the more I imagined and dreamed at night about going to places I read about and building something there. *The Swiss Family Robinson* series in *Classic Comics* was one of my favorites. Jules Verne's *Travels to the Center of the World* ran a close second.

—⚏—

From earliest memories, when I imagined being a physician, I saw more than being a clinician. I wanted to have an outsized impact on a medical field. I wanted to make a difference that transcended patient care alone. I had no idea how I would do this or what I was going to do to accomplish that. I had no roadmap. I only knew, as many adolescents think they know, that I would achieve that goal if I applied myself. This is where randomness or serendipity, the opportunities encountered, and choices you make transform your life's path.

In life, we have choices to make virtually every minute of every day. Most choices are made without deep thought, such as drinking a glass of water when we are thirsty, eating food when we are hungry, going to the bathroom when the need arises, and resting or sleeping when we are tired. Much else during our lives reflects our conscious goals, perceptions, attitudes, and even the intuitions we accumulate through our lives, a result of unaccountable interactions we have with people who surround us and the planet we live on. In all this complexity, it may be an oversimplification to view people too narrowly as being either inherently optimistic or pessimistic, as seeing the glass half full or half empty. For an optimist, failure is not a deterrent; much remains to be attempted. For the pessimist, failure is expected, so why try? Then as now, I have looked at failure not as a defeat but as a learning experience.

2

Family Roots and Growing up in Milwaukee

My family roots trace back to hardworking Russian immigrants on both sides. My paternal grandparents were Joseph Levin and Anna Toybe Rymland, who emigrated to the United States in 1905. Married in their early twenties, they settled in Milwaukee, Wisconsin. My grandfather was not afraid of trying something new. He worked as a stockyard hand, cloth presser, peddler, farmer, saloon owner, grocery store owner, and, in later years, was a property owner. My father, Jack Don Levin, was born in 1907, the eldest of five children. As a result of my grandfather's many careers, my father was exposed to various environments growing up. He experienced living on a farm, helping in a family-owned saloon, and, later, working in a family-owned grocery store. He told me he learned to swear in three languages after working in his parents' polyglot saloon in the south side of Milwaukee.

Going to college and getting an education was important to my family, especially to my father whose parents were intelligent but unschooled immigrants. My father graduated as a Civil Engineer from The University of Wisconsin-Madison in 1927 at 20 years of age and was the first in his family to graduate from college. While a student, he worked his way through school doing various jobs that included shoveling coal into the furnaces of campus buildings. He was on the wrestling team at the University of Wisconsin and liked to play tennis. He was a life-long student who enjoyed learning and remaining active. He learned to ride a 10-speed bicycle at the age of fifty and continued riding a bike well into his 70s. He was an intelligent and idealist man who was interested in everyone around him.

My father had a good analytical mind and was gifted in mathematics and had a prodigious memory. While in college, he had been encouraged to leave engineering and earn a PhD in physics. I think he would have done very well, in that field, as he was a good teacher and liked people, but in his youth, he liked the idea of adventure and being footloose to work on large construction projects and experience different cities and places in the United States. He had a wanderlust and a desire to see and experience work and life outside of Wisconsin. He enjoyed meeting new people from different places and trying to understand, in a very gentle manner, what brought them to where they were at the time.

So, after graduation, my father went to Chicago and worked as an engineer building their subway system and may have worked on the Montgomery Ward building before joining the United States Treasury Department as a Civil Engineer in 1931. This led to building border stations along the US-Canada frontier and exposure to the mountains in the west where he learned to hunt elk, deer, and bear. He was also involved in the construction of post offices for the government in the South and Midwest from 1927 to 1943.

My maternal grandparents were Rudolph and Rose Ottenstein who emigrated to the United States as teenagers where they met and married in Milwaukee, Wisconsin. My grandfather worked as a fruit and vegetable peddler and worked out of an old Ford truck when I was a child. My mother, Gertrude Marilyn Ottenstein, was born in 1913 and was the eldest of three children. My mother did not attend college since she felt obligated, because of the Depression, to work during her teens and into her twenties to help support her parents and ensure that her two brothers, Harold, and Bernard, would be able to afford college and then medical and dental school. It was a different time and place, otherwise I am sure she would have gone to college herself. Family pictures show a good-looking young woman with a happy disposition. She had a great singing voice and sang in local dance bands in the 1920s.

In 1935, my parents met and married in Milwaukee, Wisconsin. I was born in November 1941, in Milwaukee, Wisconsin and was a younger brother to Laurie, my sister who was four years older than me. My father's government work and various assignments working on construction at a woman's prison and Army base as well as building health facilities led to moving and living in Illinois, Ohio, Iowa, Nebraska, Oklahoma, and Texas. From stories I was told, my mother tired of living in a different city every year and wanting to live near family, convinced my father to move our family of four back to Milwaukee, permanently in 1943. My father took an engineer position with Froemming Brothers in their shipyard supervising construction of destroyer escorts (they built 27 ships between 1943 and 1945). He advanced in the company as the post-war intent of the company was to move into building construction, a goal upended by the death of the senior Froemming brother after the war ended. As a result, and because of limited opportunities for a civil engineer in Milwaukee at the time, my father took a job as treasurer of a wholesale appliance company in 1946.

Our family of four moved to our house, a duplex on 48th Street in Milwaukee in 1944. I vividly recall the day a moving van arrived at our house in Milwaukee. My mother wanted me out of the way. I was two-and-a-half years old. "Ride your bike," she told me, and she suggested I ride my tricycle on the sidewalk of our block. My father had adjusted the bike for me when we were living in Brownwood Texas, adding blocks to the pedals so I could reach them with my short legs.

Unafraid, or too innocent to know better, I went off on my ride. I made a turn from the house where we now lived at 48th and Locust Streets and continued my way along the sidewalk. I must have crossed a street and gotten disoriented as I could not figure out how to get back. Probably crying in fear at my dilemma, I attracted the attention of a nice lady who figured out where I belonged and set me back on course. I continued to pedal the tricycle, found my way back to 48th Street and to our new home and told my mother that a lady had helped me cross the street. My mother was angry with me, although she must have been relieved, as well. She didn't forbid me from riding in the neighborhood anymore, she simply told me not to cross streets alone. Looking back, I realize my parents rarely refused my requests to do something or create something. They were supportive of my efforts and were not worried about failure. From this event and other similar ones, I learned that success can be preceded by failure and that failure was no big deal; it was just part of the learning process.

My mother was a very accomplished and positive person who was well-organized and capable. She was generally upbeat about life and the obstacles we endured. She was not one to complain and was always there when I needed her. To save money, she sewed clothes for my sisters and pajamas for me. She knit sweaters and scarves to ward off our cold Milwaukee winters. She baked cookies and pastries and canned fruit and jam. She also played golf until she was 85 years old. My mother was social and liked most people, although she would freely voice opinions about people and events she disagreed with. She liked to play bridge and occasionally Mah-jongg with friends. Over the years that we lived on 48th Street, I remember her hosting occasional dinners, picnics, and life events with her friends. My mother cherished family and had a wonderfully supportive large family that was part of my life as a child and continues in my memories today.

—⚭—

Being the son of a civil engineer was a lot of fun and a big influence on my development. At an early age, I learned to measure with a ruler and tape measure, how to use a right-angle straight edge, and draw rough plans on paper. I learned how to build using a hammer and nails at four years of age and how to use a coping saw before starting kindergarten at Sherman School. My Dad would let me use any tool so long as he was convinced that I knew how to use the tool safely. My maternal grandfather, Rudolph Ottenstein, was a fruit and vegetable peddler who worked out of an old Ford truck and always had enough wooden crates from the fruits and vegetables he sold to supply me with wood for my many projects. I used a claw hammer to carefully remove the nails. Holding the thin wood away from the ends of the boxes, I was careful not to break it. I would keep the nails I removed and straighten them for future use.

One summer before starting kindergarten, I built my first "airplane." While my airplane, made from wood crates, had a rudimentary wooden propeller and even a place to sit, I was disappointed that the plane would not take off as planned. It was at that point that reality collided with imagination. Nonetheless, seated in the airplane made of fruit boxes, I imagined all sorts of travel, places I could see, and things I could do.

I also remember vividly, in kindergarten, when given the task of making something for Mother's Day, while the other children in the class were drawing on colored paper to make cards for their mothers, I opted to make a wooden tray for my mother. Today, it is difficult to imagine a kindergarten teacher allowing a student to build a wooden tray using a coping saw, hammer, and nails and, later, apply varnish to protect the wood. My teacher at Sherman School was Ms. Richter. Whether she thought I would ever succeed and finish the tray I never knew, but I did finish the tray and in time for Mother's Day. My mother used the tray for over 4 decades. Fortunately, I happily survived the existential "risk" of hitting my thumb with a hammer, cutting myself with a saw, or inhaling toxic fumes from an open varnish can.

Both my parents had a positive outlook on life and gave me

confidence to attempt anything I set my mind to. I remain grateful to have had parents who nourished and influenced my life the way they did. In addition to intellectual curiosity, gratitude has always been a large part of my disposition.

—∿—

In 1946, my sister Deborah was born. As a middle child and boy between two sisters about four years older and younger, we did not often play together. In addition, my older sister Laurie, had some serious medical issues at ages eight and sixteen that kept her bed-ridden for months at a time and added extra stress to the family which probably forced my independence earlier than was typical at my age. As a result, I spent a good deal of time on the asphalt playground of the Sherman Elementary School. There I learned to play chess, kick ball, hopscotch and ringers, a game that used rubber gaskets from Mason jars that we would throw on a board with hooks hanging on it. Older boys might gamble nickels playing ringers for points and we would watch them for a while before boredom led me to more action such as playing a running game on the playground. As I grew older, I played slow pitch softball and, eventually, fast pitch softball. I gravitated to pitching as I liked the physical activity better than waiting for a baseball to reach me as an infielder or outfielder. Our baseball teams were organized by age range on the playground and supervised by high-school students who worked part-time on the playground. For a couple of years, our team was quite good, and we competed against other play-ground baseball teams. Unlike today, parents were never in sight on the playground and did not drive us to games at other schools, so we biked to them on our own.

3

Teen Years and Boy Scouts

When I was about thirteen, my dad decided to get back into construction and took a job with a local real estate company that wanted to expand into construction. There, he found more happiness. He built small multi-story office and apartment buildings and organized and created a facility in Cudahy (Wisconsin) to build three-bedroom houses in a factory and deliver them by truck in the early morning and place them atop prepared sites with full concrete basements. As a teenager, I worked at his building sites and later at his factory where he built the houses. In the beginning, it was mainly cleanup work at the construction sites, but over the years I learned many useful skills. I worked during school vacation and summer break and progressed from working as a laborer, planting trees and bushes and laying sod, to insulating walls and attics of houses, helping to dry wall rooms, roof houses with shingles, and periodically, drive a twelve-wheel tandem dump truck. I enjoyed working on my dad's construction sites and found it, at times, hard work, but also great fun. I also learned to interact with a variety of people from different walks of life who were older than I was. The work had a side benefit, it paid well, so my parents thought a regular allowance for me was unnecessary.

—⁓—

Some of my fondest memories of my teen years are being with my extended family of relatives and family friends. My maternal Ottenstein grandparents were laid back, more social and religious than my paternal Levin grandparents. The Ottenstein half of the family were easier to be with and we spent more time with them. They were more gregarious, liked to tell jokes and laugh and always had a good supply of food for a growing boy.

My maternal uncles, especially Harold Ottenstein, a general practitioner, had a great sense of humor and was always fun to be around as I grew up. He and his wife, Ruth, had one child, a daughter, Carol, who was six years younger than me. I always found it easy to talk with my uncle, especially in my teens. He was generous with his time and, once I was in high school, he would regale me with stories of strange diseases he had encountered. I could tell he was pleased when he made a difficult but correct diagnosis. I also saw his humanity when I visited his office for minor medical problems or needed a physical for a sports team. When I was in college at The University of Wisconsin-Milwaukee, I would sometimes stop by his office that was on the way home from the campus just to visit for a couple of minutes. Once, before Christmas, he asked me to join him for a ride. We went to visit three of his patients, each with children at home. We brought them bags of groceries, a turkey or ham, and some small presents for their children. Harold told me about the families, what kind of work they did and if they had been laid off or hurt and unable to work. What impressed me was he had been doing things like this for years, but I doubt anyone else in the family knew about it. This was, to me, an example of a physician who cared for his patients in a holistic way.

—※—

While family and friends remained important to me growing up in Milwaukee, Scouting had a profound effect on me and my parents, especially my father. In 1948, when I was seven years old, my mother signed me up for Cub Scouts and became a Den Mother, sharing the responsibility with another mother, whose son was in our Den. In 1952, at age 11, I became a Boy Scout in Troop 1, a troop that my father and some of the fathers of boys in Sherman School started although my dad had never been a Boy Scout himself. He nevertheless knew a great deal about the Boy Scout movement as he had helped his younger brothers when they became scouts. In later years, because of his contributions to leadership training in the Milwaukee County Council of the Boy Scouts of America, my dad was awarded the Silver Beaver award. He remained active in scouting leadership roles until he died at age 77.

Scouting provided many opportunities for me. I enjoyed striving to achieve goals, solving problems, using my hands to create things, and being part of group activities. One goal I set was to earn the Eagle Award, which I did before my 14th birthday in 1955 when I became an Explorer Scout. By then, many of my friends had dropped out of scouting to pursue other activities, but I persisted because of the opportunities the program afforded me, and I enjoyed the outdoors. At that time, the Explorer program goals were for young men to enjoy a sense of adventure in the outdoors, learn how to get along socially with others, be of service to the community and explore lifework possibilities. Being goal driven, I worked hard to earn the Explorer Silver Award before my fifteenth birthday. This award was akin to the Eagle Award in Boy Scouts, but I thought easier to attain. About this same time, I was elected to the Order of the Arrow, a Scouting program that was more like a fraternity in that it had special handshakes and somewhat secret activities, all based or related to Native American lore.

In 1957, I attended a National Boy Scout Jamboree in Valley Forge as a senior patrol leader for youngsters from different communities in Milwaukee and its suburbs. With the title came responsibility and expectations and it further opened my eyes to what one person can do within a group to help young boys achieve their goals. Each experience and opportunity taken in my early life informed to enable future paths I took.

13

My last activity as an Explorer Scout happened in the winter of 1958. I was invited by the leadership of the Milwaukee County Council to be part of a committee of Explorer Scouts and leaders to organize *Operation Snowbound*, a winter weekend exercise to rescue victims of a simulated air crash in a forested area near Milwaukee. At the second meeting, I was asked to be leader of the group. Some of us on that trip did not come from families that ice fished or hunted wild game in the countryside, so we lacked proper boots, parkas, hats, and the type of sleeping bags needed to stay warm when winter temperatures dropped below zero let alone to -20 F below zero, the temperature that we experienced the Saturday we set up our tents and camped outside in the snow. To make *Operation Snowbound* a success I had to convince Milwaukee County Explorer Scout troops to participate. We also had to come up with some clever equipment solutions for those scouts without proper equipment so they would feel comfortable participating in Operation Snowbound. For the exercise to be successful, we had to improvise. For instance, many of us lacked proper insulated boots so wore three pairs of thick socks inside galoshes to keep our feet warm. We wore two pairs of gloves on our hands, and if we did not have an extra pair of gloves, we wore socks on our hands inside the gloves. Some wore two hats to stay warm. I think most of us slept in our clothes with a blanket inside the sleeping bag to stay warm.

It was a challenge to help organize *Operation Snowbound* and an even greater challenge to be responsible for many aspects of the winter event. I recall my father and other adults being there to help us, but we appreciated that they stayed in the background and let us do as much as we could without their help. We pitched tents of different sizes, made outdoor latrines, cooked meals, and had competitive winter games. Again, creating an event and helping to carry it out successfully was a wonderful experience that supported my confidence and belief that anything was possible.

Additionally, scouting programs helped me learn how to lead and work with people of different backgrounds, religions, ethnicities, and levels of competence. It prepared me to attempt goals that transcended my own narrowly focused life. I have always believed that if you think your research program has a chance to cure some brain tumors, you have to project confidenceand optimism. So, I would argue, my experiences in scouting helped prepare me for various kinds of survival tests in live.

In the summer of 1955, I was confined to home bed rest because of viral pneumonia. My uncle Harold, the family general practitioner, advised a summer of inactivity. Besides growing four inches that summer, I read a great deal. One book, *Wind, Sands, and Stars* made a great impression on me. This book by Antoine de Saint-Exupéry, a famous French aviator, was a memoir comprised of interconnected essays drawn from his experience as an international postal pilot during the 1920s to 1930s, when international flight routes were being established and flying was a risky venture. After crashing in the mountains, he wrote, "To be a man is, precisely, to be responsible." Saint-Exupéry added, "It is to feel, when setting one's stone, that one is contributing to the building of the world." Being a romantic at heart, those words of Saint-Exupéry formed a primary challenge in my life. Doing something that needed to be done, even though difficult or messy to achieve, was, I believed, an obligation to others and to society. I always felt that my father followed that same credo.

In junior high and high school, I became interested in how the nervous system and especially the brain worked. How did we form new memories? Why can we form some memories quite easily while have so much trouble memorizing other material such as schoolwork? Sports made me aware of big differences in athletic ability. I wondered how much of that disparity was due to visual acuity, response time (reflexes), and coordination and how much could be learned by some people but not by others? I also wondered how much of creative activity was acquired in life or innate in some individuals?

To better understand the nervous system, I went to public libraries and bookstores to read about physiology, neuroanatomy, and psychology. I read books about Sigmund Freud, Carl Jung, Harvey Cushing, Michelangelo, Julius Cesar, and other greats. While my curiosity increased, I learned little other than that the brain was too complex for me to parse effectively at my age and level of education, especially with the limited amount of factual scientific information that existed in the 1950s. In some ways, I was accumulating too many facts with too little knowledge, a problem I would also experience in my first year of medical school. Reading and learning are not always coupled, especially when young, to grasp all the complexities needed for comprehensive understanding.

Even as a youngster, I wanted to be a physician and do research that would positively influence many people rather than individual patients. I also realized how important leadership skills would be. Leadership opportunities abounded in the Boy Scouts, Explorer Scout and Order of the Arrow. I learned from them and by observing physician uncles interact with patients and their families and watching my father and others manage workers in his company. I realized that few people working alone can accomplish as much as a group can together under the aegis of good leadership. Early life experiences and observations forged my beliefs that almost anything is possible, and that failure is not an endpoint of defeat, but an opportunity to learn, and that people working well together can accomplish a great deal. This belief system created the cornerstone of who I am. I wanted to leave a footprint in the path of life.

Throughout my life, failure was never a stopping point, but occurred as it does in most lives. I learned from failure and moved on. Metaphorically hiding under the bed in defeat was not a winning tactic. I tried to instill that philosophy while mentoring pre- and postdoctoral students, young faculty members, research nurses and administrative assistants. Completing a task and fulfilling a goal was satisfying but not a dwelling place. There was always another goal to achieve. The fun in life has always been moving forward and doing new things that added value to life.

I have always been an optimist, even as a small child. I believed, even expected, that I could do anything I set my mind to if I put in a good effort. Of course, this is not completely true as I would learn. I discovered limitations in my ability and understanding in relation to sports, school, and interpersonal relationships. While I was better than most of my classmates at sports, there was always someone better than me. This awareness usually stimulated me to renewed effort and lowered my expectations. As I found external limits, I set internal ones as well. In academics, I took the same position. I needed to excel, but rarely felt pressured to be the best at a given subject. I did need, however, the satisfaction of achieving goals I set for. In my teens years these included getting a good or better grade in a class, the Eagle Award in Boy Scouts, the Silver Award in Explorer Scouts, getting on a basketball or track team, becoming a ham radio operator, building an analog computer for high school physics class, learning how to drive a stick-shift car and a dump truck, learning how to insulate a house, or fix a TV set.

17

4

College Years, Medical School, Marriage, and Internship

I began my undergraduate studies at the University of Wisconsin-Milwaukee (UWM). For the first two years of college, I lived at home. This was for economic reasons, and I did not see any real downside since most of my friends also planned to go to UWM and live at home. Most of my boyhood friends expected to go on to graduate school. UWM was a great educational decision since most of our courses were taught by faculty professors and not teaching assistants or hired lecturers. Fraternities were important, especially because I was living at home, and they sponsored dances and provided opportunities to play intramural sports such as two-hand touch football and basketball.

As I planned to apply to medical school during my third year of undergraduate study, I was taking science courses and their laboratories every semester. It was through my introductory chemistry laboratory that I had my first serendipitous contact with my wife to be. It was fate, *bashert* in the Jewish tradition, as we were assigned to our laboratory benches in alphabetical order by last name. Because Ellen's last name was Mendelson, she sat on a bench to the right of me two-days a week for the whole semester. On my left was a friend who also had an interest in her, but I pursued and eventually, we started dating when she had a break in her busy social schedule.

Ellen moved to The University of Wisconsin-Madison for her third year of undergraduate study because the courses required to complete her major were not offered in Milwaukee. Consequently, I transferred to Madison for my junior year, as well. While Ellen and I liked being together, there were family pressures, especially from my mother. My mother lived through the depression and seen couples with their lives ahead of them dropping out of college because they had unexpected children. Because of this external pressure and the move to The University of Wisconsin-Madison for our third year of undergraduate study, we broke up for a short time, but I was persistent, or, perhaps, as Ellen would say, "unrelenting."

Pursuit of Ellen was assisted by my decision to room with Herb Oxman, a college friend from UWM. We found a small ground-floor unit to rent on a street that passed nearby Gilman House, where Ellen was living. I did not know this when we secured our rental, but proximity made it convenient to plan my walk to classes to pass by Gilman house or run into her along the walk to classes. I was strongly goal driven, in love as in academics, and was unwilling to give her up.

Ellen was studying for a bachelor's degree in Medical Technology. Her coursework included many classes I would eventually take in medical school. I always thought her coursework was harder than mine, a truth reflected by the fact that each year, graduates in medical technology went on to medical school at the UW and elsewhere. To Ellen's dismay, technological progress made this very important field of study obsolete in the decades that followed.

During my undergraduate years at The University of Wisconsin, I became enamored with psychology, especially physiological psychology, where I thought true knowledge would be found. This led me, in my junior year, to take a research course with Jerome S. Schwartzbaum, PhD, testing rats with amygdaloid legions to see how they responded to aversive stimuli. I worked with a post-doctoral fellow, Michael H. Kellicutt, on this project, which was completed by the end of the semester and led to a peer-reviewed publication. This was the only publication in my career that, after putting in months of work, I declined an opportunity to co-author. From what I recall, I wanted to get home to my summer medical research job at the Allen Bradley Medical Research Foundation of Marquette Medical School (today it is The Medical College of Wisconsin). There, I worked on wound healing in an electric field and learned surgical techniques to operate on rats and dogs.

—⁓—

In the fall of 1962, I entered The University of Wisconsin Medical School after three years of undergraduate study. I made mistakes that first semester and my grades suffered as a result. I read too much and did not study efficiently enough to earn good grades on required medical school tests. I was driven more by medical curiosity than a desire to get good grades. Given that perspective, my first year, especially the first semester, was difficult and challenging. Fortunately, by the second semester my study habits improved along with my grades.

Ellen and I decided to marry after our UW graduation as her graduation coincided with my undergraduate graduation in June 1963. Three-year premedical students received their BS degrees after completing their first year at The University of Wisconsin Medical School. We were married on a Saturday night at the Milwaukee Jewish Community Center. Because of Ellen's Clinical Laboratory one year internship requirement at The University of Wisconsin Hospitals, she could not miss any days of work, so we had a short two-day honeymoon in Chicago over the Labor Day weekend and then drove back to Madison so she could complete her internship.

After completing her clinical internship and passing the state licensing exam required for a practicing Medical Technologist in Wisconsin, Ellen took a research position as a Project Associate in The Departments of Biochemistry and Neurosurgery working in the research laboratory of David Gilboe, PhD, an Assistant Professor of Biochemistry in the Department of Neurosurgery. Dave had been her biochemistry professor as an undergrad. This job opportunity worked out well for both Ellen and me, as Dave was a very nice man and a good mentor. I got a summer research job with Dave during that summer before my sophomore year in medical school. My project was to study amino acid changes in the blood of uremic dogs I had surgically nephrectomized and kept alive by peritoneal dialysis. The plan was for me to analyze, over my school year, the plasma I had collected for amino acid changes using the new technique of thin layer chromatography that I had learned. As sometimes occurs in research, something unforeseen happened, the deep freeze where the samples were being kept suffered a power failure over a weekend and all sample were lost and I was unable to complete the experiments I had worked so hard on during the summer before my sophomore year. Fortunately, I had other research opportunities in his laboratory during the summer and vacations before my junior year, as well that led, in time, to two publications.

In the summer of 1964 after my second year of medical school, Ellen and I took our belated honeymoon and first vacation. We drove our used light green Chevrolet Corvair from Madison to San Francisco, California, camping and visiting many National Parks along the way. We visited Ellen's girlfriend and roommate, Susan Holtzman, who had married a physician a couple of years my senior, and who was working as a radiologist at the Alameda Naval Base near Oakland, California. On our trip, we saw the Badlands, Mt. Rushmore, Zion Park, Bryce Canyon, and Yellowstone Park, where we had snow and cold weather in July that forced us to stay in a small cabin at the foot of the Grand Tetons. After we returned from our trip, my father then told us that one summer in Montana there was a blizzard on July 4th in Yellowstone that led to one or more deaths. Fortunately, we lacked that knowledge before our trip, and just managed our way through the cold and mild snow.

On our way back to Madison from our California adventure, we stopped at Las Vegas before visiting the Grand Canyon. Out of curiosity, we stopped at a casino on the strip. As midwestern kids we had never been to a casino. I think we lost a dollar or two on the slots and then ventured outside for a walk around the strip before heading back to our car. The Corvair, like many cars of that vintage, did not have air conditioning and the temperature in Las Vegas in late July can reach more than 100 degrees. While walking around Las Vegas we forgot that we had purchased two bottles of Chablis that we had left in the back of the car. We had purchased them after a wine tour at the Beringer Winery in St. Helena, California. When we returned to the car and opened the car door, the unmistakable aroma of white wine permeated the inside of the car. Both bottles had blown their corks because of the heat and the pressure of the bottle contents sent wine all over the back seat. Fortunately, it was a white wine and so, with a little water, the seat looked fine, but the aroma prevailed for days. Being cautious, we travelled most of the day with the windows open to air out the car and we stayed under the speed limits to avoid explaining the wine smell to a state trooper if we were pulled over for exceeding the speed limits.

During my junior year in medical school, I was feeling confined and wanted a distraction from my medical school curriculum. Luckily, I saw an adult education class that offered oil painting at night once a week for beginners. I had never tried oil painting, but I prided myself on having some artistic ability as I had done pen and ink drawings of buildings, boats, and hands that showed some competence. Ellen and I both signed up for the course that was being taught by an older artist named Calder, who lived in Madison because his son was on the art faculty at The University of Wisconsin.

He taught the technique of the old masters based on layering of colors starting with drawing in charcoal and painting with umber and progressing through the palette of colors as needed. Our class was limited to painting inanimate objects and still lives. I was fascinated by the development of shadows in folds of material as it required a color such as Prussian blue to be layered on after umber before the final color to allow the darkness of the shadow to show through. My last painting was based on a post card sized picture of an actual six foot tall painting by Francisco de Zurbarán entitled *St. Francis of Assisi in His Tomb*. It depicts a standing monk contemplating a skull he is holding in his hands. I had seen the painting at the Milwaukee Art Museum, and I thought it would be good practice to paint a facsimile of the painting on a thirty-inch canvas as an example of my ability to create believable shadows and folds of a cloth garment. It was eventually completed to my satisfaction and that of our teacher. The oil painting was framed and hung in our apartment and later in other abodes until Ellen decided that it was too dour a painting to hang in a home with children. While the painting resides today in a box in storage, both of us felt that taking the painting course was a wonderful experience and had provided a much-needed distraction from my studying and her research work.

In the fall of 1964, I applied for a Cerebral Palsy Fellowship that would allow me to accept a Neurology Clerkship at the National Hospital at Queens Square in London for the summer of 1965. Most of my classmates did general medicine preceptorships in community hospitals around the state of Wisconsin, but I was already thinking about the neurosciences and especially neurosurgery at the time, so the National Hospital clerkship was much more appealing to me. The Cerebral Palsy Fellowship provided partial monetary support for the trip to London. Upon receiving word that I had been awarded the fellowship, Ellen applied for a job at the National Hospital at Queen Square in their Department of Special Chemistry that was run by a well-known neurochemist, John

Cummings. She was successful getting the job which helped to pay for our living expenses in London. So, we were able to spend a wonderful summer in London working hard during the week and traveling by foot, train, and bus during weekends to visit places in London as well as other cities that we could reach by train and still be back at work by Monday morning.

In the middle of my junior year of medical school, Dave Gilboe approached me after speaking with one of his best friends, Vincent T. Oliverio, PhD, a senior faculty member in the Experimental Therapeutics Branch of the National Cancer Institute (NCI). Dave Gilboe and Vince Oliverio had remained friends since Vince had been a Project Associate in Oncology (postdoc) at the McArdle Laboratory for Cancer Research at The University of Wisconsin between 1955 and 1959. Because of my research in Dave's laboratory and his strong recommendation, Vince suggested to Dave Rall, MD, PhD, that he offer me a Research Associate position in the Experimental Therapeutics Branch of the National Cancer Institute (NCI) upon completion of my internship in 1967. As I found out later, these positions were normally given to young physicians after completion of a residency, not after an internship.

At the time of the offer, I did not know much about the National Institutes of Health (NIH) and the National Cancer Institute (NCI) and its opportunities, but Dave thought the position would allow me to do research in areas that might interest me. I think Dave believed I should solidify my research career before completing a residency that might make that path harder to achieve later. Having a research position at the NCI after internship would turn out to be a pivotal opportunity and prelude to my career.

By the beginning of my senior year in medical school, the Vietnam War had escalated and drafting young physicians finishing internships started to increase. As a result, the number of Research Associate positions offered by the NIH was reduced as the NIH was part of the Public Health Service. I remained lucky, however. David Rall, being Head of the Laboratory of Chemical Pharmacology, for whom I would be ostensibly working, made me a Staff Associate so that I would be guaranteed the NCI position. Over the years, I came to appreciate how very fortunate I was and how important that Staff Associate position was to my early academic career. That job combined with research studies and publications it produced led to important opportunities over the ensuing four to five years.

By the end of my junior year in medical school, I thought neurosurgery was my calling. I liked doing research in the brain and was convinced I had good surgical skills based on surgeries I had done and my experience assisting in neurosurgery as a medical student. I looked for surgical internships with Melvin Marcus, another medical student in my class who, incidentally, became an internationally known academic cardiologist and professor at The University of Iowa Medical School prior to his untimely death in his late fifties from colorectal cancer. I recall that Mel, a gifted pianist, could play the piano at a local Madison bar some nights to make extra money while simultaneously studying from a medical school textbook. He was a pleasant, kind, and gentle man, a legend in our class and someone I remember fondly.

By the middle of my senior year, I decided to chart a new course. I had reservations about pursuing a neurosurgical career. I realized that I really liked doing research and wanted to continue doing medical research into diseases of the central nervous system and did not think being a neurosurgeon would allow that time and privilege I would need to succeed in research and remain a practicing physician. I also believed surgery under the microscope was going to be common in the future and was concerned I did not have good enough binocular vision to excel at microscopic surgery. As a child I had been diagnosed with a strabismus called amblyopia ex anopsia, and it had not been surgically corrected when I was a child. To some adults and physicians in Milwaukee in the 1940s, muscle surgery to correct a strabismus was considered a cosmetic procedure and, as such, was performed more on girls than boys. As a result of not having corrective surgery, my eyes did not fuse properly, and my right eye function was suppressed in my brain. As an example, in Boy Scouts I realized that I could not shoot a rifle right-handed because I was unable to sight using my right eye.

Because I changed my internship preference from surgery to medicine so late in the academic year, I had to apply for internships to places without having internal medicine recommendations or time for interviews. As might be expected, I did not match to my first three choices. Fortunately, I was accepted at St. Louis City Hospital, a Washington University-affiliated program where I worked six days a week and was on call every other night for the year, July 1966 to the end of June 1967. Being a city hospital carrying for many non-paying and poorly insured patients at the dawn of the Medicare program, the city hospital received inadequate funding and was understaffed. While we had very few nurses, we did have some of the best medical residents and faculty I could ask for at that stage in my training. The residents I worked with were frequently from the Barnes Hospital ward service and were excellent teachers and mentors. By the end of that internship, I was confident that I had become a good physician.

My experiences as an intern remain unforgettable. We were understaffed to almost a dangerous degree. I recall days when I had one nurse dispensing medication and caring for inpatients on four floors of the hospital. To ensure proper medication distribution, I would alternate ward beds with reasonably well patients in between sicker patients to help me oversee patients taking their medication. As dangerous as that might sound, it worked out well. I do not recall getting into trouble with oral medication for my patients. As some patients were repeat admits, I had a familiar routine with some, knowing I could treat and discharge them quickly. This was especially true of patients with the "miseries," a term our hospital population used to refer to diabetes mellitus and heart failure and those with "shocks." I rapidly discovered "shocks" was a term some patients and their family members used to describe a rapid onset medical condition, frequently a myocardial infarction or a stroke.

One of my patients, whom I still recall today with a smile, was a man about sixty, of eastern European descent, who had a leg amputated in WWII and suffered from diabetes and heart disease. I admitted him on four different occasions during my internship. On the third admission, I was stabilizing him and expected to discharge him from the hospital after the weekend. That Saturday, I was working in the hospital and got a call that he was at the corner bar having a beer and could I send over security to pick him up?

To this day, I remember the conversation that followed. "Has he finished his beer yet?" "No," said the bartender. "Send him back after he finishes his beer," I said.

Starting then, when the patient was hospitalized, I took his artificial leg away when he was in bed to prevent another corner tavern experience.

Being understaffed presented unusual logistic and medical problems. For instance, we had no medical technologists or technicians to do blood draws on our ward, so interns drew blood. I developed a system, especially for male patients who were sometimes difficult to deal with. I would point to the antecubital vein and tell them that it would be my first stick. If that failed, I would try for a vein near or on the back of the hand, then the femoral vein, then the femoral artery, and if that did not work because they moved, I would take blood from the dorsal vein of the penis. Of course, I never had to do that, but it sure got their attention. They always cooperated and held still for me to draw blood.

Help was so scarce at St. Louis City Hospital that as interns we usually had to transport our patients to X-ray since the Radiology Department could not give up an X-ray technician for that purpose. So, accustomed as I was to being independent and doing everything myself, I tried to use my time efficiently. Sometimes, this would mean doing a procedure at night so I would be able to do something else in the morning. One such experience, which I thought nothing of at the time, became a legend on the medical service.

A woman in her seventies came from the emergency room to my ward at about 9 p.m. with shortness of breath and fatigue. I took a blood sample, did a hematocrit, and stained a slide with a drop of her blood for a differential count in the small laboratory adjacent to our hospital ward. Given the shortage of medical technologists at the hospital, it was not unusual for interns to do their own complete blood counts (CBC) and differentials in our ward laboratory. When I read the slide, I thought that she likely had leukemia and was curious as to what type of lymphocytic leukemia it was. Having a little time and a willing patient, I did a sternal bone marrow puncture, obtained a good sample, stained the slide, and determined that she had lymphocytic leukemia. That morning, I presented the case at our early morning rounds with our attending physician and residents. I had assumed that all the house staff would have done the same thing but based on the facial expressions of the attending faculty, chief resident in medicine, and my fellow house officers, I realized that I was an outlier. None of them would have done the bone marrow that night. Since I did, she was able to start chemotherapy that afternoon. I do not know how she fared since she was transferred to another floor and medical team, but at least I knew that she was able to be treated within a day of being admitted and maybe fared better because of my efforts.

While I worked at St. Louis City Hospital, Ellen worked as

a research technician for Hugh Chaplin, Jr., MD, Chairman of the Department of Preventative Medicine at Washington University School of Medicine, doing research into the association between heavy-chains and light-chains in urine and blood and cancers such as multiple myeloma. Her research with Dr. Chaplin went well and our year went quite fast with limited time to enjoy the city of St. Louis, although we did see the St. Louis Cardinals play baseball once and enjoyed Verdi's Aida performed by the St. Louis Municipal Opera Theatre in the park with elephants and other parade animals.

At the beginning of July 1967, after finishing my medical internship, Ellen and I purchased our first new car, a Pontiac Le Mans, packed up our limited possessions and drove to Rockville, Maryland and to the Congressional Towers, an apartment complex that would be our home for the next two years while I worked at the NIH in Bethesda. For the first three months after arriving and settling in Maryland, we bought supplies in preparation for our daughter Lisa's birth. In addition, Ellen, who had been frustrated as a child to never having the opportunity to take piano lessons, wanted to learn piano and she started lessons at a nearby music store. After practicing piano at the store for several weeks, we decided to purchase a new Yamaha upright from the local store in 1967. That piano moved nine times and now resides in our daughter's home.

My good fortune in getting a Public Health Service commission and a two-year staff research position at the NIH in 1967 was pivotal to my career and the choices I made on the path that would lead me to become a neuro-oncologist.

5

The National Cancer Institute and It's Impact on my Path to Academia

During my undergraduate and graduate education, internship, and residency, the United States conscription, or the draft as it was called, led to the reality that virtually all young male physicians were obligated to perform military or public health service. Since the NIH was part of the U.S. Public Health Service, many future academicians found their way to the NIH instead of one of the branches of the armed forces if they had a strong interest and expertise in medical research. As a result, many bright physicians-scientists populated the NIH campus in Bethesda. A number of these "graduates" of NIH programs became department chairs and the faculty of medical schools throughout the United States for several generations; some even went on to receive the Nobel Prize in Medicine. Among medical school faculty, these young men were often referred to as the "two-year wonders," referring to the two years of obligatory service, although many chose to stay longer than two years at the NIH.

Luckily for me, I became one of those researchers. My focus was the regional delivery of drugs to the CNS and the study of anticancer drugs in intracerebral tumor models. As mentioned earlier, because of the friendship of Dave Gilboe and Vince Oliverio, Dave P. Rall, MD, PhD, the Head of the Laboratory of Chemical Pharmacology, invited me to join his laboratory at the NCI as a Staff Associate in July 1967.

When I started, Dave Rall was forty-one years old. He was the first medical scientist I had met with combined MD and PhD degrees, both obtained from the Northwestern University Medical School in Chicago, Illinois. What I remember most about Dave's appearance is that, unlike me, he had a full head of wavy hair while I was on my way to early partial baldness. He wore glasses, which he took off when talking, and he always seemed to have a twinkle in his eyes and a smile on his face.

Dave had an advanced and intuitive understanding of the anticancer drugs of the time and a special interest in brain tumors and how the limitations of the blood-brain barrier impacted the chemotherapy of brain tumors. He was a dedicated physician and researcher and a good role model. Over the years, after completing my training, I came to understand how important his insights and dedication would be to the United States government. His commitment, vision, and administrative skills helped establish the National Toxicology Program and later he led the National Institute of Environmental Health Sciences.

I recall with fondness the laboratory branch administrator, Emilie Olausen, who greeted me when I arrived for my first day of work at the NCI on July 10, 1967. Emilie was a petite woman in her thirties who had a beautiful smile, a sharp wit, and a no-nonsense approach. She was the organizational and management force that made the Laboratory of Chemical Pharmacology in the Experimental Therapeutics Branch of the NCI work.

On the day I arrived, to my disappointment Emilie told me the two senior laboratory faculty I would likely work with, Joe Fenstermacher and Dave Rall, were away doing research on elasmobranch (fish) at the Mount Desert Island Biological Laboratory in Maine. In their absence, she advised I begin researching one of two areas, either how drugs move in the brain or how anticancer drugs work. She made it clear, too, that those were the only research areas I would be allowed to pursue without Dr. Rall's approval. She closed with

"Have a nice day and if you need supplies, come see me." Over my two years at the NCI, Emilie was a great help and a good friend. She assisted me in buying equipment, obtaining services, having instruments machined, and getting contracts for radioisotopes and radiolabeled drugs.

Both areas of research Emilie proposed sounded exciting to me as I did not have a preconceived research plan when I arrived at the NCI. For me it was like being in a toy store, the toys being new research freedom and opportunity. Within a month, I decided to work in both areas and took a path that has occupied me to this day. I studied how to better understand regional brain and tumor pharmacokinetics and the pharmacology of anticancer agents to develop improved experimental therapies for people with CNS malignancies. The base of knowledge and research and the network of researchers at the NCI laid a foundation for varied and informed approaches to chemotherapy for CNS cancers that has served me well over the many decades since my NCI days

In my first few days at the NCI in 1967, besides meeting Emilie, I met two NIH Research Associates who were older than I and who had completed residencies. William Shapiro, MD, had just completed his neurology residency at Cornell University. Bill had trained in neurology at Cornell Medical School and the Memorial Sloan-Kettering Cancer Center (MSKCC) and returned there after completing two years at the NCI. Bill spent many years at MSKCC on the neurology faculty before moving to the Barrow Institute in Phoenix to chair the Department of Neurology until his retirement in 2015. Bill was an important figure in neurology and neuro-oncology over four decades and, for many of those years, he did research with his wife, Joan Rankin, PhD, an outstanding laboratory scientist.

The second Research Associate was James Ausman, MD, a neurosurgeon. Jim did his residency at The University of Minnesota and earned his PhD in Pharmacology at George Washington

University while at the NIH. After leaving the NCI in 1972, Jim embarked on an important career as an academic neurosurgeon (University of Minnesota, Henry Ford Hospital, University of Illinois, and UCLA), a journal editor and a researcher. We had something in common, both of us were originally from Milwaukee.

During the summer of 1967, Bill and Jim viewed me as their intern by reason of the fact that I was a "the new kid on the block," was five to six years their junior, and had not done a residency. Initially, I was very sensitive to our age and training differences, but within months we became friends and remained good colleagues for decades.

I initiated some studies with Bill Shapiro that focused on three intracranial mouse models that were chemically derived, transplantable, and histologically either high-grade gliomas from glioma 26 or glioma 261 cell lines or what we called "ependymoblastoma" from the EP or EpA cell lines. In those years, Bill was interested in antitumor activity of drugs in rodent models, and I was also interested in how drugs and their biotransformation products distributed in tumor and adjacent brain, and how they exerted antitumor activity. I also collaborated with Jim Ausman using a rodent tumor model and a monkey tumor model study as well as in a brain hematocrit study I had started in medical school.

During my two years as a Staff Associate in the Laboratory of Chemical Pharmacology of the Experimental Therapeutics Branch of the NCI, I also worked with Joseph D. Fenstermacher, PhD, a physiologist and Senior Staff Associate, and Clifford S. Patlak, PhD, a biomathematician who was Head of the Theoretical Statistics and Mathematics Section in the National Institute of Mental Health. Joe and Cliff were my adopted mentors at the NCI and Cliff continued to collaborate with me into the early 1980s, first during my residency at the Massachusetts General Hospital and, later, while I was at the UCSF.

Joe Fenstermacher was thirty-three years old when I met him. He had a modest beard, wore glasses, had more hair on his head than I did, and was the father of four children. He earned a PhD in the Department of Physiology at The University of Minnesota and had come to the Laboratory of Chemical Pharmacology for postdoctoral research. I started working with and learning from him almost immediately when he returned to the lab in August that year. He invited me to participate in his research using ventricle to cisterna magnum perfusion (V-C perfusion) of radiolabeled chemicals and drugs in dogs to understand how chemicals moved in the extracellular spaces (fluids) of the dog brain. Joe and Cliff had developed a technique to answer important questions relevant to how chemical compounds and drugs move in brain parenchyma. Also, instrumental to my research, was Ernest Owens, a laboratory technician who was working with Joe. Ernie showed me how to get around the lab and how to set-up some of the experiments efficiently. Participating in this research that summer allowed me to jump-start my brief NCI research career.

Cliff Patlak earned his PhD in Nicolas Rashevsky's internationally acclaimed Mathematical Biology Program at The University of Chicago. When I met Cliff in 1967, he was forty-one years old and working in the National Institute of Mental Health Building 36 next door to Building 37 where Joe and I worked. Cliff was delightful, an avuncular man with a good sense of humor.

I fondly recall Cliff, seated in his small office surrounded by stacks of papers in what I thought was disarray, working on an equation or computer program. When I came into his room, he looked over his glasses and smiled. I would say hello and explain my problem or request. This included asking for his help or insight into a laboratory experiment and a problem programming a mathematical formula. While I had a basic understanding of calculus, I never became sufficiently independent to generate the equations I needed during those years. This shortcoming did not, however, hamper me from approaching research as a quantitative venture requiring statistical validation.

I worked with and learned from Cliff during both years at the NCI and for another twelve or thirteen years while a resident in Boston at Massachusetts General Hospital (MGH) from 1969 to 1972 and then as a faculty member at UCSF between 1972 and 1988. We published six papers together between 1970 and 1981, and Cliff advised me on several other papers.

In addition to the influence of Joe and Cliff, I was influenced by David Rall and Vince Oliverio as well as other scientists in the Experimental Therapeutics Branch.

The V-C perfusion studies with Joe were initially done in dogs because we needed a large enough brain to measure tissue levels of radioisotopes from continuous white matter samples in the brain. Having a lot of experience doing surgery on dogs during my medical school years, I helped answer a series of questions about the extracellular movement of standard chemicals and made con-tributions that speeded up analysis. I figured out how to increase experimental throughput using computer programs and expanded the repertoire of study animals to include, rat, rabbit, cat, and monkeys and developed new subarachnoid-to-cisterna magnum perfusion techniques.

The major throughput problem in this type of research was needing to use radioactive compounds, usually two isotopes in the same experiment. So, in addition to having to quickly remove the brain and prepare carefully measured pieces for scintillation counting, the final output of the scintillation counter had to be manually transferred and calculated and normalized by tissue weight to counts per minute/mg weight value and then, using a set of mathematical formula and plots Cliff developed, arriving at a singular number, the diffusion coefficient.

When I started this research with Joe, the post-experiment computations required almost a full day. To shorten computation time, I initially tried doing calculations using Fortran programming and punch card readers, but it took too much time and effort. Since computers and paper tape printing by teletype and reading by teletype were becoming possible at the NCI in 1967, I learned to program in the computer language called Time-Sharing BASIC. Once we added a tape printer to our scintillation counter, I wrote software that could reduce the time by a factor of 10 to calculate the two isotopes, correct for weight of tissue pieces, and compute the concentration of chemical/mg tissue as a function of distance from ventricular surface and then, using the computed values, plot the numbers on special complementary error function paper to obtain a diffusion coefficient. This efficiency allowed us to increase the number of experiments we could do per week by a factor of three.

After working on V-C perfusions for a year, I thought I could measure the diffusion from the subarachnoid space into brain cortex to see if the same rules governing the movement of molecules from the fluid of the subarachnoid space covering the brain into the cortex and the white matter below the cortex were the same as the movement of molecules from the ventricular cerebrospinal fluid into periventricular white matter. My goal was to understand the universality of how molecules moved in the brain to better apprehend how drugs, such as anticancer drugs, could be expected to move and distribute. To achieve this research goal, I did what Joe Fenstermacher called *gedankenexperiments* (German for "thought experiment") to develop a technique. One worry was whether an animal would sustain a sharp needle puncture through the sagittal sinus without producing an experiment-ending bleeding complication. I turned to my neurosurgery colleague, Jim Ausman. He assured me that a single pass of a small and sharp needle would be tolerated without undue bleeding since the sinus was venous blood and not subject to high pressure like arterial blood.

With this final concern resolved, I embarked on the first experiment to measure extracellular passive distribution of standard chemicals from the subarachnoid space into brain parenchyma to understand drug movement in the brain and brain tumors. I remember these experiments because everything worked as planned the first time and all other times in four different animal species. It is rare that experiments with so many variables work as planned and I relished the accomplishment. As a result of these experiments, I was able to show commonality in passive extracellular transport among four mammalian species. While, at times, I felt bad having to sacrifice dogs, cats, monkeys, and rabbits for my studies, I rationalized it as necessary to determine if the physical rules for the passive distribution of non-metabolized chemicals and drugs would be the same among the animals and, therefore, regional brain pharmacokinetics could be safely extrapolated from animal brains to human brains. I thought these experiments needed to be done once to be sure since it would allow other mammalian brain tumor models to be used to understand drug movement in the brain and brain tumors, which was the overriding goal of my research then and for decades to follow. Also, at the time, we never envisaged advances in imaging that might have mitigated this approach, although even today, neuroimaging modalities still have not reached the level of precision needed for distribution and metabolism studies in CNS tumors and adjacent brain such that we achieved in the 1960s.

—⚘—

Ellen and I enjoyed living at the Congressional Towers in Rockville, Maryland during my two years at the NCI. Our first child, Lisa, was born in the fall of 1967 at the Bethesda Naval Hospital, which was located directly across Wisconsin Avenue from the NIH. This too was an experience as the Vietnam War was expanding and those of us in the Public Health Service at the NIH were considered "yellow berets" by many of the enlisted officers and nurses at the hospital. We were more welcome at Walter Reed General Hospital but being new to the NIH and to military experience, we stayed at the Bethesda Naval Hospital for the birth of our first child as it was closer to our home. In retrospect, this was a mistake as it negatively impacted Ellen's care and was an uncomfortable experience for both of us. After the delivery when we visited the nursery, we found very few cribs occupied by a baby, attesting to the fact that having a baby at the Bethesda Naval Hospital during the Vietnam War was not a common event. Looking out over the cribs that day, Ellen, and I saw our daughter's arms and legs, in constant motion in her crib. The nursing staff thought she was disturbing the other infants and being unfriendly to "yellow berets," encouraged us to take Lisa home ASAP. Lisa remains a high-energy and very physically active person, to this day.

My early memories of Lisa were of an infant and child who liked to see the environment around her. At a couple months of age, we discovered that putting her in a backpack produced quiet, giggling, and happy moments for her and for us. The most interesting thing was she did not fall asleep in the backpack but looked around attentively as we walked. Believing in research as we did, Ellen took Lisa to participate in an NIH study to better understand how infants track with their eyes over early developmental time. We learned that Lisa tracked very well for her age, an observation we had made while also carrying her around our apartment.

On some weekends we piled into our new tan 1967 two-door Pontiac Le Mans. It had an eight-cylinder engine, a three-speed manual Hurst transmission, and bucket seats, a young man's dream car. I could "lay a strip of rubber" starting from second gear. I never had a speeding ticket but did get close once on a trip to Vermont.

When we could, we drove to visit the national parks, historical sites, and museums within a hundred miles. I even found time and energy to take a sculpture class on Saturday mornings at the Corcoran Gallery of Art in Washington, D.C. Between research at the NIH, living in Rockville, and enjoying the many experiences the Washington, D.C. area offered, we had a wonderful two years and made life-long friends. I am certain that had I completed my residency before starting at the NIH, I would have stayed at the NIH for many more years.

6

The NIH and the Brain Tumor
Study Group

The birth of modern medical oncology resulted from a convergence between a major government financial commitment to oncology drug development and bright, forward-thinking entrepreneurial clinicians and scientists who built wisely using the federal funding they directed. Critical to funding this effort was establishment in 1955 of the Cancer Chemotherapy National Service Center (CCNSC) at the NCI to support the development of second-generation anti-cancer drugs, primarily through NCI contracts. This spawned new anticancer drugs as well as a large network of cooperative clinical trial groups such as the Eastern Solid Tumor Group that became the Eastern Cooperative Oncology Group (ECOG). The new cooperative groups were needed by the NCI to test novel anticancer agents in people in an organized and statistically acceptable fashion.

Around this time, Charles "Gordon" Zubrod, MD, who led the development of antimalarial agents for the United States Army in 1956, was asked to head the Division of Cancer Treatment of the NCI. And in 1961, he was asked to become the Scientific Director of the NCI. In these capacities, and with a significant cancer budget from Congress, he and his colleagues at the NCI moved forward with contracts and grants that led to the development of new anticancer drugs.

Zubrod's early interest in natural products led him to establish a broad program for collecting and testing plant and marine sources.

At the outset, this program was controversial, but it was very successful, leading to the discovery of taxanes in 1964, and camptothecins in 1966. Both drug classes were isolated and characterized by the laboratory of Monroe Wall, PhD, at the Research Triangle Institute, and later developed for the clinical treatment of breast, ovarian and colon cancer. These drugs are still used today. In addition, working on an NCI contract, Barnett Rosenberg, PhD, at Michigan State University, made a serendipitous discovery that led to the discovery of cisplatin and its pivotal use for the curative treatment of testicular cancer. It and its analogs are still used today for testicular cancer as well as several adult and childhood cancers.

About the same time, a second group with NCI contracts was led by John Montgomery, PhD, a medicinal chemist at the Southern Research Institute in Birmingham, Alabama. Montgomery synthesized nitrosoureas that biotransformed in tumor cells to alkylating moieties that could cross-link DNA, that is one end of the drug molecule would react and bind to one strand of double helix DNA and the other end of the drug molecules would bind to the other DNA strand. These studies yielded the first effective nitrosourea chemotherapy agents for the treatment of infiltrative gliomas of the brain: BCNU (carmustine, 1,3-bis(2-chloroethyl)-1-nitrosourea) and CCNU (lomustine, 1-(2-chloroethyl)-3-cyclohexyl-1-nitrosourea). BCNU was given intravenously and CCNU could be given orally and, therefore, allowed more dosing flexibility. Over the years, John and his colleagues, Glenn P. Wheeler, PhD and Frank M. Schabel, Jr., PhD at Southern Research Institute gave me insight through their research and publications and through advice they sometimes offered about my laboratory research. Additionally, radiolabeled anticancer drugs, 14C-BCNU and 14C-CCNU and other labeled anticancer agents were provided to me through an NCI contract with Southern Research. I used these drugs to study and better understand regional pharmacokinetics of anticancer drugs in mammalian brain, subcutaneous rodent tumors, and intracerebral rodent tumors. Access to radiolabeled compounds allowed me to conduct meaningful preclinical research. This research helped my development as a cancer and pharmacology researcher and laid the groundwork for the early years of my academic career at UCSF.

While my two years at the NCI were occupied by laboratory studies, some of the Research Fellows I met while at the NCI were working as physicians in outpatient clinics and the hospital. From these contacts, as well as from Bill Shapiro and Jim Ausman, I heard about meetings of neurosurgeons who were part of a new Brain Tumor Study Group. At the time, this group was no more than a curiosity; and I did not know much about it or its membership for years to come. Nonetheless, its creation was important and a harbinger of therapeutic neuro-oncology.

Since the Brain Tumor Study Group was an important beginning of cooperative clinical trials for high-grade gliomas, I would like to reimagine those times for the reader through discussion with colleagues and friends from those years as well from my experiences. While writing this memoir I had the opportunity to speak with two prior colleagues and friends, Michael Walker, MD and Carl Leventhal, MD, about their experiences and recollections from the early years of the Brain Tumor Study Group as they were the NINDS executives who guided the program for many years. I am grateful to Mike and Carl for these recent discussions to expand and corroborate my understanding of how and why the Brain Tumor Study Group came into being.

The establishment of the Brain Tumor Study Group was a result of the fact that Dave Rall felt it was time to start thinking of clinical trials for high-grade gliomas. So, with the encouragement of Gordon Zubrod in 1965, Dave invited two young NIH Staff

Associates, Michael D. Walker, MD, a neurosurgeon, and Carl M.
Leventhal, MD, a neurologist with some neuropathology training,
to visit other neurosurgeons and neurologists in the United States
to determine who might be interested in being part of a national
cooperative to conduct clinical trials for gliomas. Mike and Carl
realized that the neurosurgeons had an interest in treating glioma
patients. However, they speculated that the neurosurgeons might be
more interested in the funding than the perceived value for patient
survival, given the dismal record of chemotherapy for cancer at the
time. Their combined efforts led to establishing the Brain Tumor
Study Group in 1966, with academic members drawn from academic
neurosurgery departments in the United States. Therapeutic neuro-
oncology thus likely had its origins in the late 1960s, through
collaboration of the following university-based neurosurgeons:
Charles Wilson (UCSF), Eben Alexander, Jr. (Bowman Gray School
of Medicine), William E. Hunt (Ohio State University), M. Stephen
Mahaley, Jr. (Duke University), John Mealey, Jr. (University of
Indiana), Guy G. Owens (Vanderbilt University), Joseph Ransohoff,
II (NYU), and Horace A. Norrell (Tulane University). Completing
the Brain Tumor Study Group administratively were Michael
Walker, Carl Leventhal and a statistician, Edward A. Gehan, PhD,
who, at the time, was also working at the NCI. Within two years,
Thomas Strike, PhD, was recruited to help run the Brain Tumor
Study Group so that Mike could continue his neurosurgical duties
at NCI's Maryland campus.

The goal of Brain Tumor Study Group was to formally test and
evaluate different forms of treatment for high-grade gliomas
(anaplastic astrocytoma, anaplastic oligodendroglioma, anaplastic
oligoastrocytoma and glioblastoma multiforme). Initially, Carl also
served as the referee neuropathologist, confirming that study
patients had high-grade gliomas. The first drug evaluated was
mithramycin, which was selected based on activity seen by Joe
Ransohoff. Unfortunately, the initial study failed to show clinical

activity for mithramycin. After this study, the group was less than optimistic about chemotherapy until BCNU came along. Consequently, they designed a clinical trial, in part, to deal with the value of surgery and radiation therapy and to determine if BCNU demonstrated activity and provided benefit to patients.

At its inception some neurosurgeons in the Brain Tumor Study Group were nihilistic about treatment for patients with glioblastoma and other high-grade gliomas; some even doubted the value of surgical resection. Other neurosurgeons, however, believed that a surgical procedure followed by radiation therapy was helpful and some believed radiation offered little benefit over surgery alone. Fortunately, some of the younger neurosurgeons such as Charles Wilson of UCSF and Joseph Ransohoff of New York University Medical School were more optimistic and anticipated that chemotherapy with surgery and radiation would provide a better option for patients based on publications showing benefit for chemotherapy in leukemia patients.

At the urging of Mike Walker and Ed Gehan, a clinical trial was designed to determine the independent value of surgery, surgery and radiation, surgery and BCNU chemotherapy, and the benefit of all three therapeutic modalities combined. By today's standards, it was not a strong statistical study. Full randomization was not possible since not all neurosurgeons were willing to enter patients on all four study arms. The study was, therefore, biased from its inception. In addition, all high-grade gliomas were thought to be similar and study eligible. This was disproved over the years. The paper published at the end of the study did show a benefit from radiation therapy after surgery and for intravenous BCNU. It took many years of clinical trials, however, to convince the medical community and gain acceptance for adjuvant chemotherapy for high-grade gliomas, years that spanned the first two decades of my career.

Mike Walker said there would be periodic meetings of the Brain

Tumor Study Group in Bethesda with the eight participating study neurosurgeons. Each neurosurgeon brought along a nurse who was working with him. Although none of the nurses spoke, after a while, Tom Strike asked the nurses questions about the trial. He found they knew more about the drugs and trials than the neurosurgeons. After that, Tom started having separate meetings with the nurses who, as a cohort, laid the foundation for the "research nurses" that all neuro-oncology programs rely on today for clinical trial conduct and integrity.

The Brain Tumor Study Group transitioned to the Brain Tumor Cooperative Group (BTCG) and then, as NIH funding changed and other cooperative efforts emerged such as the regional Northern California Oncology Group (NCOG) and national the Radiation Treatment Oncology Group (RTOG), the free-standing BTCG program disappeared.

7

Becoming a Neurology Resident and First Research Grant

Getting a neurology residency in the 1960s was different than it is today. There were few residency matching programs when I applied for a neurology residency. Information about residency programs required a letter of enquiry, an application, and maybe an interview. In my second year at the NCI, I decided to apply to Cornell Medical School and the Massachusetts General Hospital (MGH). I also considered applying to a couple other hospitals in case I was rejected by both programs. In retrospect, the decision to limit myself to only two neurology residency programs, was a big gamble, but at the time I was confident, maybe overly so, of my ability and future potential.

In the case of Cornell, I never made it to the hospital for an interview as I had met Fred Plum, the chair, at a neurology meeting and was a bit too cocky for him and so was not encouraged to interview in New York. I was, however, encouraged to interview in Boston for the MGH residency. So, I flew from Washington National Airport to Logan airport and took a cab to the MGH for interviews that I remember vividly to this day. From interviews with faculty and neurology residents, it quickly became obvious to me that I had underestimated the value they placed on completing an Internal Medicine Residency. Lacking patience, I had decided against taking two years to obtain internal medicine training as I was anxious to get on with my research and academic career and

I believed it would be a waste of valuable time. I wanted to get on with my research!

Even though faculty and senior resident physicians interviewing me said I had only a slim chance of being accepted without internal medicine training, I still felt that I belonged there. Near the end of the day, I realized that I had not been scheduled to see Dr. Raymond Adams, the Department Chair, so I spoke to his personal secretary and told her that I had flown up from Washington, D.C. and was disappointed that he did not have the courtesy to interview me. His secretary was a nice woman who said that she would see is she could arrange some time with Dr. Adams. About two hours later I was ushered into an office darkened by the falling sun as seen through the window behind Dr. Adams' chair. There I was, alone at the end of the workday, with one of the true giants of neurology.

In the dim light of that room, I tried to think quickly to encourage Raymond Adams to want me to join the residency. We talked about my research and why I wanted to be a neurologist, why I wanted to join the MGH program, and what I thought I could bring to the academic field. He told me, like the faculty and neurology fellows who had interviewed me earlier, that since I did not complete an Internal Medicine Residency before applying, I would be placed lower on the list of neurology resident candidates. "That's too bad," I said, "because I'm a very good laboratory researcher and am likely better than any of the neurology residency applicants I am competing with. Not accepting me would be your department's loss as I will be a productive academic neurologist going forward." That was unbridled chutzpah but reflected my confidence in my research future and my future academic career.

My research at both The University of Wisconsin Medical School and NCI had been very productive with ten research articles in preparation, submitted, or in press. Of these, I was first author of seven articles. Being a bit cocky at the time, I went on to tell him

I was confident I would be able to sustain my research activity after leaving the NCI, especially since I had been doing research since my undergraduate years, first in physiological psychology, and later in wound healing and experimental surgery at the Allen Bradley Laboratories of the Medical College of Wisconsin before entering medical school. I knew my interest in research was visceral and I was good enough to sustain an academic medical research career. Furthermore, I loved doing research. Ray Adams reconsidered. He became my main supporter and the driving force behind the residency committee's decision to offer me a neurology residency slot at MGH for July 1969.

And so, my residency at MGH began. Ellen and I had found a charming old, but very well-maintained upper rental unit in a duplex in Brighton, a neighborhood in the northwest corner of Boston. Our street was also home to students from Boston University who we did not see much of during the day but who occasionally caused some problems at night for our daughter, Lisa, who was frequently awakened by flashing colored lights from the students living in the apartments across the street and/or groups of students playing loud music while drinking or smoking marijuana outside on their porch. Because of this and the fact that I disliked the very crowded and unpredictable roundtrip MTA trolley ride from Brighton to Park Street near the MGH, which included a dreary walk in the early morning and late at night and usually having to wait in the cold on an island on Commonwealth Avenue for the MTA to arrive, we started to think about moving out of the city when our year lease was up. Later that year we did decide to move even though the 26-mile commute to the MGH would either involve driving or taking a freeway bus to downtown Boston.

We had saved money over the years and made some money in the stock market while at the NCI and since I was thinking of staying in Boston after completing my residency, we decided to buy a house in Framingham, a small city west of Boston. The house we chose was a single-story three-bedroom wood tract house with a small living room but a large den and a big, grassy backyard, perfect for children to play in. It was near a bus stop that could take me, by non-stop bus, to downtown Boston and put me in walking distance to the MGH. It was also near Highway 90, a toll road that allowed easy access to MGH via Storrow Drive when it was necessary for me to drive the car to work.

Ellen was happy to move to the Framingham house as it provided more space to raise Lisa and a second child soon to be born. Since I was required to work at the MGH, in preparation for our move, Ellen packed and moved our possessions from the old Brighton house to the new Framingham house, driving Monday through Wednesday with our car filled with small items. On Thursday, the movers moved all the large pieces of furniture including Ellen's piano to our new house. On Friday, since Ellen was two weeks past her due date and had chosen natural childbirth and was suffering from seasonal asthma, she was admitted to Boston Hospital for Women for induction and the birth of our second child.

I had correctly predicted, based on the way Ellen carried Lisa, that our first child would be a girl. Since Ellen was now carrying her baby a good deal higher, I opined it would be a boy as that was what I had been led to believe from my medical school experience. Thus, we focused on boys' names before the birth much as we had focused on girl's name before Lisa was born. I am sure Ellen had decided on a girl's name in case I was wrong. We did not have ultrasound routinely available for either pregnancy, so learning the baby's gender at birth was always an exciting experience.

While I stayed with Ellen until she went into the delivery room, I did not know the sex of the baby until Ellen and the baby were wheeled out. By agreement or, more correctly, in cahoots with Ellen, the obstetrician led her out of delivery and with a straight face said that I had a new daughter. While I thought that was fine, Ellen said my expression showed such disappointment, that she quickly fessed up that it was a boy, as I had predicted. Based on the size of his feet and hands, the pediatrician thought my son, Jason, would likely grow to be above average in height, which turned out to be accurate.

During my first year, Barry Arnason was an attending neurologists I liked and felt some camaraderie. He graduated from the MGH Neurology residency, was a great teacher, an interesting person to have a lively discussion with and a friend. I think how we had gotten into the residency brought us together. He told me that he was from Winnipeg, Canada and thought that he was accepted into the neurology residency by Ray Adams because one summer during medical school Barry had tagged whales in the Saint Lawrence Seaway. He also said that he thought I must have made an impression on Adams during our interview since he would say hello to me by name when we passed in the halls of the hospital. Barry said that even after he joined the Department of Neurology as an assistant professor, Adams would frequently get his name wrong the first year.

Learning from Ray Adams, Barry Arnason, Edwin Pierson Richardson (EP as he was called by the residents), the other faculty and fellows in neurology and neuropathology in those years was a wonderful experience. It provided me with a better understanding of how to dissect disease processes in the CNS. Ray Adam's approach to neurological diseases was based on understanding disease processes rather than based on associating neurological symptoms and signs with disease names. His approach provided an ideal structure for studying diseases and conditions of the CNS. It was a methodology that served me well and provided a format to understand diseases of the time and those that would be discovered in the future.

Barry, like other attendings, invited the residents and their wives, if they were married, to a dinner party or weekend lunch at their home. Ellen and I remember a Sunday brunch at Barry's classic old house near the water in Marblehead, Massachusetts, a twenty-mile drive northeast of our home in Framingham. It was an old stone and brick two-story home with heavy wood doors, carved wood trim, and beautiful plaster walls that had been built by a sea captain long before. We had a great time that day and even though we had thoughts to return to Marblehead someday for a day or two, we never had the opportunity to go back.

It was 1970, and my second year of neurology residency was coming up. Before it started, I applied for and received a research grant from the American Cancer Society (ACS). Thinking ahead towards a research career, I decided also to apply for a NINDS Fellowship for partial salary support for the year to ensure that I would be able to do my research and, if necessary, take an additional year to complete my residency.

During the second year of my neurology residency, when we rotated through neuropathology, psychiatry, and neurophysiology, I worked afternoons, evenings, and weekends doing my research in laboratory space of Bradford DeLong, a pediatric neurologist at MGH. My research was quite original and involved research in rats to better understand paths that radiolabeled sodium and coupled water could take in the rat brain hoping that it would improve our understanding of the paths of brain edema formation. I was surprised to find two gradients for sodium movement in the white matter—one toward the ventricle and the other toward the subarachnoid space. In later years, I assumed that scientists working with sodium imaging would study this in people with normal brains and compare that to others with brain edema and hydrocephalus as I was sure these studies would inform a better understanding and management of the two neurological conditions. Even with my periodic encouragement, no one utilized sodium imaging to validate my findings in the human brain. In that study, I was fortunate to work with Cliff Patlak again, with whom I had worked previously while at the NCI.

A chance discussion one day, in my second year of residency, led to another research project that year. While talking with Barry about my research into sodium transport in the rat brain, he mentioned that his laboratory was working with diphtheria toxin to produce demyelinating lesions in the rat brain and in peripheral nerves and he wondered whether either would be good demyelinating models for me to study after I had completed my brain studies. I felt sciatic nerve studies would prove very informative since, unlike the brain, demyelination would be more localized and easier to study. In addition, since I had never studied blood to sciatic nerve movement of molecules and there was scant literature on it at the time, I thought it might lead to some new insights. So, I embarked on studies in my borrowed laboratory to study how radiolabeled sodium and water move across the blood-nerve capillary interface (blood-nerve barrier) under normal conditions and after damage to the myelin covering of the nerve. Because there were no comparable studies in the literature, I agreed to the collaboration. Barry also thought the study was worth doing and introduced me to Ewa Chelmicka-Szorc, MD, a post-doctoral medical scientist working with Barry on demyelinating neurological diseases who was interested in collaborating with me and creating lesioned rats for me to study.

These studies were important as the blood-nerve barrier has specific properties and is more permeable to most standard compounds such as inulin. I also wanted to determine how systemic hydrocortisone impacted permeability and sodium (and therefore water) distribution in affected demyelinated sciatic nerves compared to normal sciatic nerves. I found increased sciatic nerve water and sodium concentration, enlarged extracellular and intracellular spaces, and increased capillary permeability to injected diphtheria toxin. When treated with hydrocortisone, nerve water decreased, as did intracellular and extracellular swelling, with a negligible effect on sodium content. Surprising at the time, it showed that the hydrocortisone effect was primarily on cellular permeability and not on capillary permeability as it is inferred to work in the case of brain edema. I have always been skeptical of the specific effects of glucocorticoid on brain tumor edema because of the many variables encountered in its study. Following my studies, I was convinced a major effect of glucocorticoids on brain tumor edema was on cellular water content and intracellular sodium integrity and less so on capillary integrity and permeability.

This finding also provided insight, many years later, when trying to taper brain tumor patients off the glucocorticoid, dexamethasone. I realized it was difficult to wean some patients off dexamethasone even when residual tumor edema appeared to be well-controlled. The patients complained about mental slowness sometimes bordering on mild confusion. I hypothesized that this "brain fog" was likely caused by inappropriate cellular Na-K gradients that leaked potassium due to mild but persistent membrane damage. Based on my prior studies of sodium transport in demyelinated nerves, I realized this condition could be partially or completely rectified using dexamethasone. I explained this to my patients and suggested we try a long taper period of dexamethasone or just riding out neurocognitive slowing as it would resolve. In the 1990s while at The University of Texas MD Anderson Cancer Center I supplemented or replaced this approach with low-dose methylphenidate (Ritalin). While no one has ever proven or disproven my hypothesis, it seemed logical to me based on what I knew of damage to glial and neuronal function in brain tumor patients and my understanding of sodium transport in the brain and demyelinated sciatic nerves and the impact of glucocorticoids on maintaining sodium-potassium gradient integrity. In addition, my clinical experience in dozens of patients fortified this understanding and therapeutic approach.

Living in Framingham during my second and third years of residency turned out to be wonderful for our young family. Our neighbors were friendly, family-oriented people and a great help to Ellen. There were other children to play with Lisa and babysitters to help Ellen, who carried most of the workload required to care for an infant and a toddler. I was generally twenty miles away at the MGH and slept at the hospital three nights a week as part of my MGH residency. In addition, during the second year I sometimes spent extra time at the MGH conducting laboratory studies. I also supplemented my meager resident's salary to help our young family so would drive thirteen miles to Concord to read electroenceph-alograms for one of the neurosurgeons during weekends in my third year.

I seemed to be always doing something or going somewhere, yet this was a wonderful time for us. The Framingham community was gracious and composed of interesting people in our general age group. As the children got older, they played outside on grass and Ellen would take them sledding or cross-country skiing in our backyard and in a local park or at a golf course. Ellen would carry Jason in a backpack while she skied with Lisa.

While living in Framingham, we were able to get babysitters every once and awhile for a weekend day to go cross-country skiing in New Hampshire or Vermont. We had some wonderful times and memories skiing in New England. One wonderful memory has stayed with me and Ellen since 1971. I had been reading local ski guides describing good trails in New England and came across a reference to Temple Mountain in New Hampshire. So, one Saturday, we hired a neighbor to babysit our children. We drove our Pontiac Le Mans to Temple Mountain. As we approached, we saw it was a small mountain with downhill skiers traversing the slopes. The article did not say where to start cross-country skiing, so I enquired at the base lodge and was directed to an old man wearing an army surplus jacket for directions. He told us to take the rope tow up to the clearing and ski from there. Neither of us had ever used a rope tow and we were novices at skiing. I tried first and was almost at the top when I saw Ellen slipping and falling off the rope tow after several attempts. Seeing her in trouble, I started to ski down to where she was trying to hold on to the rope. By the time I skied down, the old man in the army jacket appeared and said that he would take Ellen up in a ski mobile. I took the rope tow up and Ellen came up on the ski mobile. The nice older man said that he would ski with us and so we followed him along some of the most beautiful cross-country trails in the mountains that we had ever experienced. I can still see the snow-covered trees and the flawless snow in the trails we skied. Curious about why he was at the mountain and free to take us, we asked, and he said, with a twinkle in his eyes, that he was Charles Beebe, and his family owned the mountain. Over the years we skied about two or three more times with him and his wife, Lucie, and were invited to their beautiful house for sweets.

Near the end of my second year of residency and with an American Cancer Society grant and NINDS Fellowship in hand, I had approached Sidney Farber, MD, the founder, and head of the Children's Cancer Research Foundation (CCRF) that was renamed the Sidney Farber Cancer Institute in 1974, after his death in 1973. My original intent was to do brain tumor pharmacology research and clinical studies at the CCRF. Initially, he was supportive and thought it a good idea. Unfortunately, however, the year I had planned to join the CCRF was also a time of transition for the Cancer Center as Dr. Farber was retiring and Tom Frei had just been recruited to head the Center and Farber was reluctant to make an appointment. Since I was not comfortable taking a chance that Tom Frei would hire me and Ellen and I had two children to support, I decided to seek a university position elsewhere that would facilitate more reliable clinical and research opportunities.

Looking for my first academic position quickly led away from the East Coast, but not without concern. Most of the MGH neurology faculty viewed moving west of the Mississippi River as leaving the mother lode of Harvard for a strange new land. My thoughts as I planned our future were that I wanted to be in a program that was associated with a strong neurosurgery department interested in CNS tumors and a state-of-the-art neuroradiology program. In addition, Ellen and I did not want to live and raise our children in New York City so my choices in 1972 were not abundant other than to "go west young man".

Initially, the Department of Neurology at Metropolitan Hospital in Cleveland was a consideration. It was headed by Ray Adam's friend, Morris Victor, and Adams wanted me to look at the program. While having a good neurosurgery department at the time of my interview, I had the impression during my interview that things were going to change in neurosurgery and take a direction that would not be helpful to me and my future academic research opportunities there would be very limited.

My second interview was with the Department of Neurosciences at The University of California San Diego. This was an interesting opportunity as one of my co-residents, Ron Kobayashi, had already accepted a position there in neurology. At the time of my interview, the medical school buildings were new, with others on the way. I had a great time giving a lecture during my interview as it was in a very modern new auditorium with sophisticated electronic controls. The problem I saw in San Diego was the main teaching hospital was in the city center, but the medical school and laboratories they promised me, were many miles away at the medical school in La Jolla. I felt that this was going to be a major detriment to my attaining a successful academic career, so I reluctantly declined their offer and traveled to the Department of Neurological Surgery at UCSF for interviews arranged by Charles B. Wilson, the Chairman of the Department. It became clear during the first day of interviews that the best opportunities for me were going to be at UCSF.

I do not know how Dr. Wilson, Charlie to those of us who worked closely with him, managed to arrange my interviews. I can only believe that he was prescient. I not only interviewed with clinicians and researchers in the Departments of Neurological Surgery and Neurology, but Charlie had arranged interviews with Sidney Riegelman, PhD, Chair of the Department of Pharmacy, School of Pharmacy, and his Vice-Chair, Leslie Benet. Sid and Les were leaders in the field of pharmacokinetics and biopharmaceutics and seemed a natural fit for my interests. Sid, however, had a different vision for me. He wanted me to have a joint appointment in the Department of Pharmaceutical Chemistry since he felt that much of my research would focus on understanding how anticancer drugs biotransform from the structure that allows them to gain entry to our bodies to the chemical structure that forms what is called the active species and how they are metabolized. Sid, therefore, arranged for me to interview with Manfred Wolff, PhD, Chair of the Department of Pharmaceutical Chemistry and others in the department. Manfred agreed with Sid and offered me a joint faculty position.

At home, Ellen and I discussed the offer and what the 3,000 mile move from Framingham to San Francisco would entail. Moving from the east coast to the West Coast would involve selling our house and car and absorb some of the expense of relocating our family to another city. We nevertheless decided it was my best academic opportunity, so I accepted the offer and we made plans to move to San Francisco in July 1972.

—ɯ—

We decided that we were not going to drive from Framingham to San Francisco, so we had to sell our car and our house. The experience of selling our 1968 Pontiac Le Mans from the steps of our home several days before we left Framingham was memorable. We advertised the car with a for sale sign in the back and side windows of the car and placed an ad in a local newspaper. The young men who responded to our ad, some with their fathers standing behind them, assembled outside in front of our house to bid for the car. This was the only time in my life that I sold a car for more than I was asking. Selling the car was a fun experience, but selling the house was not. The lawyer for the buyer was making the sale difficult for us and to generate more expenses for us to line his own pockets. Fortunately, my brother-in-law, Jerry Stein, was a real estate lawyer in Milwaukee, made some calls to the Framingham lawyer. Jerry's intervention clearly demonstrated the benefit of having a lawyer in the family. It was also the end of the training era of my life and the start of the academic era of my life.

With sadness, but anticipation, we sold our home in Framingham and began the next journey of our lives in San Francisco where I had an entry-level academic position at UCSF. In early July 1972, Ellen, I, and our two children, Lisa, age 5, and Jason, age 2, went to Logan Airport for our flight to Billy Mitchell Field in Milwaukee to spend a week with our families while our possessions were on route by moving van to San Francisco. This was the first airplane ride for our children, and they were very excited and eager for the adventure, Lisa more so than Jason. After a few days in Milwaukee, I flew to San Francisco to await the arrival of the moving van. Ellen and the children were to fly out to San Francisco to join me the day our furniture arrived. We had been quite depressed by the small number of rental units available for us and the cost of rent relative to my annual salary of $22,000, but we had finally found a house to rent after we were advised to contact a UCSF Radiologyy Resident who had just completed his training and was moving to Mill Valley north of San Francisco. The two-story blue stucco clad house was in the Richmond District on 15th Street between Lake and California Streets.

When Ellen and the children arrived at San Francisco airport, I picked them up in a rental car and drove to our new rental house in the city. The previous tenants said they would leave a house key after they moved out. I met the moving van at the rental house to unload everything in the one-car garage while they were in the process of moving out. Later, when I brought my family to the house, I made an unhappy discovery. No key had been left outside for us. Fortunately, one of the old double-hung windows at the side of the house could be opened. With a little boost Lisa could climb through the window and was given instructions on how to open the front door. Once inside, we found the keys the previous tenants had left for us. That evening, we walked from our new home to eat dinner at a new Szechuan restaurant called Yet Wah. There we had a fantastic dinner for the four of us for only $12. This was our introduction to the city and the start of our new life in California, which we called home for the next sixteen years.

8

UCSF Academic Life and Opportunities

When I look back on the early years of neuro-oncology, two names standout: Jerome B. Posner and Charles B. Wilson. Both helped shape the early history of the field of neuro-oncology but in very different ways. This is also reflected in the fact that the East and West Coasts of the United States had an outsized importance to the development of neuro-oncology for different reasons. Although leaders in many other areas of the country contributed meaningfully to the early history of neuro-oncology, my perspective is on early major forces at work that shaped the field focuses on the East and West Coasts.

In 1970, the importance of oncology was starting to grow and expand. Medical oncology was becoming prominent on the East Coast, where it was dominated by the Memorial Sloan-Kettering Cancer Center (MSKCC) and the Beth Israel Hospital in New York and the NCI in Bethesda. At this time, the Cornell Department of Neurology provided academic coverage to MSKCC with the appointment of Jerry Posner to head the Neurology Department. Jerry was a trainee of Fred Plum who as Chair of the Department of Neurology at Cornell Medical College provided Jerry with the opportunity to chair the Department of Neurology at MSKCC. Jerry focused his clinical acumen on how cancer and its treatment produce neurological diseases. He was a consummate clinician and teacher to many generations of neurology residents. Because of his work, MSKCC studies emphasizing the neurology of cancer became an important aspect of the field that would become neuro-oncology.

On the West Coast, the oncology focus was at the UCSF Medical School and Stanford Medical School in Northern California and UCLA in Southern California. While UCSF had been early to initiate and develop cancer research and care, the institution reduced programmatic commitments to medical oncology when Hollie Smith was recruited to chair the Department of Internal Medicine in the late 1960s. About this same time, Charles Wilson was recruited from The University of Kentucky to head the Department of Neurological Surgery in 1968.

From the beginning of his chairmanship at UCSF, Charlie made clear his strong interest in brain cancer and a desire to develop better therapies. His own direct experience in brain cancer research was limited to the development of rodent tumor models that he did with Marvin Barker while in the Department of Neurosurgery at The University of Kentucky prior to coming to UCSF. Nonetheless, he had a clear vision of what he wanted to accomplish at UCSF in his department: he wanted to foster brain tumor research. To that end, he quickly established the Brain Tumor Research Center and applied to the NIH for a program grant through the NCI, which was very unusual at the time. I recall that Charlie said that he was encouraged by Congressman he knew who served on a budget committee overseeing the NIH budget. While being new to NIH grant writing, Charlie's grants to support resident training in clinical and laboratory brain tumor research and a Program Project grant to support brain tumor research were both approved after their initial application. The latter grant was the first multi-year brain tumor research grant in the United States, and, with that grant, the Brain Tumor Research Center support was guaranteed for several years. The rest is history as the Brain Tumor Research Center remained continuously funded by the NIH to this writing.

Charlie's goal for the Brain Tumor Research Center was to

create a laboratory environment to conduct radiation and cytotoxic chemotherapy research that would help to improve future clinical therapies. Initially, Charlie also agreed to support immunology research, but that research area turned out to be nonproductive and was dropped from the program after a couple of years. While Charlie was not a laboratory scientist, he was very well read in the field. His neurosurgical practice was too large and his commitment to his patients too strong for him to pursue his own research agenda. Nonetheless, he had an outsized impact on the Brain Tumor Research Center by recruiting and supporting research investigators to successfully compete for the first Program Project grant (called a PO1 grant) in the United States for glioma brain tumor research. In addition, principal investigators in the Brain Tumor Research Center were also strongly encouraged to obtain their own NIH research grants (called an RO1 grant) to support their individual research. This strong push into NCI-funded research, along with private philanthropic funds from grateful patients, provided a strong financial basis and cushion for young scientists to move forward in laboratory research at the Brain Tumor Research Center.

Charlie also joined the new NCI-sponsored brain tumor clinical program, the Brain Tumor Study Group (Chapter 6), which was established primarily by neurosurgeons to conduct clinical trials in patients with high-grade gliomas. At the inception of the Brain Tumor Study Group most were skeptical about the benefit of chemotherapy. It was into this milieu that I was recruited in 1972, to be a Principal Investigator in the Brain Tumor Research Center and to conduct pharmacology research.

My initial appointments were in the Departments of Neurological Surgery, Neurology, and Pharmacology in the School of Medicine and in the Department of Pharmaceutical Chemistry in the School of Pharmacy. Charlie had recruited me to conduct anticancer drug pharmacology research at the Brain Tumor Research Center, so these appointments fit in nicely with my academic goals and interests.

UCSF was a very exciting place to be in the 1970s and 1980s. In addition, we were driving distance to colleagues and potential collaborators at Lawrence-Livermore Labs, Lawrence Radiation Laboratories, UC Berkeley, and Stanford University and Medical School. My colleagues and I felt as if we were at the center of the medical scientific universe and the Brain Tumor Research Center was the epicenter for brain tumors. Times and opportunities were different then, and I was required to work and contribute to each department in which I had a faculty appointment. This was critical to my academic growth and the research I would ultimately do in experimental therapeutics, pharmacokinetics, pharmacology, and drug development.

As those who have trained or worked with me know, I had and still have little patience. Consequently, although I had been hired primarily for my pharmacology and research expertise, I wanted to contribute more. So, within a year, I was seeing patients in the clinical Brain Tumor Chemotherapy Service and, with that, the imperative to improve therapy for CNS tumor patients became incorporated into my psyche and the driving force for the rest of my career.

When I arrived at UCSF, my original laboratory was not yet available as it was yet to be vacated by Elizabeth Roboz Einstein, an esteemed biochemist and neuroscientist who had purified and characterized myelin basic protein and had done important research in neurodegenerative diseases and multiple sclerosis. Since I could not get my lab going quickly, I ended up following Charlie Wilson on his morning hospital rounds. These rounds started at 6:00 AM so as not to interfere with his morning surgeries. These rounds were different than what I had experienced at MGH on my two one-month rotations on neurosurgery because almost all the patients I saw were Charlie's patients and the vast majority had some type of brain tumor and were either postoperative or were inpatients receiving intravenous BCNU. In those days, patients received intravenous chemotherapy as inpatients, not treated as outpatients like today.

By mid-1973, I decided that my neurology training had given me insight into the care of these patients, and I had an aptitude for conducting clinical trials using the same cytotoxic drugs I was studying in the laboratory. Charlie agreed and encouraged me to join the Brain Tumor Chemotherapy Service, even though he already had a neurosurgery fellow who was helping with the chemotherapy patients being treated on Brain Tumor Study Group protocols. Within a year, I was overseeing all the patients on the Brain Tumor Chemotherapy Service. Within another year, I was running the program as Charlie was happy to focus on surgery, residency training, and overseeing Brain Tumor Research Center hiring and grants. In 1977, I officially became the Chief of the Brain Tumor Chemotherapy Service, which I would later rename the Neuro-Oncology Service.

9

Growing Impact of UCSF on the Field of Neuro-Oncology

Living in the San Francisco Bay Area and working at UCSF in the 1970s and 1980s was fun and scientifically exciting. UCSF and other institutions in the Bay Area were changing the life sciences and creating biotechnology companies like Genentech. The School of Pharmacy—the most prestigious school of pharmacy in the Western Hemisphere at that time—had typically garnered more NIH grant support than any other school of pharmacy in North America during the past forty years. In addition, the Department of Pharmaceutical Chemistry in the School of Pharmacy had received more grant support than any school of pharmacy in North America at the time and, from what I understand, to this day. This was also the time of Michael Bishop and Harold Varmus, whose large laboratory programs in the School of Medicine would eventually lead them to receive the Nobel Prize in Medicine.

In addition to research at UCSF, exciting research was being conducted at The University of California at Berkeley, the Lawrence Livermore Laboratory and Stanford University. It was not unusual to collaborate with research and clinical investigators at two or three of these institutions to solve a problem as quickly and efficiently as possible. It was a time when young researchers like me thought anything was possible. It was also an enabling research environment that accepted failure as precondition for success. Research setbacks were an inconvenience to advancing research, not viewed as roadblocks, the way they are sometimes considered today.

When I started to work at UCSF in July 1972, my primary appointment was in the Department of Neurological Surgery. I also had an appointment in the Department of Neurology since I was a neurologist, and it was logical that I might want to practice neurology in addition to conducting research in the Brain Tumor Research Center and the Department of Neurological Surgery. Of significance also were joint appointments in the Department of Pharmaceutical Chemistry in the School of Pharmacy and in the newly created Clinical Pharmacology Program that was headed by Kenneth Melmon, MD. That appointment led to a joint faculty appointment to the Department of Pharmacology. The latter two appointments were arranged by Charlie Wilson and were very important as they were instrumental to some of the collaborations and research I would do at UCSF.

During the next 16 years, I was an active member in the four departments and programs. In addition, I periodically lectured medical students and pharmacy students on cancer pharmacology and pharmacokinetics. My laboratory research efforts focused almost exclusively on regional pharmacokinetics of anticancer agents in normal brain, irradiated brain, and intracerebral rodent tumor models and the CSF pharmacokinetics and toxicity of anticancer agents in beagle dogs. I was also involved with training fellows in clinical pharmacology and neuro-oncology. At my request, in 1977, I became the first academician designated in the professorial series as an Associate Professor of Neuro-Oncology at UCSF.

In 1981 I was promoted to Professor of Neuro-Oncology in the Department of Neurological Surgery and Pharmacology in the UCSF School of Medicine and Professor of Pharmaceutical Chemistry in the UCSF School of Pharmacy.

Joining the Department of Neurological Surgery and Brain Tumor Research Center in 1972 were important and enabling research decisions. These choices ran counter to the conservative culture at MGH. There, clinical faculty were expected to follow a traditional path - get a prestigious clinical appointment at one of the Harvard-affiliated hospitals, do some clinical case-based research, and, if you found a position that allowed time for research and had space to accommodate research maybe try to obtain some research support. Whatever roles you chose to embark on, do so in a methodical and measured pace that allowed you to stay within the bounds of the department structure. No matter how I viewed these paths, I found them much too slow and restrictive for me. At UCSF, I felt like I was on a frontier. Taking chances, doing new things, deviating outside a comfort zone became my normal, rather than adhering to the orthodoxy of tradition. This perspective was reinforced by other research faculty in the UCSF Schools of Medicine and Pharmacy.

To fully appreciate the environment I would come to cherish and the opportunities and scale of research being conducted in the Brain Tumor Research Center and elsewhere at UCSF, I will describe some of the research being done during my sixteen years there. I also will describe the Brain Tumor Chemotherapy Service that I grew and changed before leaving UCSF in July 1988.

When I arrived in San Francisco July 1972, the UCSF Medical Center was a constrained space unable to comfortably accommodate all the programs that would develop in the ensuing decade. All neuro-oncology programs at the time were nascent, providing great opportunities for dedicated researchers and physicians willing to work in somewhat limiting physical spaces. A good example was our outpatient examine room.

Walking down the seventh-floor corridor from the Department of Neurosurgery offices in the hallway of Moffitt Hospital, you would pass our neuro-oncology clinic room on the right side of the hall, just before reaching the main hospital. As you walked into the modified four-bed hospital room you would see a maroon couch that doubled as an examining "chair" for ambulatory patients and adjacent seating to accommodate family members or their friends accompanying the patient. Walking over to the couch, you would pass a gray-blue cloth covered divider and counter on the left, behind which a nurse, and later, where a receptionist would seat. To the right would be another divider separating the examining couch from two desks and chairs where our fellows wrote their notes.

In my years at UCSF, I never heard a patient or family member complain about our limited clinic space. In some ways, the space was a homey environment. The converted four-bed room was, however, too small to provide space for us to give IV anticancer drug therapies, so we "borrowed" an EEG telemonitoring room when it was not in use. On the upholstered bed of the telemonitoring room, our nurses and, sometimes fellows, prepared IV bags for IV drugs including BCNU, dacarbazine, vincristine, 5-fluorouracil (5-FU), bromodeoxyuridine, and many other drugs that were experimental and never made it into the clinic. It was more convenient and less expensive for us to treat our patients in inpatient rooms or in the UCSF medical hematology-oncology small treatment area. It would take many years before we had an infusion center at UCSF that we could refer patients to for IV therapies. Not until 1987 were we able to obtain more conventional clinic space in a medical office building across Parnassus Street to house the Neuro-Oncology Service.

In our converted four-bed hospital room, we examined patients and consented them for many clinical trials that helped mold the field of neuro-oncology. Between 1973 and 1988, we initiated approximately thirty clinical chemotherapy, radiation therapy and combined radiation-chemotherapy trials for CNS neoplasms. Our group produced the first methodology to evaluate and semi-quantify CNS tumor response and progression as well as collecting observations and approaches important to best practices in neuroimaging at the time.

Here we started the first community program using disposable intravenous pumps for long-term chemotherapy. We were among the first to use the experimental disposable intravenous infusor pumps (Centrisil, Travenol Laboratories, Chicago) to deliver 3 day/week infusions of 5-FU and 4 day/week bromodeoxyuridine infusions for hyperfractionated radiation therapy studies. We mailed infusion pumps loaded with drug for multi-week treatments to our patients. Either the patient or a family member that we trained exchanged new pumps for empty used pumps. Today, that procedure is not feasible given existing regulatory restrictions used to "protect" patients and validate insurance billing. In the more than 10 years of conducting clinical trials, we never had an infection from an intravenous pump used at home or an error with a pump that put any patient at risk.

Looking back at those years at UCSF, I am appreciative of the opportunities I had, the friendships made, colleagues I worked with, and the clinical team that led to so many advances in therapeutic neuro-oncology for adults and children. The laboratory and clinical research we accomplished in the 16 years I was at UCSF would be hard to accomplish today given the academic and hospital focus on costs, professional salaries, and burdensome regulations and costs associated with clinical trials.

I have always been driven to achieve goals that I felt were important to me, my patients, future patients, and the greater world if my research was successful. Making the time to do this was critical and led, sometimes, to putting my family activities second to my work. In retrospect, I probably took my family for granted when I really should not have. This was a culturally conditioned partnership in those days and fell within normal expectations. Ellen, and I each grew up in families where our parents were partners in marriage and trusted each other. Our mothers were expected to support their husbands who worked long hours without complaint. Consequently, from the beginning of our married life, Ellen and I viewed marriage as a partnership and our financial independence was important to us. Between my part-time summer work and Ellen's job after undergraduate graduation, we paid for the rest of my medical school education without being in lingering debt.

I expected Ellen to be responsible for managing our money and making the necessary purchases and never questioned her choices and judgment. Once we had children, her family responsibilities increased more than mine since I was so focused on my career. Ellen took responsibility for raising our children and ensuring their participation in religious activities, various sports, and for their music lessons. She also ran the house, worked outside the house, did volunteer work, and served as an officer in our synagogue.

Besides being mother to our two children and Chief Operating Officer of our household, Ellen worked part time as a Research Associate in the Lymphoma Research laboratory of Marshall Kadin, MD, at UCSF. After a year doing lymphoma research Ellen went to graduate school to earn a Master of Clinical Laboratory Science degree from UCSF. She then worked for a time as a Medical Technologist at Kaiser Permanente in San Rafael to retain her Medical Technology license and then taught Medical Technology at San Francisco State University. Following that, she joined my research laboratory and collaborated with me on my National Cooperative Drug Discovery Group (NCDDG) grant to create drug inhibitors of the catalytic site of the c-Src protein tyrosine kinase. She worked with Lazlo Nadasdi, PhD, a peptide chemist I had recruited from Hungry to conduct the peptide research portion of our NCDDG research.

Ellen and the children made it possible for me to devote most of my time to my UCSF research and patients, working six to seven days a week. There were also laboratory parties and later Brain Tumor Research Center parties at our home. Ellen donned the party planning hat when we entertained Brain Tumor Research Center colleagues at our home, coordinated events and did most of the cooking and food preparation. While I sometimes helped with these parties, none of them would have been possible without Ellen's skill and hard work. Her help and support became even more important when we moved to The University of Texas MD Anderson Cancer Center in late 1988.

—∞—

Joining a funded program and research center provided our family with financial stability and a framework that allowed my creative investigations to succeed. I felt I could do any research needed to solve a problem when I joined UCSF.

Our Program Project grant has a rich history. It was the first NIH PO1 on brain tumors to be funded by the NCI in the United States under the aegis of the NIH. The overall intent of this initial proposal was to bring together a diversified group of scientists and physicians to study malignant brain tumors, with the goal of using laboratory findings to design and conduct successful clinical trials. The Program Project provided the means for Brain Tumor Research Center investigators to carry out translational research, making it one of the first cancer centers in the world to do so.

The first application was funded for a two-year period. During this time, Charlie Wilson, the original principal investigator, assembled a team of young physicians and scientists with expertise in clinical trials, biochemistry, biophysics, cell kinetics and pharmacology. Fundraising was initiated, and laboratories were outfitted.

The organization required to conduct clinical trials was put into place. Laboratory support personnel were hired and initial collaborations with other scientists and physicians were established.

With the initial funding of this Program Project in 1972, the Brain Tumor Research Center was effectively born. The new investigators devised then state-of-the-art projects using their scientific and medical expertise and applied for the first competitive renewal in 1974. The NIH grant renewal was funded for a three-year period. Funding for Program Project Grants and later a SPORE grant continually funded brain tumor research in the Department of Neurological Surgery for the next thirty-five years.

Because brain tumor therapy and research are major aspects of neuro-oncology today, I think it is important to recount early attempts to understand and treat brain tumors and the subsequent evolution of Brain Tumor Research Center research over the years.

Two overlapping programmatic activities were supported by the Brain Tumor Research Center. The main activity was to conduct applied and goal-directed laboratory research to inform better clinical treatments for people with high-grade CNS tumors. The second program area was the clinical service to translate laboratory research into testable clinical trials for chemotherapy and radiation-chemotherapy protocols to improve the survival of people with CNS malignancies.

In 1973, I began treating patients on the Brain Tumor Chemo-therapy Service in the Department of Neurological Surgery. Shortly after I was promoted to associate professor in 1977, and the UCSF dean, Julie Krevans, allowed me to be called an Associate Professor of Neuro-Oncology, the Chemotherapy Service became the Neuro-Oncology Service.

10

The Importance of Conferences to the Nascent Neuro-Oncology Field

Writing a manuscript on the results of laboratory research or clinical trials is a great way to communicate contributions to a field, but often is not enough to spur new studies or encourage others who aspire to contribute to a field. Having an opportunity to meet someone in person to discuss research can be quite valuable at times. I have found that casual discussion with colleagues sometimes has a profound effect on research direction or consideration of a future research hypothesis. Sometimes these casual and post-talk discussions provide new insights not anticipated and collaborations not expected; both can be opportunities to create something better or new in research. It is wise to keep in mind that sometimes serendipity leading to a research or medical breakthrough has its nidus in unexpected discussions with colleagues.

From experiences at the NCI, MGH, and opportunities at UCSF, I understood that sharing research knowledge, teaching principles and networking were necessary to expand the laboratory and clinical research needed to advance CNS tumor research to help patients live longer. So, one day in 1974, after leaving our weekly laboratory research conference, I commented to Charlie in the hallway that, based on the literature at the time, it seemed that few people were doing brain tumor research in the world and that we and others would gain a great deal if we could have a meeting to discuss and share information and research ideas for brain tumor therapy. Charlie agreed immediately and suggested that I look at

Asilomar Conference Grounds in Pacific Grove on the Monterey, California coast to host a meeting. He recently had a UCSF retreat there and liked that it was driving distance from San Francisco. I enquired and found that lodgings were inexpensive, group meeting rooms were good size, and catered food services quite good and reasonably priced. In addition, it was easy walking distance to the beautiful Monterey shore. It seemed like a perfect place for interacting with attendees, networking, and discussing CNS tumor research in a leisurely and open environment.

With Charlie's advice and help, I put together the California Conference on Brain Tumor Therapy at Asilomar in Pacific Grove, CA on November 24-26, 1975. Charlie and I raised funds from the American Cancer Society (California Division), the NCI, Bristol Laboratories, Upjohn Company (with Jim Swenberg's help), and, of course, the Brain Tumor Research Center and our Department of Neurological Surgery. Through contacts I had established from the NCI and Southern Research, Charlie's contacts with the Brain Tumor Study Group, and Mike Walker of the NINDS, we invited 37 people we thought might be interested in attending our first conference. The invited clinicians and scientists came from 14 states and two countries and had different backgrounds and degrees (MD, PhD, DVM, MS). We provided housing, meals, and helped with travel costs for the 31 people (84%) who attended the California Conference with the funds we had raised.

Attending the first conference, besides Charlie and me, were, in alphabetical order: Jim Ausman (Neurosurgery, Mayo), Darell Bigner (Pathology, Duke), Ron Blasberg (NCI), Julian Bloom (Radiation Oncology, Royal Marsden, London), Derek Fewer (Neurosurgery, Winnipeg), Emil Freireich (Leukemia, MD Anderson), Phil Gutin (Neurosurgery, USPHS & NINDS, Baltimore), Corwin Hansch (Medicinal Chemistry, Pomona College), Wolff Kirsch (Neurosurgery, University of Colorado), Simon Kramer (Radiation Oncology, Jefferson School of Medicine, Philadelphia),

John Leith (Radiobiology, Lawrence Radiation Laboratory), Joe Ransohoff (Neurosurgery, NYU), Lucien Rubinstein and Mary Herman (Neuropathology, Stanford), Frank Schabel, Jr. (Southern Research), Bill Shapiro (Neurology, MSKCC), Charles Tator (Neurosurgery, Sunnybrook Hospital, University of Toronto), John Venditti and Isidore Wodinsky (Medicinal Chemistry and Tumor Biology, NCI), Mike Walker (Neurosurgeon) and Tom Strike (NINDS), Gordon Zubrod (Medical Oncology and Director of University of Miami Cancer Center). In addition, there were also seven other attendees from the Brain Tumor Research Center and Neurological Surgery at UCSF: Marvin Barker, Edwin Boldrey, David Crafts, Takao Hoshino, Lawrence Marton, Mark Rosenblum, and Kenneth Wheeler.

The first conference program covered six topics: 1) carcinogen-induced and transplantable rodent tumors, 2) chemotherapy and radiotherapy of rodent brain tumor models, 3) regional tumor pharmacokinetics, 4) anticancer drug structure-activity relationships in CNS leukemia and brain tumors, 5) the CSF pathway for drug delivery and approaches to drug combination therapies and 6) clinical discussions of external beam radiation, adjuvant chemotherapy, and chemotherapy for recurrent tumors. Emil "Jay" Freireich, MD, a renowned leukemia physician, from The University of Texas MD Anderson Cancer Center, was the keynote speaker at our banquet and spoke on "An Outsider's View of Brain Tumor Therapy." By all accounts, the conference was a great success with open scientific discourse where differences in opinions could be voiced and discussed.

The second conference was held two years later since progress in brain tumor research and treatment was not occurring at a fast enough pace to warrant yearly meetings. The second meeting was called the Brook Lodge Workshop on Brain Tumor Therapy and was held at Brook Lodge (an Upjohn Company facility) in Kalamazoo, Michigan on October 24-26, 1977. It was organized by Jim Swenberg, a DVM and toxicologist for the Upjohn Company and the meeting's sponsor. This meeting attracted 40 participants from 32 institutions and six countries. The workshop sessions were on 1) brain tumors and their milieu in the brain from structural, morphological, biochemical, and immunologic viewpoints, 2) immunology of brain tumors and therapeutic potential, 3) experimental approaches to evaluate drug activity in cell culture and animals, 4) understanding the effects of alkylating agents on DNA and glioma and metastatic rodent tumor model growth, and 5) clinical studies. The clinical studies reported on irradiation for primary and metastatic CNS tumors, intra-tumor drug delivery, and polyamine markers of tumor recurrence. This meeting resulted in a 1000- to 2000-word summary for each talk that appeared in Japanese and English.

The Third Conference on Brain Tumor Research and Therapy was held again at Asilomar, in Pacific Grove on October 29-31, 1979, and was organized and co-chaired by me and Charlie Wilson with substantial input from other members of the Brain Tumor Research Center. There were about 48 attendees at this conference from six countries. For this meeting, I was able to get support from the NCI, Bristol Laboratories, Upjohn Company, and E.R. Squibb & Sons. The Brain Tumor Research Center at UCSF provided administrative support for the meeting gratis. By the time of this conference, the field was maturing, and clinical trials were presented from the Brain Tumor Study Group and the Brain Tumor Research Center at UCSF, EORTC (Brussels), and the Royal Marsden Hospital (London). There were talks on regional pharmacokinetics, drug permeability studies, intraarterial drug delivery, and osmotic opening of the blood-brain barrier therapy. There were also more sophisticated studies of tumor phenotype, tumor cytogenetics, and new intracerebral nude (special immune-deficient mice) mouse models. Quantitative effects of alkylating agents on clonogenic cells from tumors, tumor cell heterogeneity, and drug resistance were being presented together with drug effects on growth and differentiation in culture. In addition, new hypoxic radiosensitizers were being studied in cell culture and in animals as harbingers of clinical trials that would follow.

While the decision to hold these conferences every two years was agreed upon by organizers and attendees alike, the location of the conference was more freewheeling and depended on who wanted to organize the conference. With tacit agreement, every other meeting was expected to be held in the USA. Over the years, even when the name of the conference changed, older attendees still affectionately referred to these conferences as the Asilomar Conference. In the pages that follow I describe a series of bi-annual conferences, some of which I helped organize, and many others organized by colleagues in Japan, Europe, Canada, and the United States. I always felt that these conferences helped lay some of the groundwork for neuro-oncology programs in the United State, Europe, and Japan.

For the fourth conference, and the first held outside of the USA, it was decided to rename the conference as the International Conference on Brain Tumor Research and Therapy to reflect its international appeal. This conference was held October 14-16, 1981, at the Nikko Prince Hotel in Nikko, Japan. The conference was organized by Keiji Sano, the elder statesman of brain tumor neurosurgery in Japan. Takao Hoshino and I helped Dr. Sano develop the program for the conference.

The Conference was a great success with wonderful memories. We had 85 attendees from the United States, Canada, Japan, and Europe. This conference covered some new topics, such as epidemiology of brain tumors in Japan and the United States as well as environmental exposure and carcinogenicity. Clinical trials from the Brain Tumor Study Group, Brain Tumor Research Center, and the EORTC were also presented. From Japanese colleagues, we heard about ACNU, a new nitrosourea that was being investigated by the IV and intraarterial routes in high-grade glioma clinical trials. Other clinical studies presented were PET results of CNS tumors, extensive radiobiological studies, clinical interstitial 125I studies, RT-drug combinations, and tumor hyperthermia studies. Laboratory studies presented were tumor cell proliferation kinetics, spheroid culture studies of drug effects, and relationships of alkylating drug activity to tumor cell cycle kinetics of tumors taken from patients at different ages. Also presented were some of the early studies of polyamine inhibitors such as DFMO and biologic response modifiers.

In 1983, the Fifth International Conference on Brain Tumor Research and Therapy returned to Asilomar in Pacific Grove, California on October 23-26. Approximately 100 attended this meeting, from six countries. I organized this meeting with the help of Dennis Deen and Marvin Barker, colleagues in the Brain Tumor Research Center. In the process of raising funds to support the Fifth Conference, we made application to the National Institute of Neurological and Communicative Disorders and Stroke (NINCDS) but were met with criticism of the exclusive "by invitation only" nature of the meeting. Fortunately. that year funding was obtained to help support this conference but not those that followed. While reviewing my 1982 NINCDS application for this meeting, I came across a sentence I had written that "Ideally, this conference should focus on new drug design, but, unfortunately, the conceptual basis for such a consideration is premature." Sadly, more than 30 years later, that statement still rings true, although scientists have made great strides in understanding the molecular genetics of the various tumor subtypes (phenotypes) and how different cellular signaling molecules impact cell division, invasion, and resistance to treatment.

In the 1983 program, we had sessions on brain metastases, monoclonal antibodies, and pediatric tumor classification, brachy-therapy, radiation dose fractionation, hyperthermia, chemotherapy for adults CNS tumors as well as investigations into the use of PET and NMR scanning and spectroscopy. One of my recollections of the fifth conference was about the final group dinner. We thought some dinner entertainment would be a nice addition to the evening, so I hired a local comedian who lived in Monterey, California. To surprise the banquet attendees, I told only one colleague, Mike Edwards, a UCSF neurosurgeon, about the planned evening's entertainment. I instructed the comedian to work as a waiter during part of the dinner while Mike and I started to tell jokes. After we told a couple of our jokes, I suggested that the waiter "could tell better jokes." And of course, he could, and he did, but some colleagues in the audience became uncomfortable as they did not know if it was appropriate to laugh at the waiter's jokes and enjoy the shenanigans. Later in the evening, the comedian told me that this was the hardest group he ever had to entertain. The lesson learned from that experience was that surprises like that were not welcomed by this group of physicians and laboratory scientists.

—⁂—

In June 1985, Jerzy Georges Hildebrand organized a European Organization for Research and Treatment of Cancer (EORTC) meeting entitled "Consensus Meeting of Treatment of Brain Tumours" that was held in Lausanne, Switzerland. This meeting was focused on the treatment of primary CNS tumors, including primary CNS lymphoma. Ellen accompanied me to Switzerland for these meetings. We stayed in Geneva our first night in Switzerland, and the next day Nicolas de Tribolet invited us to stay at the de Tribolet family Chateau in Motier that was built in 1715 where he would be hosting a reception and dinner for some of the meeting attendees. I found the Chateau quite enchanting and fascinating. The kitchen, on the first floor, had a large walk-in fireplace for cooking food. Nicolas told me that Jean-Jacques Rousseau spent a couple of years in Môtiers when he was banned from France because of his revolutionary writings and was often a guest of Nicolas' ancestors. Since Nicolas had recently been promoted to Professor in the Department of Neurosurgery in Lausanne, he invited me to go with him into the basement wine cellar before the reception and dinner and to retrieve a bottle of Mouton Roth 1965 that his father had put away many years before just for this occasion of Nicolas becoming a professor. Nicolas had waited for me to arrive to share this bottle of wine and to celebrate his promotion together.

That night we slept in a second-floor bedroom furnished in antique family furniture after enjoying a wonderful dinner and late evening discussions sitting around the fireplace with Nicolas, his wife, Vernique, and George Hildebrand. Ellen and I have fond memories of the time we spent in Môtiers, and the wonderful time we had visiting Switzerland before and after the meetings.

The Sixth International Conference on Brain Tumor Research and Therapy was held at the Grove Park Inn, Asheville, North Carolina, on October 21-23, 1985, a decade after these conferences were started. Approximately 130 attended. The co-chairs were Cliff Schold, Charlie Wilson, and Darell Bigner. This meeting was funded by the NIH, the Association for Brain Tumor Research, Burroughs-Welcome, Bristol-Myers, Dupont, and the neurosurgery departments at The University of North Carolina, Duke, and Northwestern. Topics were oncogenes and growth factors, carcinogenesis, drug mechanisms, immunobiology, drug delivery, tumor imaging, chemotherapy, and radiotherapy. This meeting had two large poster sessions where attendees who had not been asked to speak were given an opportunity to show and discuss their research in a room where posters could be mounted on boards for viewing by attendees as they walked by the posters. During those years as today, attendees at conferences such as the International Conference on Brain Tumor Research and Therapy had to justify requesting travel money from their institutions to attend the Conference, and it was easier to obtain travel funds if the attendee was presenting either a platform presentation or poster at the Conference.

Masakatsu Nagai and I were co-chairs of the Seventh International Conference on Brain Tumor Research and Therapy held at the Yamano Hotel in Hakone, Japan on October 18-21, 1987. The meeting was funded by the Association for Brain Tumor Research, the Friends of Brain Tumor Research, the Preuss Foundation, the Stanley Gore Memorial Fund, the Japan Brain Tumor Foundation, and 24 pharmaceutical companies in Japan. NIH support was not available because of the invitation-only nature of the conference. About 150 physicians and scientists attended this conference. There were 94 abstracts at this meeting that were published in the Journal of Neuro-Oncology and a meeting space provided for formal poster sessions for those whose abstracts were not accepted for presentation. Topics covered were oncogenes and growth factors, genetics and lineage-specific expression, cytokines, and immunotherapy, radiotherapeutic approaches, cell proliferation, drug resistance and cytotoxic chemotherapy.

This was a memorable conference for many reasons. In addition to attending the scientific sessions of the Conference, Ellen and I had time to visit the nearby Hakone Open Air Museum where large sculptures of Henry Moore, Picasso, and others were set amid the garden. Nearby, we also were able to visit the Picasso Museum that housed a large portion of his ceramic works. In addition, post-Conference we and some of the other speakers and organizers stayed a day at a local Ryokan, a traditional Japanese inn, where we lounged in yukata, a multicolored bathrobe, and experienced life of the Japanese traveler of a past time. At night, after a delicious Japanese banquet, we drank and sang karaoke style long into the night. Of the many pictures we have of that night, I have two showing me singing with Keiji Sano and with Nicolas and Veronique de Tribolet. Unfortunately, smartphones did not exist then, so we have no recording of our singing that night.

The Eighth International Conference on Brain Tumor Research and Therapy was held in Zermatt, Switzerland on September 11-13,

1989. The meeting was chaired by Nicolas de Tribolet and co-chaired by Darrell Bigner and Paul Kleihues. The Conference focused on the evolving areas of molecular genetics, oncogenes, cell differentiation, tumor invasion, new treatment modalities, and mechanisms of resistance to cytotoxic drugs. The town of Zermatt is in view of the Matterhorn Mountain and quite visually stunning. One afternoon after the day's meetings, we embarked on the Gornergrat Railway. We were served red and white wine as well as cheese and dried meat during the train trip. Some colleagues and attendees of the Conference drank a bit too much and were a bit tipsy upon arrival at Gornegrat. Attesting to their health and determination, they managed to walk the 3 kilometers back down the mountain to Zermatt; likely sobering up on the trek back to Zermatt.

The Ninth International Conference on Brain Tumor Research and Therapy was held at the Asilomar Conference Grounds in Pacific Grove on October 15-18, 1991. The conference was chaired by Charles Wilson and co-chaired by Darrell Bigner and Nicolas de Tribolet. The focus of this conference was on clinical trials, new radiation approaches, new chemotherapy and immunotherapy approaches, normal CNS tissue damage from irradiation, and poly-amine metabolism in CNS cancer patients. The ninth International Conference on Brain Tumor Research and Therapy was unique in that it was the first conference covered in programmatic detail as a journal article.

The Tenth International Conference on Brain Tumor Research and Therapy was held at the Stalheim Hotel, in Voss, Norway on September 6-9, 1993. The conference was organized and chaired by Ole Didrik Laerum and co-chaired by Darrell Bigner, Paul Kleihues, Nicolas de Tribolet, Nicolas Vick, and Charles Wilson. The abstracts from this conference were published. As this was my first trip to Norway, Ellen joined me for the meeting and for some vacation travel afterwards. We have many good memories of the meeting and the small boat trip we took through the fjords near Voss. We also remember, as part of that boat trip, stopping at a small town on the fjord where we tasted goat cheese made by a group being taught a French method that produced an excellent cheese without even a hint that it was made from goat milk.

The Eleventh International Conference on Brain Tumor Research and Therapy was held at the Silverado Country Club, Napa, California, on October 31-November 3, 1995. The conference was organized by Charles Wilson and co-chaired by Paul Kleihues and Nicolas Vick with the program organization the responsibility of Dennis Deen in the Brain Tumor Research Center. This meeting was the largest Conference at the time with 276 participants. Abstracts of presentations and conference posters were published in the Journal of Neuro-Oncology. A social event for this conference was memorable for its location. One evening we were bused to the Jarvis Winery in Napa. From the road it was not much to see, but once inside the door, we were invited into their winemaking facility, a 45,000 square feet cave. The cave had been bored into the Vaca Mountains using British technology and equipment to produce parabolic shaped tunnels and caves. Inside the cave was a running stream and an artificial waterfall coming out of rock and an alcove displaying a large amethyst quartz rock. It was not only a visual masterpiece, but a technical masterpiece as well. Ellen and I enjoyed walking around the underground winery eating appetizers, tasting different wines, and talking with friends.

As an aside, years later, while flying from Beppu to Narita Airport (Japan) I was seated next to a young man who I made small talk with as the plane was preparing to take flight. I thought by his accent that he was Australian, but he informed me that he was English but did spend a lot of time in Australia. I inquired what he did for a living, and he told me that he worked for an English company that made tunneling equipment. So, I said that I had been in the caves of the Jarvis Winery that had been dug using tunneling equipment. "That was our equipment and I worked on tunneling the winery" he said. As a scientist, I felt that the probability of that exchange occurring on a short internal flight in Japan was somewhere near one in a million.

Subsequent International Conferences on Brain Tumor Research and Therapy continued bi-yearly through 2018, as the 2020 conference had to be canceled because of the SARS-CoV-9 pandemic.

—◊◊—

I was invited to attend and speak at the first meeting of the Asian Society for Neuro-Oncology (ASNO) that was held in Kumamoto, Japan in November 2002. It was a memorable event since the society had recently been created by the brain tumor societies or neuro-oncology societies of Japan, Korea, China, Taiwan, and Turkey. The goal was to create an educational international neuro-oncology society to promote neuro-oncology in all Asian countries and to build up a close and friendly connection with EANO and SNO and to have a voice in the World Federation of Neuro-Oncology (WFNO). Over the years since its founding, ASNO has grown to include Australia, Hong Kong, India, Indonesia, and the Philippines. Ellen and I both enjoyed the meeting as we visited with old friends and made some new ones. What I remember best was during an evening banquet being asked to give a short extemporaneous speech. In the presence of many colleagues and friends who were older than me, I decided to start my short talk with the observation that at 61 years of age "this was the first after dinner speech I have given where I was the youngest speaker." As everyone burst out laughing at this remark, I did not have to say more than to congratulate the organizers of the meeting and wish the new ASNO great success in the future.

—◊◊—

After my departure from the UCSF faculty and my move to The University of Texas MD Anderson Cancer Center to Chair the Department of Neuro-Oncology in 1988, I felt a distance being created between me and those taking over the reins for planning future International Conferences on Brain Tumor Research and Therapy. Since these conferences were UCSF-centric, I accepted that reality.

In retrospect, at the time of the 1995 International Conferences on Brain Tumor Research and Therapy at the Silverado Country Club in Napa, I had underestimated the extent that my neuro-surgical colleagues liked and wanted to continue these Conferences. Conversely, these conferences were becoming less important to me as I was putting my efforts into the creation of the Society for Neuro-Oncology and its first annual meeting that would be in 1996.

I had my reservations about the structure of these International Conferences that had to be limited in size and, therefore, were by invitation and/or permission to attend. I also thought that they allowed too many speakers resulting in very short talks, sometimes only to 4 minutes in length. My concern for the meeting structure also grew as it diverged from my original vision and the intentions of the original organizers of the conferences. Without much tact on my part, I put forward my belief that the new Society for Neuro-Oncology would better be able to organize meaningful meetings for physicians and scientists interested in CNS tumors and could potentially replace the International Conference on Brain Tumor Research and Therapy with more productive meetings. This position was a minority opinion and not well received. In fact, to some of the organizers of the International Conferences it was, in retrospect, a hurtful commentary on their efforts, over the years, to organize and attend prior International Conferences. For my candor and impatience, I was organizationally disinvited from the group that would plan future international conferences. As a result, and to ensure the purpose and direction of future conferences did not change into another Society for Neuro-Oncology conference, Charlie made it clear that he would keep these Conferences going with planning and organization through UCSF.

Since I viewed starting these meetings and, later, starting SNO to be ventures akin to raising a child, I watched with disappointment the direction the International Conference on Brain Tumor Research and Therapy was taking. I was proud that the idea gestated at UCSF in 1974, was still going strong and, to an extent, did meet some of the needs of the field from a neurosurgical perspective. It was still a place to network and help make a better neuro-oncology world and move the field foward.

Over the years since that fateful day in November 1995 when I was critical of the direction the International Conference on Brain Tumor Research and Therapy was taking as I felt they deviated too far from their original intent, nonetheless, I must admit that in 2014, when I attended the Twentieth International Conference on Brain Tumor Research and Therapy at the Ritz Carlton Hotel in Truckee, California, I found it gratifying to see how the neuro-oncology communities had embraced and sustained the special meetings Charlie Wilson and I first conceived four decades earlier. At that conference and with the perspective of many decades, I have mellowed and changed my opinion on the value of these conferences and accepted its idiosyncrasy, importance, and networking value. My memories of the meetings, the meeting places I visited, and the friends I made through these meetings remain with me today and, hopefully, those memories will continue for many years to come.

11

The UCSF Brain Tumor
Chemotherapy Service Goes Digital

The Brain Tumor Chemotherapy Service aspired to be as scientific and as innovative as possible. One initial goal I set was to develop criteria and methodologies to accurately define tumor progression and therapeutic failure. Another goal was to define therapeutic benefit, such as stopping the tumor's growth (called stable disease), or an actual improvement (called partial response). While complete response was sometimes seen in other cancers, like Hodgkin lymphoma and testicular cancer, it was virtually unheard of in patients with primary CNS tumors. The laboratory research that would one day impact the treatment of CNS tumor patients was initially focused upon brain and spinal cord tumor patients with the emphasis being on cytotoxic chemotherapy, irradiation, and chemotherapy modification of the radiation response.

In the beginning, before the computerized tomography (CT) era, we developed criteria for following patients using clinical examination, electroencephalogram (EEG), and radionuclide scintiscan. We published these criteria in 1977. At the time, it seemed that the most reliable test to define tumor progression was the blinded EEG reading with the nuclear scintiscan being a close second in reliability. This EEG reading predicted progression based on increased regional distribution of slow wave activity. We also studied and understood the impact of the timing of IV-injected radionuclide tracer on the size of the tumor and, therefore, the risk of a false positive determination of tumor progression. By comparing scintiscans taken at one- and two-hour intervals after IV injection of technetium-99m DTPA, we were able to demonstrate the need for strict adherence to a specified time between injection and imaging to ensure that we were accurately designating treatment benefit or progression. In our 55-patient study, we concluded that a two-hour scan interval was most accurate as a long a delay between radionuclide tracer injection and scintiscan imaging allowed too much radionuclide tracer to diffuse from tumor into the surrounding brain.

Fortunately, neuroimaging technology accelerated quickly in the 1970s. When our initial papers on criteria for evaluating patients were in press, we were already participating in the birth of the CT era, and we developed new and more insightful criteria with which to evaluate CNS tumor progression and response. We no longer needed the EEG or radionuclide scintiscan to evaluate patients for progression or response. The CT scan alone was more accurate for defining response and progression than the radionuclide scintiscan and it was also a great help to neurosurgeons planning operations. The CT scan was a tremendous advance until the arrival of magnetic resonance imaging (MRI). While the MRI required much more machine time to obtain a full set of diagnostic algorithms, it provided so much more information. Initially, we found that it helped us to better understand the impact of radiation total dose, fraction size, and ports of delivery on the tumor and the surrounding brain. It also clarified other pathologies that could occur independently of infiltrative tumor. MRI technology has improved and become more sophisticated over time and, therefore, more informative to clinicians.

In the 1970s and 1980s a brain tumor diagnosis was more commonly an admitting diagnosis at UCSF than pregnancy, lung cancer, breast cancer, pneumonia, or heart failure; such was the magnitude of the neurosurgery program that Charlie oversaw. Charlie alone accounted for about 750 of the neurosurgical cases a year. Because of his draw as a neurosurgeon and our prominence as a program that coordinated post-surgical chemotherapy and radiation therapy for people with CNS tumors, our Brain Tumor Chemotherapy Service also grew proportionately in size. Most of our patients were not admitted as we established an outpatient IV service and utilized medical oncologists in the community for the convenience of our patients. I tried to create treatment plans for almost all the adult and pediatric tumors we saw, and, for many tumor pathologies, we created formalized clinical chemotherapy, chemoradiation, and radiation therapy studies in adults and children. We did all of this with me, the only non-surgical faculty member, a research nurse, a data manager, a receptionist, and one or two clinical neuro-oncology fellows.

During the 1970's I felt that we needed to have maximum efficiency to fully understand and conduct so many clinical trials and follow such a large patient population. I was reasonably computer savvy having programmed and used computers while at the NCI. While there, I had been using early primitive computers made by Wang and programming via a teletype terminal for programs to calculate my experiments and otherwise support my research. I also utilized these programs in my research when at the MGH. So, when I got NCI funding on our PO1 grant to purchase a Finnegan chemical ionization mass spectrometer (CI/MS) to conduct BCNU pharmacokinetic studies in humans, I looked around for a minicomputer to control the Finnegan and analyze measurements from it. After careful study, I purchased a Data General minicomputer that would allow foreground and background operation so that CI/MS could run in the foreground, and I could run MS-DOS and time-sharing BASIC language programs in the background.

Shortly after the Data General computer arrived, I decided that I needed computer-based word processing software. After some searching, I found and purchased a sophisticated word processing software package that ran on MS-DOS; it was called XyWrite and was the word processing software used by some editors and writers in newspapers and publishing houses at the time. After installing XyWrite, I wrote all my papers and grants on the computer. I even devised a reference and bibliography system so I also had online references that could be directly included in manuscripts and grants. As a result, my writing, and data collection productivity as well as that of my neuro-oncology fellows increased dramatically.

Within six months of installing XyWrite, I began to imagine the benefit of having a computer-based record system to better follow my patients and clinical trials. I had created forms for me to use to follow each patient's treatment, to tabulate blood counts, and to record the various measures we used to ascertain if the therapy they were on was working.

Since our clinical program was growing each year, I needed a more efficient system than paper forms and records to follow our patients and the various treatments they were receiving. Realizing that I could not buy the relational management data system I sought and being impatient to embrace the more efficient clinical future I envisioned, I approached Christopher "Kit" Dove, a computer programmer and soon to be husband of one of my laboratory technicians, Mary Freeman, and asked him if he could help me create a database system. Kit had graduated Yale with a mathematics major and liked to do computer programming to solve problems. At the time he was working on contract for various banks to improve their computer operations. He was a gifted programmer and wonderful human being, and he tentatively agreed to helping me develop a relational database in BASIC to run on my Data General minicomputer that I could use to follow patients and to conduct clinical trials more efficiently. Kit wanted to know exactly what I was looking for and how exactly the database would be used. He explained to me that writing the program code would not be difficult but designing the program around its intended use would be the hardest thing to do correctly. He disliked rewriting software code, something I understood from my own programming experience. Thus, I went through, what would be called, software design psychotherapy with Kit for a couple of months until he felt confident that I knew what I wanted, and he could safely design the structure of the software and be sure that I would be satisfied.

As a result of Kit's computer programming skills and commitment to our program, he was able to finish one of the first, if not the first relational database management system in the USA designed to manage cancer therapy information. The time-dependent information that was entered into our computer program included information like patient age, gender, height, weight, body surface area, past medical history, and non-chemotherapy drugs being taken. In addition, it included the extent of each surgery and its relevant pathology, all radiation therapies with doses and schedules, each chemotherapy drug with doses and dates of administration, adverse events, laboratory studies, neuroimaging type and date of studies, as well as physician scores reflecting the patient's clinical status and neuroimaging results for each visit. Prior to initiating our relational database coding, and unknown to us, the NCI had contracted the Rand Corporation to develop a relational database for patients on cancer therapy. From what we were told, Kit beat their team to the development of a functioning cancer therapy relational database. I always felt privileged to have known and worked with Kit Dove and fortunate that he was willing to create this relational database for us. It truly was a game-changing addition to our clinical program.

All patient data was manually entered through a Tektronix terminal by our data manager, initially Tana Pischer (Schimberg) and later, Pam Vestneys (Silver), as well as by moonlighting pharmacy students who worked nights and weekends. We were so immensely successful in this process that by about 1978, we were able to collate information on all active patients and going forward were able to track their medical course, weekly. Our research data manger and I ensured that the data entered was correct based on the computer record generated compared to paper records that we continued to keep in the clinic for each patient.

Kit had written the software knowing that I could read and understand program code and would be able to generate my own Boolean searches to pull out any information I wanted such as specific patient populations, treatments, pathology, MRI results, secondary diseases, medications taken, each surgery and each radiation course, or any data that was entered into the computer as a string variable and/or string variable with a numerical modifier. I took the computer output and utilized other programs I had written for basic statistical analyses to enable us to analyze patients for time to progression, overall survival, drug doses administered, radiation dose, radiation fraction size and schedule, other medical conditions, and toxicity to therapies.

In addition to writing all the Boolean searches and doing most of the basic statistics on the computer using software I had written, I also ensured that the computer was backed up daily and that the computer platters were secure. We stored one backup platter of patient files in a secure laboratory cabinet, and each week, about every other day, I would take one platter home.

Periodically, I provided my neuro-oncology fellows with study printouts and asked them if they wanted to write a manuscript on the study. No one said no to that inquiry and the opportunity to publish an article in a peer-reviewed journal. One of my fellows, Marc Chamberlain, a pediatric neurologist by training, was legendary in this regard. I could give Marc the data on Friday afternoon, and he would show me the first draft of the paper on Monday morning. Being able to have such easy access to full data for all our patients in a computerized relational database allowed our Brain Tumor Chemotherapy Service to leapfrog programs for many years and address population-based questions requiring large databases before it became commonplace in other academic neuro-oncology programs.

Another good example of the value of this database was an evaluation of glioma tumor growth patterns to understand the incidence of tumor multifocality. Ali Choucair, a neurologist and one of my fellows, found that from a population of 1047 patients the median time from diagnosis to detection of a second lesion was about 60 weeks and of 630 anaplastic glioma patients, only 9% developed multiple lesions within a median of two years. Ali also wanted to determine the risk of bleeding for patients treated with anticoagulation for deep vein thrombosis. When we queried the database, we found that among a group of 915 patients with a malignant glioma and a Karnofsky performance score equal to or greater than 60, only 4% developed venous thromboembolism and that no patient treated with the standard of care at the time, IV heparin for seven to ten days followed by oral warfarin, suffered an intracerebral bleed.

Another example of the importance of having a relational database management system in the 1970's and 1980's was the ability to ask a variety of questions about treatment and patterns of treatment outcomes. For instance, another fellow, William F. Hoffman, a neurosurgeon who had recently completed his residency in Missouri wanted to know how many glioma patients would suffer neurological and/or neuroimaging worsening after external beam radiation therapy (EBRT) and at what intervals of time after completion of EBRT. To determine this, I set up a Boolean search and found 262 patients with a total of 1290 MRIs who fit the criteria. CNS worsening occurred up to 18 weeks after EBRT, as ascertained from clinical examination, MRI scans, and glucocorticoid dosage. Interestingly, the progression we observed was not always true tumor growth, as 28% (7/25) of such cases subsequently improved without medical intervention. This subgroup experienced a sub-acute radiation treatment effect that is more commonly referred to as pseudo-progression today.

I also did a study in the 1980s that I never published that questioned whether having more information on the neurological examination would yield results like or better than our analog score of -2 (worse), 0 (stable) or +2 (better). As expected, having more neurological examination data available was not helpful. In fact, there was no correlation between findings of the neurological examination and overall neurological status that could be applied across all patients in a study, since tumor location and extent of resection drove neurological findings and obscured the value of scoring groups of specific physical signs or symptoms. From our perspective, it was clearly inferior to the global analog scoring system (+2, +1, 0, -1, -2) that we were using.

12

UCSF Research Opportunities and the People who Made it Possible

Even before starting at UCSF, I had a clear vision of what I wanted to do but lacked a clear roadmap of how to get there. I wanted to create new, more efficacious, and less toxic treatments for people with CNS tumors. I understood this would require well-designed research, discovery of new therapies and drugs, expanded collaboration, and a little serendipity. I was confident I would conduct some of that research and discovery and that I would know how to navigate the path with others I had met previously, those I was working with at UCSF, and those I would meet in the future.

The Brain Tumor Research Center was the ideal place to be when I started my academic career in 1972. Charlie Wilson's vision of the Center when he created it in 1968 was straightforward. Goal-directed laboratory research of chemotherapy agents and radiation therapies would, when translated to the treatment of people with primary infiltrative tumors such as high-grade gliomas and medulloblastoma, lead to patients living longer and with less toxicity from new treatments. Those of us in the Center joined this endeavor because we believed in its goal and our ability, through collaborative laboratory research, to eventually make a difference for our patients and other people in the world suffering from these tumors. We all were on a mission.

—※—

In the current milieu of molecular and genetic profiling of cancers it is instructive to consider the research conducted in the Brain

Tumor Research Center and the treatment changes, medical knowledge, radiobiologic advances, and pharmacology and regional pharmacokinetic insights this research fostered between 1972 and 1988, the time I worked at the Center. Those years were among my most productive research years and some of the most enjoyable ones as I was imbedded with a group of very bright and committed scientists who also enjoyed working and socializing together.

In my effort to create new and more effective treatments for patients with CNS tumors, I started working with alkylating agents at the NCI between 1967 and 1969 to determine the basis and limits of their efficacy; I continued that research work into the late 1970s at UCSF. At that time, as today, those drugs were understood to be of limited efficacy, generally palliative in their use, and capable of engendering at least five different mechanisms of failure or resistance to their antitumor efficacy. Resistance to therapy, even in the modern era of targeted therapies, remains a major limitation in cancer treatment. Thus, the investigators in the Brain Tumor Research Center pursued studies to better understand these drugs and how they might be used more effectively in brain tumor treatment.

It was my honor, in 1972, to be the first faculty member to be recruited specifically as a Brain Tumor Research Center Principal Investigator. Our early group of investigators established consequential and enduring collaborations with other scientists and clinicians at UCSF, Lawrence Livermore Laboratories, University of California Berkeley, and others. This set a precedent for the extensive collaborations that continued with subsequent investigators on the Brain Tumor Research Center Program Project (P01 grant).

Kenneth Wheeler, PhD, a radiation biophysicist, also joined the Center in 1972, shortly after I did. Ken was a warm and gregarious scientist who conducted high level and rigidly controlled experiments. Ken obtained his PhD in Radiation Biophysics from The University of Kansas, did a postdoctoral fellowship in Radiation Biology at

Colorado State University, and was then recruited to the Center. He was an expert in DNA damage and repair in mammalian cells. Some of his research focused on the cytotoxic effects of BCNU, alone and in combination with radiation *in vitro* and *in vivo* in the 9L rat brain tumor model.

Dennis Deen, PhD, joined Ken as a postdoctoral student in 1975 and became a Principal Investigator in 1977 on the biophysics project shortly after Ken left UCSF in 1976. Like Ken, Dennis received his PhD in Radiation Biophysics from University of Kansas. He had a down-home demeanor that belied a razor-sharp scientific intellect and research sense. Much of the research in the Wheeler-Deen laboratory focused on the effects of BCNU-induced alkylation on DNA damage, especially how it resulted in stable DNA cross-links. Over the years, I periodically collaborated with Ken and, later, Dennis as we investigated the impact of chloroethyl nitrosourea biotransformation to its alkylating and carbamylating intermediates and their effect on DNA damage and its enhancement of radiation-induced cellular damage.

Laurence J. Marton, MD, joined the Brain Tumor Research Center in 1973 and became a Principal Investigator in 1975. He had originally planned to be a neurosurgeon while in medical school at the Albert Einstein College of Medicine but changed his mind after one year as a UCSF neurosurgery resident. After the first year of residency, he went to the NIH for two years of research and, following that, returned to UCSF in 1973 to pursue his interest in polyamines and their relationship to cancer. Larry also completed a residency in Laboratory Medicine at UCSF, while serving as a Principal Investigator in the Brain Tumor Research Center. His ability to perform both roles combined with strong administrative and communication skills led to his promotion to Professor and, eventually, Chair of the Department of Laboratory Medicine at UCSF, a position he held until 1992, when he moved to The University of

Wisconsin to become Dean of the School of Medicine and Public Health and, later, became Chief Scientific and Medical Officer of the SLIL Biomedical Corporation.

Another of the early investigators was Takao Hoshino, MD, a Japanese-trained neurosurgeon with a strong commitment to brain tumor research and international research collaboration. Takao started doing research in the Department of Neurological Surgery at UCSF in 1968, before the creation of the Brain Tumor Research Center. Afterward he returned to Japan for clinical work and then moved to Israel to do research before returning to the Brain Tumor Research Center in 1973 as a Principal Investigator. He was a pioneer in tumor cell cycle kinetics and became the world's authority on cell kinetics of CNS tumors.

Mark Rosenblum, MD was a UCSF neurosurgical resident that Charlie encouraged to take research time from his residency to investigate the effects of nitrosoureas using an in vivo treatment and *in vitro* assay to provide quantitative survival information. Mark continued his research after completing his residency in 1979, joined the neurosurgery faculty, and became a Principal Investigator in the Brain Tumor Research Center in 1980. Eventually, he was recruited to Detroit to Chair the Department of Neurosurgery at Henry Ford Hospital and become a Professor at Wayne State University. Mark initiated experiments in which animals with intracranial tumors were treated with a nitrosourea drug followed by rapid tumor removal and a clonogenicity assay of cells removed from the tumor at various times post-treatment. The post-treatment survival kinetics of 9L tumor cells were revealed by these early studies.

In the early years of the Brain Tumor Research Center, we were a dedicated family of scientists and very talented Staff Research Associates. All our Staff Research Associates were college graduates who worked hard and, at times, passionately, for the betterment of our research and improved patient outcomes. My first laboratory contact when I started at UCSF and the Brain Tumor Research Center was Marvin Barker, MS who had being working with Charlie in the Department of Neurosurgery at The University of Kentucky and had come with Charlie to UCSF. Marvin brought with him the expertise to implant intracerebral tumors in rats and mice, an expertise that became one of the cornerstones of our research for the first decade of the Center's existence. With Charlie's backing, Marvin also managed our laboratory administrative offices and coordinated grant submissions.

I worked, either directly or collaboratively with so many wonderful people in the Brain Tumor Research Center that I hesitate to name them least I forget someone. Some of the Research Associates in my lab I was privileged to work with were Anne Byrd, Deborah J. Byrd, Judit Csetey, Mary Freeman-Dove, Boon Hoshino, Felix Karim, and my wife, Ellen. Staff Associates working with other Center principal investigators I interacted with were Shirley Hervatin, Kathy Knebel, Warren Lubich, Carol Maroten, Dolores Vasquez, and Mary Williams. Also, invaluable to the function of the Center in those years was Bennie Usog, a jack-of-all-trades technician who kept the dishwasher running to clean our research glassware, performed photography and darkroom duties, and produced most of the slides for our talks using a Kodak carousel slide projector. Our technical Staff Associates were invaluable to our research and the training of many of Neurological Surgery residents and post-doctoral fellows who passed through the Center. The reason that I still know the names of all the Staff Associates and technicians in the Center is that they were like family, and we treated each other with kindness and respect and liked to socialize when the opportunity arose.

During the first decade of my academic career at UCSF, many of us had the perception that we were the center of the therapeutic neuro-oncology universe. This was also strengthened as UCSF was then the center of enormous advances in cellular biology, genetic drivers of cancer, radiobiology, crystallography and three-dimensional modeling of drug docking and binding, to name a few. Additionally, scientists at UCSF were creating new companies, such as Genentech, Chiron, and Cetus, which would move science forward and provide unprecedented collaborative opportunities. From my perspective, considering the clinical trials I had initiated and published, the twenty-one neuro-oncology fellows I had trained, and the accolades we received from physicians throughout the world, those of us in the Brain Tumor Research Center believed that we, on the West Coast, were the critical drivers of the field of therapeutic neuro-oncology.

—⚏—

To provide a flavor for the research of the Center in the early years, I will recall some of our research and the direction it informed us. In 1975, Larry Marton and I collaborated on one of his projects to evaluate the potential of assessing cerebrospinal fluid (CSF) polyamine levels to reflect tumor burden and the growth of CNS tumors. The correlation between these levels and gliomas near a ventricular surface was good, but imperfect as a predictor of tumor growth. However, for medulloblastoma, its predictive efficacy was excellent. In fact, cerebrospinal fluid (CSF) levels of one or more of the polyamines (putrescine, spermidine, and spermine) predicted predicted tumor progression two to three months before we were able to see imaging changes on the CT or MRI. As a result, I followed my medulloblastoma patients using MRI and lumbar puncture to measure the level of the polyamines in the CSF for a couple of years, but eventually stopped doing the CSF studies because young patients were complaining about having to travel to UCSF to have a lumbar puncture every eight to twelve weeks. In addition, since I could not offer them any new therapies at the time that could take advanatge of the lead time in early tumor growth provided by CSF polyamine levels, I also agreed that we should stop providing that service to our medulloblastoma patients.

Larry's interest and research in polyamines led to seminal studies that he and I did with DFMO (alpha-difluoromethyl-ornithine, eflornithine), an irreversible inhibitor of the enzyme ornithine decarboxylase (ODC). While studies showed that DFMO had antitumor activity against some glial rodent tumors, the observation that DFMO could potentiate the antitumor activity of the alkylating agent BCNU turned out to be a clinical opportunity that I wanted to test. These studies also led me to embark on radiolabeled-DFMO regional distribution studies in rodents with intracerebral and subcutaneous glial tumors to better understand how DFMO worked. Eventually, my DFMO studies led to several clinical trials in humans and the establishment of two late-stage pharmaceutical companies to try to bring DFMO (eflornithine) to market for the treatment of anaplastic astrocytomas (see Chapter 27).

Takao Hoshino was a pioneer in tumor cell cycle kinetics and became the world's authority on cell kinetics of CNS tumors. In the 1970s and 1980s, he used radioactively labeled thymidine (3H and 14C) in rodents with intracerebral tumors. The Hoshino laboratory carried out an ambitious project that defined the cellular kinetics of untreated 9L cells *in vitro* and in vivo. He defined the cell cycle phase durations of untreated 9L cells and quantified perturbations in the cell cycle caused by BCNU and two other chemotherapeutic agents. He was the first medical scientist to use ^{3}H-thymidine to measure cell proliferation and cell kinetics in human glioma *in situ*. In collaboration with Joe Gray, PhD and his colleagues at Lawrence Livermore Laboratory, Takao became one of the first investigators to use the newly developed technique of flow cytometry to study the cell cycle kinetics of tumor cells. In later projects within the P01 grant, these techniques were used to study the kinetics of human brain tumors *in situ* and *in vitro*.

Takao trained numerous Japanese neurosurgeons in brain tumor research at UCSF. Many of them returned to Japan to continue laboratory and clinical research. He and I became good friends and colleagues, soon after I joined UCSF, and remained friends for decades, until his death from gastric cancer in 1993. He introduced me to Japan and was, in part, responsible for many of my travels there and for many of the friends I made there over the years.

He was a magician making things happen in Japan. I would like to share a fond memory of my first visit to Japan, in 1974. Takao had arranged for me to be invited to attend and speak at a brain tumor meeting sponsored by the Japanese Neurosurgery Society. Takao had friends throughout Japan, both in medicine and in commerce. This turned out to be very helpful to me. On my first flight to Japan, Takao planned to travel with me to Tokyo to make sure I did not get lost or have a problem, as I did not read or speak Japanese. I arrived at San Francisco International Airport on the morning of my planned departure, ready to start my new adventure. When I attempted to check in at the international gate for Japan Airlines, we realized that I did not have a visa. Takao had forgotten to mention I would need one. "No problem," he said, and he began conversing in Japanese with the ticket agent. A minute later, the agent said, "Come back tomorrow with your visa and I will get you on the flight." Not being much of a world traveler at the time, I asked where I needed to go to get the visa. While the agent explained my next steps, Takao was on the phone. Afterwards, he handed me the address for the Japanese consulate in San Francisco. They would issue a visa for me in the morning with enough time for me to make the early afternoon flight. I not only made that flight, but when I boarded flight the flight attendant gave me the impression that they were expecting me. In addition, even though I was traveling coach, my assigned seat had two adjacent empty seats beside it, so I could lie down and sleep. For me, it was a special flight.

At Narita Airport, which is about 48 miles from Tokyo, Takao met me at the terminal and drove me to a reception for a visiting Canadian neurosurgeon who would be returning home in a couple of days. I have no idea where I got the energy to stay at the reception for two hours, drink a beer, and carry on a conversation after the long flight, but I did. Perhaps the explanation is that I was thirty-three years old, and I was hyped up for the trip and the new experiences that awaited me in Japan. In addition, over the years, I have also found that it is easier for me to fly west than to fly east from San Francisco.

Mark Rosenblum had established a research program in the Center during his residency that he continued after joining the Department. Working with Dolores Vasquez, a Staff Research Associate, his lab carefully established the dose-dependent tumor log cell-kill relationship of BCNU in human glioma cell cultures. At about the same time I was investigating BCNU in various intra-cerebral rodent tumor models, I was also treating patients with high-grade gliomas with intravenous BCNU using a schedule of three consecutive days every six weeks. Following laboratory research and efficacy studies in rodent models, I concluded, based on Mark's *in vitro* studies and my rodent model studies, that a higher BCNU dose one day every six weeks would work equally well and be easier to give to patients without hospitalization. I quickly took it to the clinic to see if it produced any unforeseen toxicity problems. Patients found this schedule more convenient, and it reduced the incidence of the vein sclerosis at the injection site. It also required less work for our clinical team and was less expensive to administer. It was a win-win for everyone. After our first publication of this dosing schedule in a clinical trial, this one-day dosing regimen was incorporated into all our patient treatment protocols and eventually became the schedule used throughout the world.

Mark's group also used a Colony Forming Efficiency (CFE) assay to investigate the clonogenicity of cells obtained from twenty-nine human tumors. This work provided a first look at the heterogencity in pathology and in response to therapy that is seen from tumor to tumor and within individual human brain tumors. This inter-and intra-heterogeneity is now accepted as one of the hallmarks of malignant gliomas. In addition, these tumors formed the beginning of the Brain Tumor Research Center Tissue Bank, which evolved into an extensive collection of human brain tumor tissue and corresponding normal brain tissue obtained during surgery. This tissue bank became a valuable resource for future research projects in the Center and elsewhere.

Philip Gutin, MD joined the Department of Neurological Surgery as an Assistant Professor in 1979. Unlike Mark, Phil had spent six months with me as a Neuro-Oncology Fellow and had developed an interest in the potential application of brachytherapy to treat high-grade gliomas such as glioblastoma. Brachytherapy is a form of radiation therapy whereby the radiation source is implanted into a tumor. After working on brachytherapy experiments in the intracerebral 9L rat tumor model with Mark Bernstein, MD, Phil decided that he needed to try this form of localized radiation therapy in people with recurrent (progressive) glioblastoma. With the help of Theodore Phillips, MD, Chair of the Department of Radiation Oncology, and other radiation oncology colleagues, the clinical trial for patients with (progressive) glioblastoma was started using ^{125}I implants. The ^{125}I implants were relatively safe radiation sources as they produced a long and low radiation exposure with a relatively short penetration distance. As the neuro-oncologist in the department, I followed Phil's brachytherapy patients. While the treatment was efficacious for some of the patients, it also produced significant radiation necrosis in the tumor and brain surrounding the tumor in about 50% of study patients. As a result, and since I followed nearly all of Phil's brachytherapy patients, I had an opportunity to participate in some of the first studies using positron emission tomography (PET) to delineate radiation necrosis in the CNS. After I left UCSF in 1988, Phil became chairman of the Department of Neurological Surgery after Charlie retired, but later moved to New York to Chair the Department of Neurosurgery at the Memorial Sloan-Kettering Cancer Center until he retired in 2019.

Phil has been a long-time colleague and friend since his years as a resident at UCSF. He has an engaging intellect and wonderful sense of humor. For a couple of years, he, Mike Edwards, a pediatric neurosurgeon, and past Neuro-Oncology Fellow, and I would meet in the hall outside the Department of Neurological Surgery office to share jokes. I looked forward to these brief breaks for the humor and the time together before returning to the serious business of treating CNS tumor patients.

13

My Laboratory Research at UCSF

The reason for the detailed presentation of the research colleagues and I conducted at UCSF in the 1973-1988 period is to provide examples and highlight my perspective on the importance of this very focused and goal-directed research on cytotoxic drugs, and in particular alkylating agents, as well as their interactions with radiation on experimental growth inhibition of CNS tumors. The research was goal directed and focused to create therapeutic strategies that would lead to clinical trials that could help people afflicted with CNS cancers. Our Brain Tumor Research Center group was passionate about their goal-directed research and the belief that their research would make a difference, especially to people with infiltrative high-grade gliomas.

I expect that many of today's scientists and physicians who conduct laboratory and clinical research in neuro-oncology might look back at that era and the research we conducted as being less sophisticated than the molecular-genetics, proteomic, and drug discovery/development research of today. I felt the same way about research that preceded mine when I embarked on my own research into regional brain and tumor pharmacokinetics, experimental therapeutics, and drug discovery and development. My attitude, however, did not last long as by the late 1980's I was humbled by the complexity of drug discovery and development to create an irreversible inhibitor of c-Src as the director of the first National Cooperative Drug Discovery Group grant. Generational research is always so. Future research should become more sophisticated and provide more new information and insight. It is also a truism that today's research benefits from the research and insights of past scientists and physician-scientists.

From my perspective, the research I will briefly summarize in the chapter that follows, truly informed the clinical trials of that era and some of the treatments we use today. While we would collaborate at times and seek advice and drugs from pharmaceutical companies and contract research organizations like Southern Research (Birmingham), Arthur D. Little (Boston), the Rand Corporation (Palo Alto), we conceived and designed our laboratory and clinical research based on research conducted in our Center.

When I embarked on my neuro-oncology path in 1967, I always assumed that tremendous progress would be made in drugs and therapeutic strategies over the years. Over the past 50 years I have absorbed the sadness of limited therapeutic gains. Even the explosion in molecular biology and genetics research has led to limited new therapies to treat CNS neoplasia. Aside from the parsing of survival outcomes into molecular-genetic subgroups, we have not created new therapies to replace alkylating agents and radiation therapy for infiltrative gliomas and medulloblastoma. I, in no way, want to minimize the importance of many informative molecular-genetic studies that have provided new insights into tumor diagnosis and likelihood of response to a therapy such that today we can offer our patients more specific diagnosis-based care and a more accurate prognosis. My request to the reader is to read through the research of that past time and realize the passion and pride I, and those scientists I worked with had for our research and its potential to impact the lives of people afflicted with infiltrative gliomas.

During this early period in the Brain Tumor Research Center's history, Charlie received two additional NIH awards in addition to the PO1 grant. One NIH award supported a post-graduate training program, and the other was a contract to carry out chemotherapy trials on patients through the Brain Tumor Study Group. These grants contributed to the running of our Brain Tumor Chemotherapy Service and our ability to hire two clinical (neuro-oncology) fellows each year. These were both important opportunities that made it easier for us to grow and expand our Brain Tumor Chemotherapy Service.

By 1975, I had two grants from the ACS: a five-year Faculty Research Award for partial salary support and one that supported a laboratory research project. In addition, Hoshino, Marton, Wheeler and I each had an R01 grant from the NCI. Thus, the investigators within the Brain Tumor Research Center were individually competitive in the grant arena, but the funding derived from the P01 grant and departmental support comprised most of the funding for the Brain Tumor Research Center core functions of our laboratories and its administrative support.

Under the umbrella of the Program Project grant and the multiple individual investigator grants our group garnered, the Brain Tumor Center research expanded quite a bit and its clinical programs and trials flourished, making it a world leader in conducting novel clinical trials for pediatric and adult brain tumors. Our Brain Tumor Chemotherapy Service population was split about 75% adult patients and 25% pediatric patients. Pediatric patients coming to our Brain Tumor Chemotherapy Service were generally referred from California and other Western states, although I did have patients coming from as far away as Italy and France. During those years we behaved less as consultants and more as primary care physicians as we assumed the responsibility to plan and implement the treatment of our Clinic patients as well as their long-term follow up. In that process we gained the respect and corroboration of radiation oncologists, medical oncologists, pediatric oncologists, neurologists, and neurosurgeons throughout the country with referrals within a 2000-mile radius from San Francisco.

—⟋⟍—

My laboratory research flourished at UCSF. Working with Robert Weinkam, PhD, a new faculty member in the Department of Pharmaceutical Chemistry, we used mass spectrometry to study drugs like BCNU and procarbazine. This relatively new technology was used for measuring drug and drug biotransformation products in biological fluids. I was fortunate to obtain a Finnegan 3200 Mass Spectrometer through our PO1 grant that allowed us to develop a new chemical ionization mass spectrometry (CI/MS) assay to quantify BCNU biotransformation and measure its pharmacokinetics in patients with high-grade gliomas. Bob and one of his graduate students, David Shiba, also used the CI/MS to study procarbazine biotransformation, a drug we used alone or in the PCV combination to treat patients with CNS malignancies. At the time, I viewed their study as seminal since it provided for our better understanding of procarbazine's mode of action and biotransformation products. David Shiba finished his PhD in Pharmaceutical Chemistry at UCSF, and shortly afterwards decided to get an MD degree and eventually became a medical oncologist and now practices in Modesto, California.

While at a distance, I continued to work with Clifford Patlak who was across the country at the NIMH in Bethesda, Maryland. At Cliff's suggestion, I also began to work with a gifted mathematician at UCSF, Herbert Landahl, PhD, who coincidentally had been Cliff's graduate professor during his doctoral studies at The University of Chicago. Herb had an interesting history prior to UCSF. He was born in Fancheng, China in 1913, and spent part of his childhood there since his father was a Lutheran minister who had been assigned to China. Because of the instability in China at the time, Herb's family returned when he was still a youngster. Herb was mathematically gifted and obtained his PhD at The University of Chicago in mathematical biophysics in 1941. I immensely enjoyed the sixteen years we worked together at UCSF. Herb was a physically and mentally active man who, with his wife Evelyn, did West Coast jazz dancing in San Francisco on a regular basis. Sadly, Herb died in 2003, at age 90, of pulmonary fibrosis, a disease that might have been a complication from his human studies during WWII to determine the mathematical basis for how gases such as nitrogen mustard disperse in the lungs. From stories he told me of those times, I think that sometimes he was his own experimental volunteer for those studies.

The years between 1976 and 1981 at UCSF were among the most enjoyable for me as I worked with Herb Landahl at UCSF and Cliff Patlak at the NINDS to develop mathematical models to understand and predict the pharmacokinetics of anticancer drugs in the brain, in brain tumors and in cerebrospinal fluid. In 1980, I decided to write a definitive paper to clarify in one article, the mathematical basis by which drugs moved in the brain and intracerebral tumors. To write the best paper at that time, I needed the input of both Cliff and Herb so I cajoled them both into taking on the challenge of coauthoring the paper. Writing a paper with these two biomathematicians turned out to be great fun. They used different approaches to solve the same mathematical problem. Cliff lamented over the fact that he would generate pages of computer code to solve a problem, while Herb would solve the problem with a two- or three-line mathematical approximation. While I included both sets of solutions, I have always wondered if anyone reading the paper understood the different approaches to the mathematical solutions presented in the appendices of our nearly forty-page paper. Cliff and Herb probably never knew how much pleasure and gratification I had writing the paper with them.

Another comment on this nearly forty-page paper is in order. For a couple of years, I had been enthralled by the word "heuristic" and was seeking to write a paper that would allow me to use it in the title. The paper with Herb and Cliff was the perfect vehicle for the word and capped off an exciting part of my research life. Unfortunately, however, completing this paper convinced me that further pharmacokinetic modeling and study of alkylating agents and other cytotoxic drugs would not improve their antitumor efficacy in the clinic. My conclusion, reached in 1980, was that new and different types of drugs were needed to treat infiltrative CNS neoplasms.

In those years, efforts made in brain tumor and cancer research were pioneering in a multitude of ways. For example, computer use was relatively new for the kind of scientific study I was doing. For much of my research between 1968 and the late 1970s, I used a teletype connected to a modem for programming and calculations. Once I purchased the Data General minicomputer to run the CI/MS assay I was able to program the mathematical algorithms that Herb derived, and I was able to establish graphic plots on a Tektronix refreshable terminal. While the computer was cumbersome, I treated it kindly, backed up the data regularly on removable disk platters about a two foot in diameter, and prayed for the good health of the platters.

Combining laboratory studies in rodents, dogs, and monkeys, with insightful mathematical algorithms, Herb and I made significant inroads into understanding how computer modeling of experimental data could aid in understanding drug action and efficacy. For some time, several pharmaceutical industry software packages used my capillary permeability data for their "teaching set of brain permeability" and as a basis for their computer-based modeling efforts.

Some of the pharmacokinetic research I published in the 1970s started while I was at the NCI. These studies examined how radiolabeled methotrexate and 5-FU moved into rodent tumors and how large molecules such as albumen moved in monkey brain from a choriocarcinoma tumor into adjacent brain. My colleagues and I were concerned about the impact that brain irradiation would have on the entry and distribution of different sized chemical compounds. We also worried about drug toxicity when drug therapy was coupled with irradiation as well as the adequacy of drug delivery to the growing edge of infiltrative gliomas. We used rodents and various radiolabeled standard compounds and drugs to see if radiation exerted a differential effect on different molecules, which is precisely what we observed. Radiation differentially affected the movement of diverse drugs and chemicals but not all uniformly.

We found that for the acute effects of irradiation, defined as a short interval between irradiation and study, the radiation fractions used in these studies produced little change in capillary permeability of normal brain capillaries to high molecular weight drugs in rats. In parallel studies of delayed radiation effects on rat brain capillaries, we found evidence that the "early" delayed effects of X-irradiation altered brain capillary permeability in a small subset of chemicals studied. The only consistent increase in permeability occurred with galactitol, a hydrophilic molecule that is normally quite restricted in its transcapillary transit in the brain.

A new research area I embarked on in the 1970s impacts my professional life to this day. While it was known that polyamines could be found in most tissues, tumors and body fluids, Larry Marton wondered if careful measurement of polyamines in CSF might predict tumor growth earlier than our neuroimaging studies would show us. Much of his research in the 1970s and 1980s focused on the development and use of a sensitive technique that utilized ion exchange chromatography with fluorometric detection on a Durrum D-500 amino acid analyzer. Working with Larry and Warren Lubich, a Staff Research Associate in his lab, we used these sensitive methods to investigate the relevance of polyamine levels in the cerebrospinal fluid to CNS tumor growth. As part of an IRB-approved experimental protocol, my neuro-oncology fellows and I obtained CSF, usually by lumbar puncture, from children and adults with various types of brain tumors. These measurements proved not to be predictive of either the degree of malignancy or the size of the tumor for several brain tumor types, including glioblastoma, different astrocytoma grades, meningioma, and pituitary adenoma. One caveat we knew might affect the level of CSF polyamines was if the tumor was not close to a brain ventricle or subarachnoid surface. As a result, our findings for infiltrative gliomas were inconsistent, however, findings for patients with medulloblastoma accurately predicted and anticipated tumor progression/recurrence. For a couple of years prior to the MRI era, I and my neuro-oncology fellows did regular lumbar punctures on medulloblastoma patients (mostly children) to allow us to treat them earlier for tumor relapse. Ultimately, I stopped assessing CSF polyamines in children because I felt that we lacked effective therapies to take advantage of the knowledge that the tumor was growing earlier than expected. Moreover, designing a clinical trial around CSF polyamine levels in medulloblastoma patients was overly challenging since medulloblastoma is a very rare tumor and I did not think that I would be able to accrue enough patients to a clinical trial under those circumstances.

This period also marked the beginning of a collaboration between Larry and Dennis Deen in the Brain Tumor Research Center and Richard Shafer in the UCSF School of Pharmacy to investigate the effects of inhibiting the polyamine biosynthetic pathway on the subsequent sensitivity of tumor cells to physical and chemical agents. Their studies showed that inhibiting the polyamine putrescine with alpha-difluoromethylornithine (DFMO; eflornithine), sensitized 9L tumor cells to BCNU. At the time, these findings were novel and exciting, because they suggested that DFMO and other relatively nontoxic polyamine inhibitors could play a role in potentiating some chemotherapies. To exploit these findings, polyamines became the central theme of a later competitive renewal of the Program Project grant and an application that Larry made as part of a National Cooperative Drug Discovery Group (NCDDG) grant on polyamines. These studies also helped inform the clinical trial I undertook in 1984 with a combination of DFMO given before BCNU in patients with recurrent glioma tumors that showed that the combination of DFMO with BCNU was safe and resulted in unexpected long-term survivors. This concept also helped to inform my randomized trials of DFMO before the PCV combination I initiated at The University of Texas MD Anderson Cancer Center.

Much of the effort in our UCSF labs was focused on how nitrosoureas, especially BCNU and CCNU, worked as anticancer agents and to better understand how these drugs worked with radiation therapy. To that end, Dennis Deen carried out a series of studies that thoroughly explicated the dose response of 9L cells to select BCNU and x-rays. In collaboration with colleagues from the Netherlands, these data were fit to the so-called alpha-beta equation, which furthered insight into the magnitude of enhancement produced by combining BCNU with x-rays. Alpha-beta analysis is still used today to design clinical trials in radiation oncology.

Perhaps the most important outcome of these nitrosourea studies came from my collaboration with Dennis and Bob Weinkham to unify cell survival data. These data were produced in dozens of laboratory experiments using several different nitrosoureas by implementing a simple drug-dose concept based on the biologic half-life of BCNU in cell culture systems and the resulting area under the drug curve.

The Deen lab also established 9L cell survival curves for cisplatin, bleomycin, spirohydantoin mustard, nitrogen mustard, methotrexate, 6-mercaptopurine, cytosine arabinoside, 5-fluororacil (5-FU), and hydroxyurea. These drugs were or had been under investigation in intracerebral animal model systems or in clinical trials, either as single agents or in drug combinations. I also had studied and published on the regional brain and tumor distribution of radiolabeled 5-FU. As a result of my publications and those of the Deen lab, I initiated a clinical trial of BCNU and a 5-day outpatient intravenous infusion of 5-FU. While it showed reasonably good activity for patients with recurrent astrocytoma and anaplastic astrocytoma, I did not think it was "game changing" therapy so did not pursue a big randomized clinical trial.

Also, during this period, the Deen Laboratory developed a multicellular spheroid model using 9L cells. This model was used to investigate the cytotoxic effects of several agents in single and multi-dose protocols. It also provided a model for culturing different types of cells together so that cell-cell interactions could be studied. One of the seminal findings of this work was the demonstration that as the percentage of BCNU-resistant cells in the spheroids was increased, the relative sensitivity of the nitrosourea-sensitive cells increased, and they became more resistant. This suggested that during treatment of human tumors, drug-sensitive cells that survived treatment would gain resistance to the drug, making the tumor more refractory to future treatment with these drugs.

It was a fruitful time for investigative research. Also, during this time, Mark Rosenblum continued evaluating drugs alone and in combination using the *in vivo/in vitro* 9L model. The Rosenblum Laboratory also investigated the efficacy of several drugs alone and in combination in the 9L rat intracerebral (IC) model and in the glioma 26 mouse IC model. Drugs studied included BCNU, spiro-hydantoin mustard, PCNU and PALA. Research that I found more intriguing at the time were studies demonstrating the induction of resistance to BCNU in the 9L model. They isolated BCNU-resistant clones, and these clones were studied *in vitro* and *in vivo*. Rosenblum and colleagues had developed a soft agar culture system that could be used for the growth of early passage human brain tumor cells and generated cell survival curves for several glioblastoma specimens obtained from patient surgeries. Their goal was to correlate the *in vitro* sensitivity of the cells to the clinical response of the patient as this was a time when many cancer investigators were searching for assays that would predict the success or failure of specific treatments in individual cancer patients. Mark, in collaboration with Takao Hoshino, also initiated studies to investigate heterogeneity of brain tumors by comparing BCNU dose response curves, DNA content measured by flow cytometry, and cell yields among different samples obtained from the same tumor. Lastly, using radiolabeling techniques, Mark and Takao studied *in vitro* cell kinetics of several human brain tumors. This work provided the earliest experimental data for human brain tumor cell doubling times, growth fractions and cycling times.

In addition to my collaborative research efforts with Brain Tumor Research Center colleagues, my laboratory pursued pharmacology and pharmacokinetic studies of CNS tumor drugs. We defined the half-lives of various nitrosoureas and investigated the impact of phenobarbital treatment on the pharmacokinetics of these compounds. This was important work because many brain tumor patients had seizures and were being treated with phenobarbital to control their seizures during chemotherapy with BCNU or CCNU. At the time, it was unclear what impact the induction of liver enzymes by phenobarbital would have on the action of these drugs. As it turned out, phenobarbital induction of liver enzymes accelerated the biotransformation and blood clearance of BCNU, thereby reducing the antitumor activity of BCNU and, likely, the other nitrosoureas. While we did not study the impact of diphenylhydantoin (Dilantin), I assumed that it would also impact the metabolism of BCNU and CCNU. On the plus side, I have a theory that phenobarbital (or Dilantin) pretreatment would be expected to reduce systemic BCNU and CCNU toxicity. To put this in perspective, drugs such as BCNU and CCNU move from the plasma of the bloodstream into brain and brain tumors very quickly, almost as fast as water moves, whereas the effect of phenobarbital on BCNU transformation is a much slower process. Hence, my thought was that phenobarbital reduced BCNU myelotoxicity without negatively affecting its antitumor efficacy because the rate constant for blood to tumor and brain was an order of magnitude faster than its rate of biotransformation and inactivation by liver enzymes. This is a hypothesis, but over time, and with the advent of nonenzymic-inducing anticonvulsants entering the clinic, I was noticing that fewer patients tolerated the same starting doses of BCNU and CCNU that I had used for years when phenobarbital and Dilantin were used for seizure control.

At the time, I was also investigating many other chloroethyl nitrosoureas. These were produced under an NCI contract that encouraged development of new drug analogs. It was hoped these might be more efficacious anticancer drugs than BCNU and CCNU, the most used drugs to treat CNS tumors. As part of that program, the NCI made these novel drugs available to me to test in rodent tumor systems. At the time, these rodent models served as reliable preclinical tests and justification for high-grade glioma clinical trials. Of the many drugs I tested, I was convinced that a drug called PCNU would be superior to BCNU and CCNU, based on my structure-activity studies. PCNU demonstrated superior pharma-cokinetic properties that produced higher tumor drug doses and presumably higher tumor levels with the same amount of toxicity to normal tissues leading to an improved antitumor activity in intracerebral rodent tumor models.

As a result of my lab studies, I decided to go forward with a clinical trial using drug supplied by the Cancer Therapy Evaluation Branch (CTEP) of the National Cancer Institute. We found that PCNU was indeed active against progressive high-grade gliomas and would have been a good candidate to expand studies for FDA approval were it not for the fact that both BCNU and CCNU had FDA approval already, so I decided not to pursue it commercially in the United States at the time. In addition, a third nitrosourea, ACNU, was being used in Japan, and a fourth, fotemustine, was being used in France. Although, I believed PCNU was the best nitrosourea of the lot, I thought that the improvement in patient survival would likely be small and not nearly as important as finding a new drug for CNS tumors with a different mechanism of action than alkylating and cross-linking DNA. I felt then, as I do today, what we needed most were anticancer agents with completely different modes of action.

Also at UCSF, I conducted drug structure-activity studies with imidazole carboxamides. The studies led to a clinical trial of a bis-chloroethyl derivative, a drug we also thought was superior to dacarbazine, an FDA-approved and clinically available drug. This was because bis-chloroethyl derivative had better brain and tumor penetration and, unlike dacarbazine, cross-linked DNA. While I thought this drug was sufficiently unique and active to possibly be worth more attention, our phase II study of 5-[3,3-bis(2-chloroethyl)-1triazeno] imidazole-4-carboxamide (NSC-82196) and other studies sponsored by CTEP were not enough to encourage CTEP to contract for additional drug supplies to enable me to do a larger phase II study. On the other hand, my structure-activity studies did help others to develop a new alkylating agent for high-grade gliomas. I was told by Edward Newlands, the clinician who was the first to bring temozolomide forward for the treatment of humans with glioma, that our published structure-activity studies were the stimulus for the synthesis and development of the monofunctional alkylating agent temozolomide by Malcolm Stevens.

During this time, our group studied the pharmacokinetics of procarbazine in plasma quite extensively. We also conducted investigator-initiated studies to search for drugs to modify the membranes of cancer cells, with the hopes of overcoming the blood-brain barrier that prevents many cancer drugs from entering the brain. Unfortunately, none of my research or that of others in the

Brain Tumor Research Center during those years led to new drugs entering the clinic for the treatment of high-grade gliomas. It took another 40 years before a drug I had worked on was far enough along in a clinical phase III trial to be close to approval for the treatment of high-grade astrocytoma (Chapter 27).

14

UCSF Laboratory Research Contributions to the Clinical Programs

In the mid-1970s, my clinical goal was to create new combination drug therapies to improve on the anti-tumor efficacy of the alkylating agents - BCNU, CCNU, and procarbazine - we were using at the time on the Brain Tumor Chemotherapy Service. I was optimistic that we could do better for our patients. As a result, I conducted many phase I (dose-finding toxicity studies) and phase I/II (phase I studies with additional patients added to determine phase II clinical efficacy) studies to compare treatment efficacy of these new therapies to our own growing patient database. We were quite confident that our methodology and carefully organized patient database records would be sufficiently accurate to alert us if a new therapy strategy were good enough to warrant running a randomized cooperative group trial.

This manner of testing new therapies and clinical ideas has its shortcomings as it reduces statistical certainty of the outcome, whether it be time to tumor failure, progression-free survival, or overall survival. On the other hand, at the time I was more interested to find a drug combination that would provide a dramatic benefit in outcome, be it time-to-tumor progression or overall survival. Philosophically, I was resigned to failing more frequently then succeeding in this quest. I relished the hope that someday the signal of a drug combination would be so strong that we would need to conduct a longer three-to-four-year randomized study.

My first randomized trial at UCSF was a study I designed to compare oral hydroxyurea during external beam radiation therapy (EBRT) in patients treated with adjuvant BCNU compared to another group treated with adjuvant BCNU who were not treated with hydroxyurea during EBRT. This study was initiated through the Western Oncology Group which was then situated in Los Angeles. Unfortunately, the Group disbanded before we had met our study accrual goal, so the results we reported were under powered. Since the clinical signal favored hydroxyurea during EBRT, we continued using hydroxyurea during EBRT for over a decade until temozolomide during EBRT supplanted it. Deep down I still think that a direct comparison of the two therapies would find hydroxyurea superior to temozolomide during EBRT.

—⁓—

During the mid-1970s, I initiated a phase II clinical trial of BCNU with procarbazine, a phase II clinical trial of BCNU with 5-FU, two different phase II clinical studies using differing dose schedules for combination chemotherapy studies of CCNU (lomustine), procarbazine (Matulane), and vincristine (PCV #1 and PCV#2) that led to many trials with PCV (PCV #2). During this same time, I initiated a study to determine the value of hydroxyurea to potentiate the effectiveness of EBRT in a randomized phase III trial of BCNU and EBRT versus BCNU and oral hydroxyurea during EBRT. At the time of this study, BCNU was the standard of care and clinical investigators like me were attempting to improve therapy by combining it with other drugs and with radiation. Under my direction, clinical trial participation grew to involve 170 patients at the time of our first PO1 renewal in 1974.

In my laboratory during the mid-1970s, we were doing related pharmacological studies to understand the mechanisms of action of the family of chloroethyl nitrosoureas that included, among others, BCNU and CCNU. These efforts, along with those of other scientists in subsequent projects in the program project, helped produce a complete understanding of the mechanisms of action for all chloroethyl nitrosoureas and the relationship between drug stability and chloroethyl nitrosoureas pharmacology.

Under my direction, the Brain Tumor Chemotherapy Service (later to become the Neuro-Oncology Service) continued to grow, and by 1980, we were treating 340 patients per year with chemotherapy.

—⚅—

In those years, because chemotherapy for CNS tumors was in its early stages of medical acceptance and because most CNS cancers are considered rare tumors, we had a large active regional program going, most patients were referred to our center. One of the larger hospital programs at the time was Kaiser Permanente. The Kaiser program provided care throughout California but had a small neurosurgery footprint in Northern California that was limited to the Kaiser's Redwood City Hospital. They referred almost all their primary gliomas and medulloblastoma patients to us for post-surgical treatment coordination and management. By the mid-1980s they would expand neurosurgery to Sacramento but continue to refer to us. Kaiser provided a great source of patients for our clinical trials. Initially, we saw these patients on our Brain Tumor Chemotherapy Service free of charge, although we tried to obtain CT scans, and later MRI scans, as well as laboratory studies through the patient's local Kaiser Permanente hospital to reduce our costs as we were not paid to care for Kaiser patients at the time. In later years, I negotiated an arrangement with Kaiser Permanente's Redwood City Hospital in Northern California for a grant of about $30,000/year for 4-5 years to cover some of our costs for nurses. This was a time when an extra $30,000 went a long way in clinical research.

—⚅—

By 1980, many changes and growth in our clinical program had occurred. We had shifted from hospitalization for IV chemotherapy to outpatient chemotherapy infusions which was an important

milestone as we had by then 779 hospital admissions for IV chemotherapy. We had also hit a milestone of 14 clinical trials that had
originated from our Center research. One of these trials was a Phase
III study comparing the effectiveness of the combination of BCNU,
radiation and hydroxyurea during radiation with the combination
of BCNU and radiation that was standard therapy at UCSF at the
time. This study was based on observations that hydroxyurea could
potentiate the cytotoxic effects of radiation on growing tumor cells
in culture and in vivo. Based on the published pharmacokinetics of
hydroxyurea, I devised an administration schedule to maintain
blood levels and, presumably, tumor penetration levels high enough
to achieve a potentiation of radiation doses. Other trials, also based
on laboratory studies, focused on BCNU in combination with 5-FU
infusions and single-agent thio-TEPA.

Another clinical protocol coming from Center laboratory studies
was the modified PCV (procarbazine, CCNU, and vincristine) protocol that became the most important chemotherapy regimen for
decades for infiltrative gliomas (astrocytoma, oligodendroglioma,
anaplastic astrocytoma, anaplastic oligodendroglioma, glioblastoma) and other CNS neoplasms. I was concerned that the combination of procarbazine and CCNU used in the first generation of
PCV might not be optimal for treating infiltrative gliomas with
respect to toxicity and efficacy. To test this hypothesis, I designed
laboratory studies using rodents with intracerebral tumors that
convinced me to refine our first PCV combination chemotherapy
(PCV-1). The new design was called PCV-3 and came about in a
deliberate fashion based on experiments conducted in our laboratories that suggested that by delaying starting procarbazine and
giving vincristine after combined treatment with CCNU and
procarbazine, might produce a maximum cell-kill during a period
when tumor cells should be in a proliferative phase. In addition, the
new combination appeared less myelotoxic to the rodents. This

insight followed my extrapolation of animal tumor cell cycle kinetic studies from Takao with an estimate of the cell kinetics of human gliomas. These studies and certain assumptions led me to modify PCV-1 by giving vincristine seven days after procarbazine. In addition, my rodent model studies further suggested that systemic toxicity of the PCV-1 could be reduced if procarbazine was administered seven days after CCNU. Thus, PCV-3 was born, which persists to this day as the PCV chemotherapy regimen.

In the first 20 years of my career, three of my studies moved into large phase III randomized cooperative group studies. In addition, another three we deemed worth pursuing but were unable to pursue because of inadequate drug supply and the unwillingness of the Cancer Therapy Evaluation Program (CTEP) of the NCI to fund a contract to obtain more drug for my studies. In the remaining studies, I felt that the results did not appear substantially better than therapies we were using at the time. One success was the randomized trial of intravenous BCNU compared to PCV that led to PCV becoming the standard of care for patients with glioma of the brain and spinal cord for decades, until it was partially eclipsed by single agent temozolomide. Another success was Phase I/II trials of DFMO (eflornithine) and DFMO-BCNU that led to the randomized phase III study of DFMO-PCV versus PCV being conducted in the 1990s that found that the combination of DFMO-PCV increased median overall survival of anaplastic glioma patients by about 2.5 years.

Over the years, Brain Tumor Research Center colleagues and I had made several innovative contributions to brain tumor therapy. These included: 1) investigation of hydroxyurea and misonidazole as radiation sensitizers in previously untreated tumors; 2) investigation of pre-radiation chemotherapy for high-grade gliomas; 3) use of multiple diagnostic studies to define progression and response according to specific criteria; 4) use of CSF polyamine levels

127

to assess CNS tumor growth; and 5) use of brachytherapy for recurrent and primary high-grade gliomas. To expand the size and statistical power of our studies, many of our clinical trials were carried out under the auspices of the Northern California Oncology Group (NCOG) and the CNS Tumor Committee that I chaired.

In terms of chemotherapy trials, we accepted both adults and children with infiltrative gliomas, medulloblastoma, pineal tumors, choroid plexus papilloma, and other childhood tumors for which we also investigated various drug and radiation approaches.

We treated children with CNS tumors with most of the same therapies being used in adults. For very small children who were treated with a drug combination, I worked with the UCSF Pharmacy to make a preparation that the child's parents could administer at home. The youngest child I treated with an oral combination chemotherapy regimen was six months of age. Since children tolerated chemotherapy with less myelosuppression than adults, I sometimes modified protocols to allow more dosing and easier administration schedules for parents. One example of this was when I started using a drug called dibromodulcitol. This was an orally administered drug that alkylated DNA, which could be given daily for days to weeks. I used a simple protocol that allowed drug to be taken daily until either the neutrophil or platelet counts dropped to half their starting level. This turned out to be a very popular chemotherapy protocol for our children until we ran out of drug that was being supplied by the Cancer Therapy Evaluation Program (CTEP) in the NCI.

Experimental single-agent and drug combinations included BCNU, 5-FU, CCNU, misonidazole, procarbazine, vincristine, and 6-mercaptopurine. Shortly thereafter, we began to evaluate polyamine inhibitors (DFMO and MGBG) as possible new drugs for the treatment of brain tumors. Some of these cytotoxic drugs were also studied in medulloblastoma and in addition to studies with dibromodulcitol, methotrexate and thio-TEPA.

—ɯ—

Critical to the team approach in neuro-oncology was having access to excellent neuropathologists. They were needed to assure accurate diagnosis and grading of CNS tumors and to help assess animal tumor models used for laboratory studies. Between 1972 and 1988, I worked serially with Surl Nielsen, Janet Townsend, and, starting in 1978, Richard "Dick" Davis. Dick was recruited away from The University of Southern California as Professor and Senior Neuro-pathologist and stayed in the UCSF program until his retirement in 2008.

Throughout my UCSF years, I sought clinical trials statistical support, which at times was problematic. It grew in importance with the recruitment of Kathleen Lamborn, PhD, to the faculty after I left UCSF. Initially, however, I worked with Robert M. Elashoff, PhD, between 1972 and 1976 when he was recruited to a Harvard program. He and I published one paper together, a 65-patient clinical trial of a BCNU-procarbazine combination that, while active, did not appear to be better than PCV. After Bob left UCSF, I collaborated with David C. Heilbron, PhD, and published a paper with him in 1980. In this study, we adapted a Weibull mathematical approach to the CT volume of high-grade glioma tumors post-surgical resection and pre-irradiation to see what impact tumor volume had on the probability of tumor progression at one year. This was one of the first papers to analyze the impact of pre-treatment tumor volume on tumor progression. We found, among patients receiving the same radiation and chemotherapy regimen, a fourfold greater chance of being free of tumor progression at one year if the enhanced residual tumor volume was in the 10th percentile (3 cc) rather than the 90th percentile (85 cc). Further, the presence of a peritumor low-density and edema increased the probability of being tumor progression-free to 68% and 32%, respectively.

In retrospect, I received the greatest statistical insight into clinical trials' statistics through my association with the Northern

California Cancer Program and William "Bill" Brown, PhD, at Stanford and John Hannigan, MS, of the NCOG between 1984 and 1990. For many of our institutional clinical trials, I relied on computer software I wrote to produce Kaplan-Meier plots. The plots and relationships were elucidated using the Gehan-modified Wilcoxon rank sum analysis and the logrank test. If I needed a covariate analyses, I contacted a statistician at UCSF when we had one on faculty, or Bill Brown at Stanford, or John Hannigan of the NCOG.

During this time, colleagues and I used the concept of time to tumor progression (TTP) as an endpoint for our clinical studies. TTP was assessed by a combination score derived from the clinical neurological exam and CT scan (or radionuclide brain scan before CT replaced it as an imaging technique). The methodology we developed provided objective, semi-quantifiable parameters that greatly helped us speed up assessment and accuracy of our clinical trials findings. In addition, the analog scale I had developed: +2 for improvement, 0 for no change, -2 for progression or worsening, and +1 and -1 for uncertainty, was easily coded in our computer database. This analog scale remains in use today at many institutions doing glioma clinical trials where T2 hyperintensity rather than gadolinium (Gd) contrast define response and progression to therapy, such as in low- and mid-grade gliomas, although I believe that computer driven tumor volumetrics will someday make the analog scale obsolete for MRI progression and response.

—⁂—

By 1980-1981, I had become very frustrated by the lack of progress in treating glioblastoma (GBM) and the lack of new drugs in the pipelines of pharmaceutical companies and academics labs around the country. I doubted that cytotoxic alkylating agents were going to advance therapy for high-grade gliomas. Because of this frustration, together with clinical colleagues, I developed a "Hail

Mary" drug combination designated as NCOG-6G91. My radiation oncology colleague, Bill Wara, referred to this protocol as the "Reggie Protocol" in honor of the baseball great, Reggie Jackson. To this day, I never fully understood why he liked calling it the Reggie Protocol, but the name stuck for much of our clinical team.

NCOG-6G91 was a seven-drug protocol that was based loosely on laboratory study results in the Brain Tumor Research Center and on my optimism regarding the value of the drug-drug interactions created by the protocol. It was "the last stand" for our group, the most aggressive protocol we could conceive of at the time with the drugs available. It also carried considerable toxicity risk for our patients, but I was confident the risk would be acceptable based on my prior experience using these drugs to treat patients.

The therapy consisted of seven drugs administered before, during, and after EBRT. The first phase, consisting of a 5-FU and CCNU combination, was initiated after surgery. This was followed by radiation therapy and concurrent chemotherapy with hydroxyurea and misonidazole. Following radiation therapy, adjuvant chemotherapy with alternating cycles of a procarbazine and vincristine combination with a BCNU and 5-FU combination were given for a year. This protocol was based on diverse experimental observations. 5-FU enhances cytotoxicity of CCNU, increasing the ability of CCNU to kill glioma cells, thereby reducing the tumor cell burden before radiation therapy. Hydroxyurea potentiates radiation-induced cell kill, improving the response to radiation therapy in patients with high-grade gliomas, and misonidazole to radiosensitize hypoxic cells. Procarbazine, vincristine, BCNU, and 5-FU were active against gliomas, and tumor cell resistance to one of these drugs did not appear to result in resistance to any of the others.

The NCOG trial enrolled 90 patients between 1980 and 1983. Of these patients, 64 patients with GBM were evaluable for TTP. This was based on their completion of pre-radiation chemotherapy,

EBRT and hydroxyurea, having begun adjuvant chemotherapy, and returning for follow-up examination. We found that patient response to the Reggie Protocol was the same as for the BCNU and PCV arms of NCOG-6G61. In addition, it was found that the median TTP for the 64 patients was 42 weeks, about the same as we had observed for the PCV arm of NCOG-6G61. At two years, however, the PCV arm was superior (20% vs 5%) to the NCOG-6G91 protocol. For studies such as these, overall survival is more important than TTP, but we did not have the patience to wait for the determination of overall survival before publishing and concluded, maybe wrongly, that we had not moved the needle for GBM treatment since the results of the "Reggie Protocol" were like those of a previous protocol, NCOG-6G61, which consisted of hydroxyurea during radiation therapy followed by chemotherapy with BCNU or the PCV combination.

Interested in fractionated radiation and chemotherapy, the Dennis Deen lab focused on exploiting the multicellular spheroid model to better understand fractionated radiation and chemotherapy. His studies included seeking to answer the question: How does a radiation sensitizer administered periodically during a fractionated radiation treatment affect the overall response of the cells to the treatment? These studies were carried out using human brain tumor cell lines because DNA repair mechanisms operable in rodent cells differed from those found in human tumor cells. This project was devised to help clinical investigators understand and interpret outcomes of their fractionated therapeutic studies, hopefully leading to new therapeutic strategies. In my case, his data helped me to understand and later, at the MD Anderson Cancer Center, pursue accelerated fractionation studies with carboplatin and bromodeoxyuridine chemotherapy and, thereby, make a final push at enhancing radiation to increase survival of patients with high-grade gliomas (Chapter 15).

I and other Center medical scientists also pursued drugs that might be used to potentiate the effects of radiation to kill more high-grade glioma tumor cells. The first drug we studied was a hypoxic cell sensitizer called misonidazole. It was known that high-grade gliomas had regions within the tumor that had low oxygen tension and were, therefore, less sensitive to the antitumor effects of irradiation. Misonidazole had been shown to improve radiation therapy-induced tumor cell kill when cells were grown under hypoxic or low-oxygen conditions. In anticipation of a clinical trial, our group conducted studies to look at CNS toxicity to the peripheral nerves and auditory evoked potentials in rats. We also participated in several clinical trials to evaluate the potential of hypoxic cell sensitizer, misonidazole, to enhancing the ability of radiation therapy to kill tumor cells and prolong survival of people with glioblastoma. Unfortunately, that approach did not work in patients.

Taking a different approach, Dennis and Takao showed that bromodeoxyuridine could potentiate radiation-induced high-grade glioma cell-kill in cell culture. In anticipation of a clinical trial, Surasak Phuphanich, my wife, Ellen, and I developed a high-performance liquid chromatographic method to measure the drug in human serum and conducted a pharmacokinetic study to inform the dose schedule for the clinical trials that followed. Our initial results in a phase II study were very encouraging, and we thought we really had a valuable drug to be used to improve on the effects of radiation therapy for the treatment of high-grade glioma patients. Unfortunately, subsequent studies by the Radiation Treatment Oncology Group (RTOG) as well as a later hyper-fractionated EBRT study with bromodeoxyuridine I conducted at the MD Anderson Cancer Center failed to support benefit.

Research into the role of polyamines and how best to exploit the polyamine biosynthetic pathway in brain tumor cells continued in Larry Marton's laboratory. In collaboration with Dick Shafer in the Department of Pharmaceutical Chemistry, new and expanded physical-chemical techniques (melting temperature, equilibrium dialysis, circular dichroism and viscoelastometry) were investigated. In addition, Dennis Deen's lab further expanded polyamine research to include chromosomal and molecular assays. The result of these studies provided a good understanding of the role of polyamines in tumor cells and the biological consequences of inhibiting this pathway. The studies helped catalyze some of my laboratory research and stimulate my clinical trials research with DFMO treatment of CNS tumors over the next two decades.

I could not have predicted this foray into polyamine research with Larry Marton would be so important for me and, maybe, for the field of neuro-oncology. Understanding the association between CSF polyamine burden and CNS tumor and tumor location, and later, studies with DFMO in the laboratory and clinic were pivotal. Before leaving UCSF in 1988 for The University of Texas MD Anderson Cancer Center (MDACC) I did not foresee that my clinical studies at UCSF would lead directly to initiation of pivotal phase III randomized trials with DFMO and PCV versus PCV in high-grade gliomas at the MDACC that, in turn, led to DFMO being on a path today for clinical approval for the treatment of anaplastic astrocytoma (see Chapter 27). To some degree, scientific researchers can look ahead, but rarely are we so prescient.

In 1985, our multidisciplinary clinical team was composed of twenty individuals. It included four neurosurgeons: Charlie, Phil, Mark, and Mike. We also had a faculty neuropathologist, Richard Davis, and his neuropathology fellow, Hans A. Kretzschmar. In addition, radiation oncology was well-represented by Bill Wara, Steven Leibel, Glenn Sheline, Penny Sneed, and the department chair, Theodore Phillips. Neuroradiology became the major methodology for following CNS tumors and defining response or progression of treatment; we were very fortunate to have two neuroradiologists, Hans Newton and David Norman, as well as their neuroradiology fellows. At the time I was still the only faculty neuro-oncologist, but fortunately I usually had two neuro-oncology fellows. Filling out our Clinical Service were one or two clinical research nurses, a data manager, and a receptionist-secretary.

Throughout my UCSF years, I worked closely with neuro-radiology and nuclear medicine colleagues to develop early neuroimaging criteria for the semi-quantitative assessment of tumor progression and response as well as for assessing radiation treatment effect (e.g., necrosis). These efforts were critical in improving our ability to define tumor response and progression to treatment with greater accuracy. We also were able to reduce false negative and false positive interpretations that might invalidate the usefulness of our treatment decisions. Over the years I have found that education and experience are required to limit errors in clinical judgement.

Clinical studies at this time included: 1) poly-drug chemotherapy and drug-radiation protocols based on laboratory leads; 2) brachytherapy with 125I for primary tumors; 3) combined hyperthermia and brachytherapy for recurrent tumors; 4) PET studies to diagnose and follow patients with a high risk for developing radiation-induced necrosis; 5) safety and efficacy studies for drugs administered directly into the CSF; 6) safety and efficacy studies of oral versus intravenous bromodeoxyuridine treatment; and 7) attempts to develop a better classification system for human gliomas.

—w—

By the time I left UCSF in 1988, the Neuro-Oncology Service (originally the Brain Tumor Chemotherapy Service) was seeing about 400 new CNS tumor patients yearly and had about 2000 outpatient visits each year. In addition, we offered clinical trials for most infiltrative primary CNS tumors.

When I look back on the sixteen wonderful and productive years I had at UCSF and the Brain Tumor Research Center, the colleagues I worked with, friends I made, patients and families I had been entrusted to care for, and programs I developed, I feel very lucky and deeply honored. Among my contributions to the field was a better understanding of some of the physical-chemical attributes of brain penetrant chemicals and anticancer drugs, regional chemical and drug tracer modeling to appreciate how anticancer drugs would distribute in tumors and surrounding brain, how drug pharmacokinetics could be used to better understand alkylator drug action and tumor cell kill, and how restricted brain permeability of a drug might nevertheless succeed in adequately penetrating the surrounding brain under specific conditions. We also did early systematic research into the toxicity and pharmacokinetic of intra-CSF administered drugs in beagle dogs. These experiments helped prevent dangerous drugs from being tested in children and adults as well as investigations to better model how intra-CSF drugs are cleared from the CSF.

Looking back today, I recall tangible contributions that helped move the UCSF program forward and, hopefully, the wider clinical neuro-oncology field. One of my lasting contributions was the generation of neuro-oncology fellows I helped train. Many of those fellows went on to productive academic careers and are training the next generation of fellows and future university faculty to treat CNS tumor patients. Furthermore, I helped establish the first methodology for systematically following and defining the benefit of treatment (i.e., radiation therapy, chemotherapy, surgery) on patient outcomes using an analog scale that enabled fairly accurate assessments of TTP, progression-free survival, and overall survival. I was also instrumental in bringing PCV therapy forward as one of the most widely used combination chemotherapy regimens in the world for the treatment of CNS tumors.

I take pride in having played a major part in developing the first minicomputer-based relational database to track and analyze the impact of treatments, diagnostic variables, and the impact of other diseases on CNS tumor patients. I am also proud of the associated analytic software for tables and graphs to collate treatment-specific therapies. Implementation of the computerized record enabled our program to conduct, analyze, and publish many clinical studies and to answer numerous associated medical and neuroimaging questions. Our persistent concern about the negative impact of irradiation on the brain, also led colleagues in radiation oncology and me to push the clinical window at the time and reduce the tumor radiation field size for infiltrative glioma patients and then to evaluate the efficacy and safety of reducing cranial-spinal dosing for young medulloblastoma patients. Both efforts were satisfying and support the Hippocratic oath to "first, do no harm".

—⚹—

My years at UCSF were productive and gratifying knowing that my passion and leadership had helped to establish and develop one of the first translational research groups in which scientists and clinicians worked together to conceive laboratory projects that had direct relevance to the treatment of CNS cancers. We all felt that the Brain Tumor Research Center was a role model for many cancer centers to follow. I am also proud of co-founding with Charlie Wilson and organizing the first meeting to bring clinical and laboratory researchers together to share their research and ideas. Originally called the California Conference on Brain Tumor Therapy in 1975, these meetings continue bi-yearly as the International Conference on Brain Tumor Research and Treatment.

Whether rightly or wrongly, we at UCSF had the perception and conceit that we were the center of the therapeutic neuro-oncology universe. Our perception of our general importance to the field was strengthened by the fact that UCSF was then the center of enormous advances in cellular biology, genetic drivers of cancer, radiobiology, crystallography and three-dimensional modeling of drug docking and binding, to name a few. Scientists at UCSF were creating new companies, such as Genentech, Chiron, and Cetus, which moved science forward and provided unprecedented collaborative opportunities. So, it is understandable from my perspective given the clinical trials I initiated and whose results I published, the twenty-one neuro-oncology fellows I had trained, and the accolades we received from physicians throughout the world, those of us in the Brain Tumor Research Center and the Department of Neurological Surgery believed that we, on the West Coast, were the critical drivers of the field of therapeutic neuro-oncology.

15

The Good and Bad About Radiation Therapy for CNS Tumors

For much of my career in neuro-oncology I was involved in efforts to increase the effect of radiation on the growth of tumors in the CNS. These studies encompassed tumor cell cultures, rodent intracerebral tumor models, and human clinical trials. The results of these studies were mixed with respect to efficacy and future patient benefit, although they helped define the effect of alkylating agents on radiation cell kill. I also participated in laboratory and clinical studies of the hypoxic cell sensitizers, misonidazole and desmethylmisonidazole, and defined their pharmacokinetics and brain penetrance, their effect on radiation on tumor growth in rodent models, neurotoxicity, and lack of efficacy in patients with glioblastoma.

Because of our lack of success with hypoxic cell sensitizers, I and radiation oncology colleagues looked at other agents to potentiate radiotherapeutic cell kill. We focused our first efforts on hydroxyurea and, later, bromodeoxyuridine and carboplatin. While we believed that hydroxyurea improved radiation therapy control of high-grade glial tumors clinically, we never completed a large, sufficiently powered prospective randomized trial to prove this benefit. The cooperative group sponsor, the Western Cancer Study Group, disbanded about halfway through our study and I did not have the foresight to attempt to continue it as a local protocol.

Western Cancer Study Group Protocol 156 started in about 1977 and was a phase III clinical trial designed to compare using radiation therapy, BCNU, external beam radiation therapy (EBRT), hydroxyurea during radiation therapy, and adjuvant BCNU (BHR Group) to pre-radiation therapy BCNU, EBRT, and adjuvant BCNU (BR Group) for the treatment of malignant gliomas. In the BHR arm of the study, hydroxyurea was administered orally on alternate days during radiation therapy. Time to disease progression was determined by comparing the results of sequential neurological examinations and radionuclide and computerized tomographic scans. Of the 130 patients entered in the study, glioblastoma patients (n = 72) demonstrated a statistically significant difference (p = 0.03) between the two arms of the study, with BHR Group MTP 41 weeks and BHR MTP 31 weeks. In addition, the subset of glioblastoma patients with subtotal tumor resection did slightly better on BHR (49 vs 31 weeks) with a p-value = 0.03. While our study was not powered for survival, we were confident that hydroxyurea during EBRT was of value and was well-tolerated with little myelotoxicity. After publication of this study in 1979, we continued to use hydroxyurea during EBRT until publication of the Roger Stupp temozolomide clinical trial results. Interesting, however, our studies utilizing EBRT with hydroxyurea followed by PCV and various nitrosourea combinations produced comparable overall survival results to the temozolomide studies.

In the Center, we continued our pursuit of agents to improve on EBRT for CNS tumors and investigated using the halopyrimidine bromodeoxyuridine (BrdU), the alkylating agent BCNU, the hypoxic cell sensitizers misonidazole and desmethylmisonidazole, and platinum analogs during radiotherapy. In most cases, these studies culminated in clinical trials. In our initial clinical studies with BrdU during EBRT we thought the clinical signal was good, however, with further study and, especially when we combined BrdU with accelerated fractionated radiotherapy in a rigorous test for efficacy, it failed to extend survival in glioblastoma patients.

One of the most frustrating studies was a trial I created to evaluate intravenous carboplatin with accelerated fractionated radiotherapy that produced some clinical success but with an unacceptable level of CNS toxicity. Based on studies with cisplatin by Karen Fu, a UCSF Radiation Oncologist, we embarked on two very aggressive trials of carboplatin, an analog of cisplatin, in combination with accelerated fractionated radiotherapy for patients with glioblastoma and anaplastic glioma. Sadly, the studies demonstrated no benefit for the glioblastoma patients. For patients with anaplastic glioma, however, we found a survival benefit, but at an unacceptable level of radiation necrosis. The median overall survival for anaplastic astrocytoma patients was 29 months and for oligoastrocytoma patients 41 months. Furthermore, 25% of anaplastic glioma patients were alive nearly nine years after treatment was initiated. Unfortunately, treatment-induced radiation necrosis, documented by surgery or autopsy, was found in 19 patients (21%). A mixed pattern of necrosis and tumor was found in another 21 (23%), and an additional 13 patients without biopsy (14%) demonstrated an MRI appearance compatible with radiation necrosis. Even more unfortunate was serious clinical neurologic deterioration and/or dementia requiring full-time caregiver attention observed in nine patients (10%).

To better understand the cause of the excessive incidence of radiation necrosis, we interrogated the variables of radiation dose, irradiated tumor volume and radiotherapy techniques used (boost and fields). We concluded the higher incidence of radiation necrosis in this patient group was due to carboplatin given to improve the antitumor activity of irradiation.

I was absolutely devastated by the CNS toxicity my protocol had wrought on these patients and redoubled my efforts to find better treatments that might lessen radiation damage to the CNS. Sadly, it would take until 2007 for me to find a possible therapy to counteract some effects of radiation damage to the CNS and until 2011 before we could establish Class 1 Evidence of the efficacy of bevacizumab (Avastin) as a treatment for radiation necrosis. In 2007, one of my MDACC neuro-oncology fellows, Javier Gonzalez, wrote a paper on our experience with intravenous bevacizumab (Avastin) for the treatment of CNS radiation necrosis in eight patients. Even with this encouragement, I could not get Genentech, the pharmaceutical company that produced Avastin to provide drug to me for a randomized trial to provide more substantial evidence of Avastin's effectiveness in treating CNS radiation necrosis. I was forced to go through a longer and more complicated process to obtain Cancer Therapy Evaluation Program (CTEP) approval and funding for a randomized study and, in addition, CTEP required that we study symptomatic patients with radiation necrosis, a process that took four years (Chapter 16).

In addition to drug studies to potentiate radiotherapeutic effects on CNS tumors, I worked with Phil Gutin on his extensive ^{125}I brachytherapy studies during my UCSF years. These studies led to some clinical benefit, but at the high price of radiotherapy necrosis and reoperation. They also led to one of the first PET studies to document radiotherapy necrosis in the CNS in a group of patents where active tumor versus radiotherapy necrosis were both possible outcomes.

In other radiation studies, I worked with Bill Wara to lower radiotherapy toxicity and improve radiotherapy efficacy in children with brainstem gliomas and cerebellar medulloblastoma. We tried hyperfractionated radiation for brainstem gliomas with some initial benefit that seemed supportable in a larger study. Since these were not randomized studies and outcomes were palliative in nature, these more time-consuming and, therefore, expensive, treatments never really caught on, either for children or adults. Bill Wara and I were a bit disappointed this therapy did not receive interest from the pediatric neuro-oncology community. We thought the hyper-fractionated dose schedule we were using produced less CNS toxicity.

In studies with Bill Wara, for children with medulloblastoma, we were able to reduce radiotherapy doses with good results when coupled with adjuvant chemotherapy. Initially, this approach attracted more concern than interest. In the first cooperative trial, early relapse was seen, and the reduced spinal dose approach was dropped by the pediatric oncology community, although we argued that in our studies, we used adjuvant chemotherapy and maybe that was the difference. Today, the lower dose approach has found acceptance for some medulloblastoma subgroups. In addition, based on modern molecular-genetic studies, it is likely that some children with medulloblastoma may be able to forgo spinal irradiation altogether in the future.

16

Radiation Necrosis and Treatments Effects: The Game Changer

Early in my career at UCSF, I understood that I and my neuro-oncology fellows could serve as consultants and send our patients back to their referring physicians for further care and the implementation of our suggested treatments. However, I did not like this approach as I felt I needed to learn as much as I could about my patients and the consequences of the tumor diagnosis and its treatment on their lives and those of their caregivers. It was important to know nuances of their neurological symptoms, psychosocial interactions with family and friends, the impact of their disease and its treatment on neuroimaging modalities, and I needed to stay informed about what the therapies were capable of doing. I also felt that because of the specialized knowledge I had gained, I would do my patients a disservice if I were to function solely as a consultant. I felt that there were not enough trained physicians who could both provide chemotherapy, oversee radiation therapy, and deal effectively with the neurological problems that our patients posed. As a result, I elected to provide a neuro-oncology service that effectively made our team the primary care teams for our patients going forward, at least if they were getting therapy, and usually for the duration of their lives. That is not to say that we did not involve the patient's local physicians(s) in their care, we did, but we were expected to take expanded responsibility for the direction of their care and the treatment of treatment complications. We were practicing holistic medicine, or more correctly, holistic neuro-oncology much before it became popular.

This approach turned out to be best for patients and crucial for training neuro-oncology fellows. It also meant that we were aware of the impact of surgery, radiation, and chemotherapy damage to the CNS. As a result of our holistic approach, we followed our patients very closely for the rest of their lives, whether it was three months or 15 years. We had to bear witness to their diminished neurological function and social interactions, changed familial relationships, with teenage children sometimes assuming responsibility for a parent, reversed roles in marriage and other marital disruption, and, at times, divorce. This clinical intimacy led to a great deal of frustration with radiation therapy for me and our team. On the one hand, we tried to improve radiation outcomes with various radiation fraction and dose schedules, and with new drugs and chemicals. On the other hand, it appeared to me, and others on our team, that CNS tumor irradiation was a major cause of morbidity, and sometimes even mortality, for our patients.

Apropos of this frustration is the following story. My memories of people I treated in the late 1970s and 1980s is overwhelmed by the impact of tumor treatment on their neurocognitive function. One man I recall was Sam. Sam was about thirty-five-years old when he first came to our clinic following partial removal of his tumor by a neurosurgeon at a hospital close to his home in Fort Bragg in Northern California. He lived alone, but near his parents. He had a married brother and worked in a lumberyard.

Sam came to his first clinic dressed in clean work jeans and a patterned flannel shirt. For support, his father and brother joined him, although his father preferred to wait for the history and examination to be completed before he came back into the room. Sam was quite amiable, with a sweet disposition, as far as I know, Sam never married. I am not sure if he graduated from high school.

From his brother I deduced that Sam was a good worker, dependable and a well-liked employee of the lumberyard. Sam's recent craniotomy was obvious; his scalp stitches were well-healed and thin wisps of brown hair were starting to grow back around the healing scalp scar. His pathology showed mildly anaplastic astrocytoma.

My examination found no specific localizing neurological signs other than a possible slowness of response to questions, confirmed by his brother as a little changed from before surgery. He also appeared to have neurofibromatosis 1 (NF1), a genetic disorder characterized by the development of multiple benign tumors of nerves and skin (neurofibromas) and areas of abnormal skin pigmentation. Since only about 15% of people with NF1 develop gliomas, usually in childhood, Sam was either an outlier or had a slowly growing astrocytoma unrelated to NF1. I could not be sure which was the true cause of his tumor.

In the 1970s we did not have the molecular-genetic studies that we have today, so I learned most about Sam's tumor from the careful report of Dick Davis, our neuropathologist who reviewed the tumor slides from his recent surgery and described the tumor as a mildly anaplastic astrocytoma. The alternative subclassification that Dick used in his reports was highly anaplastic astrocytoma, which today, with our sophisticated molecular-genetic profiling, we would know to be a tumor that would soon become a glioblastoma. As such, Dick's insights, based on light microscopy and some basic immunohistochemistry stains, was of enormous help in planning the best therapy for Sam and other glioma patients.

We treated Sam with either 54 Gy (180 cGy x 30 fractions) or 58 Gy (190 cGy x 30 fractions) of whole brain irradiation. This was the usual practice at UCSF at the time. Sam also volunteered to be in a randomized trial of oral hydroxyurea every six hours every other day during radiation therapy followed by adjuvant BCNU (BHR arm) versus radiation therapy alone followed by BCNU (BR arm). This study had started as Western Cancer Study Group Protocol 156 but continued as a UCSF study after the demise of the Western Cancer Study Group halfway through study accrual.

Sam did well for a couple of years, aside from some complex partial seizures. He worked at the lumberyard and drove, sometimes alone, but usually with his brother or father, to see me at UCSF every six to eight weeks. In the third year, he came to clinic every three months. During that year, he said he was having trouble keeping up with work and, as a result, was given more menial tasks to do at the lumberyard. His CT scan showed marked white matter changes in both hemispheres.

By the end of that year, it was becoming clear that Sam was having trouble living alone. His family did what they could to protect and help him but living alone became too difficult and too dangerous as his deficit led him to unintentionally cause a small fire in his cabin cooking breakfast one morning. As a result, the family turned off the gas to the stove and brought him his meals or had him eat with them in their house. It also became clear that driving 150 miles to our UCSF clinic was becoming difficult for the family. Because of this, Sam had CT scans taken locally and mailed to our UCSF clinic.

In the fourth year, Sam's family brought him to clinic because the CT scan showed worsened disease. By then we had MRI at UCSF, so we rescanned his brain. At the time, it was unclear how much of what we saw was radiation effect and how much was tumor as the MRI changes were in a new location. I felt it was likely that his neurocognitive slowing was a result of his original whole brain radiation therapy and chemotherapy. His family was accepting of that as "he never has been quick in his thinking," they said. Sam and his family encouraged reoperation since we were confident the new lesion could be safely resected so we moved forward with surgery. Unfortunately, as we suspected from the MRI, the resected tumor proved to have transformed to glioblastoma. I think I saw Sam once more in clinic as I had arranged PCV chemotherapy to be given by a local medical oncologist near his home.

Sam and his family accepted the impact of the CNS tumor and its treatment side-effects, knowing they could occur. I was less accepting; he was a shell of the man I first met.

Young children affected by whole brain radiation therapy caused even more indelible memories. I vividly recall a youngster of about six years with a left frontal glioblastoma that was nearly totally resected by Mike Edwards, a neuro-oncology fellow, a gifted neurosurgeon who became an assistant professor in the Neurological Surgery Department at UCSF after his fellowship. Jimmy was a bright little boy with a big smile. After surgery he was still able to move all limbs, walk about the hospital room, and converse in short sentences. After about two weeks, he was referred to Bill Wara, an outstanding and committed radiation oncologist in the Department of Radiation Oncology at UCSF who had developed a technique for irradiating young children without having to use general anesthesia. At that time, we were still giving whole brain radiation to treat children with glioblastoma, so that is what Jimmy received. Bill reduced the radiation dose outside the focused tumor dose to hopefully protect some of the normal brain as best he could while still providing whole brain coverage. About three or four weeks after completing radiation therapy, Jimmy started on PCV chemotherapy.

Jimmy's parents were accomplished and successful in their respective music and literary fields, so it was with great fear and trepidation that they approached this journey with their only child. Jimmy's father had been traveling to Europe for his research, so Jimmy's mother cared for him at their home in the San Francisco Bay Area. All went well for the first six months, and then Jimmy started to have behavioral problems. His MRI showed white matter changes associated with radiation damage that covered most of the left brain and parts of the right hemisphere.

Jimmy's neurocognitive function deteriorated, and his mother was having problems managing him at home, especially with her husband away. Both factors, contributed to a rift in the marriage. Eventually, Jimmy was hospitalized at an extended care facility and undoubtedly medicated. From a tumor perspective, Jimmy did well, but from a quality-of-life perspective, he did terribly, living in an institution for over a year. I never knew whether he died of the tumor or the treatment he received. I did know, however, that whole brain irradiation was a disaster to his young developing brain.

These two cases are only a small part of my experience with the effects of whole brain radiation therapy for infiltrating gliomas and medulloblastoma that formed the basis for my discomfort with radiation therapy. At the time, the 1970s and early 1980s, my radiation colleagues and I believed that the neurocognitive damage a patient suffered from brain irradiation was a gamble that would affect, at random it seemed, about 40 percent of patients.

17

The Day we Changed Radiation Treatment for Gliomas

In my years at UCSF, we held a weekly multidisciplinary Brain Tumor Board meeting on Thursday mornings. These conferences were critical to our team approach to the treatment of CNS tumor patients and the centerpiece of the Brain Tumor Chemotherapy Service. The room the Board met in was an old and nondescript room in the basement of Moffitt Hospital that belonged to the Department of Radiation Oncology as we did not have a room of similar size in our department. I still remember the trek to the basement room that was reached by stairs and was at the far end of the department's space. The floor in the room was covered in asphalt tiles in a nondescript grey that appeared worn and in need of replacement. Chairs formed a U-shape around a table in the center of the room where presenters and others sat. Charlie Wilson and I sat facing the radiology view boxes.

Over the years our Tumor Boards became more sophisticated as neuroimaging technology advanced. Between 1972 and 1976, we relied on the neurological examination, radionuclide scintiscan and EEG to determine response (tumor regression) or deterioration (tumor growth) during brain-tumor chemotherapy and chemo-therapy-radiotherapy. In these early years, the light-backed view boxes used for viewing X-ray and other imaging films were primarily used to view skull X-rays. Within a few years that changed, and our knowledge and understanding of tumor behavior increased dramatically with the development of CT in the mid-1970s. After the advent of CT, MRI was introduced at UCSF, and we started to learn even more about the impact of tumor and treatment effects on the CNS. It is humbling to realize how much we did not know about tumors before CT and MRI, and how much we learned in the years that followed and are still learning through constantly developing neuroimaging technologies.

Operationally, after CT and MRI were introduced at UCSF in the mid-1970s, the Tumor Board took on more formality with sequential CT and/or MRI images presented by either Dave Norman or Hans Newton, UCSF faculty neuroradiologists and early leaders in CNS imaging, or one of their neuroradiology fellows. The patient's history and treatments, if any, were presented by a neuro-oncology fellow or rotating neurosurgery resident. In the CT-MRI era, this was followed by a presentation of sequential neuroimages. In all cases, we expected the neuroradiologist to be able to provide a judgement and score number as to whether the tumor was stable (0), larger (-2), smaller (+2), or, occasionally, uncertain (-1 or +1).

Neurosurgeons in attendance were usually Charlie Wilson and Edwin Boldrey, a prior department chair and oldest member of the department, as well as other faculty neurosurgeons if a patient of theirs was being presented. Radiation oncology was usually represented by Bill Wara and Glenn Sheline and sometimes the Radiation Oncology Department Chair, Theodore "Ted" Philips, attended. Sometimes, our neuropathologist, Surl Nielsen in the 1970s, Janet Townsend in the mid-1970s, and Richard Davis starting in the late 1970s, commented about the pathology or showed photomicrographs. At UCSF, nearly 40% of the chemotherapy (neuro-oncology) fellows had been trained in neurosurgery; the remainder being trained in neurology with but two exceptions that I can recall, Mike Prados who had completed training in pulmonology, and Alfred Bowles who had completed a surgical internship and was trying to decide which residency path he would take. For each case presented we discussed, and sometimes argued, about what would be best for the patient: surgery, radiation, and/or chemotherapy. Sometimes, the Tumor Board decided to do nothing but watch, which meant repeating CT or MRI scans and discussing the case again at a future date. These structured Tumor Board conferences also allowed neuro-oncology and neuroradiology fellows and, at times, neurosurgery residents an opportunity to have their knowledge and judgment tested in front of a group. Some of our neuro-oncology fellows who went on to academic careers in neurosurgery were David Crafts, Michael Edwards, Philip Gutin, and Mitchel Berger. Those neurologists going into academic neuro-oncology careers included Dorcas Fulton, David Macdonald, Geoffrey Barger, Surasak "San" Phuphanich, Ali Choucair, and Mark Chamberlain. Michael Prados, an internist/pulmonologist succeeded me at UCSF. Names from the neuroradiology fellowship are equally well known today in academic medicine, such as William Dillon, Dieter Enzmann and Pat Turski.

I would like to trace the path of where my angst regarding radiation toxicity to the CNS led as it is instructive and of historical importance. It happened during one Tumor Board in the fall of 1983. On this day we changed how radiation therapy was administered to treat infiltrative gliomas. The Tumor Board meeting started no differently than on any other Thursday morning. I made rounds on inpatients with two fellows, Surasak "San" Phuphanich and Geoffrey Barger, and Peggy Seager, one of our neuro-oncology clinic nurses. The evening before, we had sent the list of cases to be presented at our Tumor Board meeting to Dave Norman's office in neuroradiology. After rounds, we walked down the seven flights of stairs from our clinic in Moffitt Hospital to the basement offices of the Department of Radiation Oncology. Our destination was the conference room situated at the far end of the Radiation Oncology Clinic.

As I walked with my fellows that day through the patient waiting area in the Radiation Oncology Department, I noticed the walls looked a little brighter because they had recently been painted, but the overall impression was of age because of the dark stained wooden doors with glass panes that were treated to allow light but not to allow recognizing anyone on the other side of the door. While we walked to our Brain Tumor Board conference that morning, we had no idea that we were walking into history.

The Tumor Board meeting started off as usual, but by the time the fourth patient was presented, I could feel frustration and anger welling up inside of me as San described how the patient had been deteriorating neurologically for months and the MRI images began to coalesce in front of us. The patient presented with a stable-appearing glioma but worsening neurological function and changes in the MRI that we had come to identify as being late radiation damage. I vented my frustration with a patient's decreased quality of life secondary to irradiation and I burst out with the words, "When are we going to stop giving whole brain irradiation for malignant gliomas?" Either I was so impassioned, or the timing was just right after the outburst, Ted Phillips, the Chair of Radiation of Oncology, and Bill Wara said, "How about tomorrow?" I was flabbergasted by the rapidity of the response. There was no heated discussion as everyone in the room either agreed or were too shocked to utter a comment. In the blink of an eye, we agreed to change the way gliomas would be treated with radiation therapy since the arrival of the first radiation therapy machine at UCSF. I had a difficult time concentrating on the rest of the Tumor Board that day as I tried to digest what the ramifications of this change in radiation treatment field would have on radiation therapy for the glioma patients.

Others in attendance at the time recall this day as a day that changed the history of radiation therapy for primary infiltrative gliomas on the West Coast and for much of the United States. It's questionable if everyone at the Tumor Board that day appreciated the impact this decision would make on the treatment of glioma patients for years to come, but the three radiation oncologists, Bill Wara, Ted Phillips, and Glenn Sheline, the two neuro-oncology trainees and fellows, San Phuphanich and Geoff Barger, and the neurosurgeons, Charlie Wilson, Edwin Boldrey, and Mike Edwards, all knew and appreciated the importance of that announcement and the potential impact it would have on patient quality of life. No one really knew what the impact would be on patient survival, but we were optimistic that improved neurocognitive function would be better for patients.

It never occurred to me that our decision to reduce the radiation treatment field would be met with such dissent from colleagues in the Midwest and East. Some in the field called or wrote editorials stating that we were going to kill people with this decision. Darrell Bigner called and admonished me, saying "Don't you know that gliomas are infiltrative, and you have to treat the whole brain with radiation therapy?" We were told that what we were doing by reducing the radiation dose was blasphemy. I remember reading an editorial in one of the neurology journals to that effect, although I have been unable to find it again. When Bill Wara attended a Pediatric Oncology Group (POG) meeting several months after our momentous decision, like me, he was strongly admonished that limited-field radiation was a very bad idea and was told that by doing so, he would kill children.

Today, limited field irradiation for infiltrative and single-site gliomas is the norm. Reducing the size of the radiation field improved survival and led to a better quality of life for our patients, although no randomized trial prospectively proved this in the 1980s. Several months after we made this decision in Tumor Board, we considered whether we needed to do a prospective randomized trial to compare whole brain to limited-field irradiation. A randomized clinical trial is, of course, the best practice from a statistical perspective. However, none of us wanted to risk hurting people with whole brain radiation unless we absolutely had to.

Happily, for us and our patients, medical history would confirm our decision as correct. With little coaxing, all radiation therapists in Northern California that were participants in the Northern California Oncology Group agreed to the change. At the time, we were accruing patients to a phase II clinical trial of radiation therapy with bromodeoxyuridine during radiation therapy followed by the PCV combination. We knew our decision to cease whole brain irradiation would impact the trial, but we felt reducing neurocognitive decline in our patients was more important than strict adherence to radiation dose fields. The benefit of combining bromodeoxyuridine with radiation was retained as we were irradiating tumor in both cases. As it turned out, reducing the tumor field size indicated that patients with limited-field irradiation survived longer. Unfortunately, since the study was not powered to compare whole brain with limited-field irradiation, we could only conclude in the paper that limited-field irradiation provided improved overall survival. In addition, we observed that our limited-field irradiation patients had fewer and less severe neurocognitive symptoms and signs than with whole brain irradiation for primary CNS tumors. Sadly, we did not have formal neurocognitive testing available at the time. Nonetheless, all members of our neuro-oncology team became comfortable with our decision to use limited-field irradiation for newly diagnosed infiltrative gliomas. We believed we had chosen the moral and medical high ground and our patients would be better off from our decision.

Late-delayed CNS radiation damage, or radiation necrosis, has always been difficult to contain and limit. Too often it is associated with neurocognitive sequalae in patients. I have distinct and sad memories of too many patients who, over the years, suffered severe cognitive impairment. It was, therefore, with great disappointment that even when we reduced tumor irradiation to smaller fields, we had to face the fact that reducing the field size for irradiating infiltrative gliomas of the brain lessened, but did not eliminate, radiation-induced brain damage.

This sad truth was reinforced throughout my clinical career. To this day, I remember many of these patients who either died of radiation necrosis or who whose lives were seriously affected by radiation necrosis and associated small-vessel strokes. One of these patients I saw many years after his surgery, EBRT, and chemotherapy was completed. We met at the unexpected venue of a Society for Neuro-Oncology Annual Meeting.

It was November, when the tree leaves turn to red and gold and drop to the ground, but before celebrating the American Holiday of Thanksgiving. I was in San Antonio, Texas, where it was still coatless fall weather with a few clouds resting in an otherwise pale blue sky. Tourists walked on the River Walk but boating on the river had not yet started for the day as I entered the San Antonio Marriott Rivercenter Hotel. The 2015 Society for Neuro-Oncology Annual Meeting had brought me to the hotel for three days of meetings to learn and talk with colleagues about the arcane field of CNS tumors.

On the second day of the meeting, I entered the hotel planning to attend a talk in the main conference area. I found the escalator that would take me down to the lower floor where the scientific meetings were held. I was walking quickly, as I often do, in pursuit of what I hoped to be an interesting talk about treatment options for a recently observed genetic subgroup of people with gliomas. I noticed a man entering from an outside door and walking toward me. He waved, signaling me to wait for him. I did not initially recognize him, but I was curious and waited until he came closer to see who this stranger might be.

As he neared, I could see he was a middle-aged man with thinning brown hair. He wore clean, but wrinkled, khaki pants and a light coat. Something about the man's appearance triggered memories of a patient I had treated years ago, but I was not sure until he said, "Doctor Levin, do you remember me? I am Henry."

In a split second, I experienced a cascade of memories. I first met Henry and his wife, Mary, at one of my MD Anderson Monday new patient clinics in 2003. They had come to show me his MRI and discuss what I thought he should do about his abnormal MRI. Henry was in his early thirties. From that meeting, I learned that they had two young children who were staying with their maternal grandmother while they were in Houston. Henry worked full-time at a hardware store and wanted to become part owner of the store. Because of his relaxed interaction with his wife during the clinic visit, I thought he and his wife got along well together.

During that initial visit, Henry's wife sometimes expanded on Henry's responses to my questions and comments, and Henry appeared comfortable with that. I had the impression that they grew up together in or near the same small town outside San Antonio and shared a long history. I explained an operation would be needed to remove much of the right frontal tumor and we would use the pathology report to develop a treatment plan for him. To counter this new intrusion in his life and the fear associated with it, I offered that the tumor appeared to be a mid-grade glioma and that surgery, as first step, would be needed to remove as much tumor as possible so we could make a diagnosis and plan therapy for him. I did not push too much further information on them as they were about to see his neurosurgeon down the hall in the clinics we shared.

I next saw Henry a week after surgery. The surgeon did a good resection of the tumor that we call a subtotal resection. Tumors like

Henry's can rarely be truly removed in toto unless they are in a lobe of the brain that can be excised without causing much neurological sequalae. The tumor was classified as an astrocytoma, so I re-affirmed the surgeon's optimistic statement to them that tumor growth could be controlled with radiation and chemotherapy. At this clinic visit, Henry sat quietly on his chair as I explained the need for external beam radiation therapy and likely post-irradiation additional chemotherapy with the PCV combination. This was, at the time, my usual practice for patients like Henry, whose MRI showed a good deal of residual tumor following partial resection of an astrocytoma. I explained we would go slowly with PCV chemotherapy and told him not to worry about it now. We would talk again after his next MRI about two weeks after completion of irradiation.

I continued seeing Henry and his wife, and sometimes his father, in clinic for the next several years. For the first year, I saw Henry at seven-to nine-week intervals, depending on his blood count recovery to the cytotoxic PCV chemotherapy that he was taking after external beam radiation therapy. I recall Henry being an easy and undemanding patient who appeared to adjust to the requirements of chemoradiation, adjuvant chemotherapy, and the endless MRI and clinic visits that occupied the first years of treatment. He was generally happy and was getting good support from his co-workers, who expected him to bounce back to his normal self after the treatments were over.

Late in year two, I was seeing Henry at three-month intervals for an MRI, review of his symptoms, and neurological examination. My plan was to extend the interval between MRI and clinic visits to four months in the third year and then to six months for years four and five. After the first year, even though the MRI showed no evidence of tumor growth, it was clear by the way Henry and his wife talked, that Henry was not functioning well at work and home and there was concern he might be laid off. Mary said that his energy level was not consistent during the day, and he had problems when too many things were going on at the same time. Chris Meyers, a neuropsychologist in our Department at The MD Anderson, had conducted formal neurocognitive testing of Henry and found that his neurological symptoms and problems were due to impaired executive function and excessive fatigue. It took him longer to do the tasks he did before the tumor and its treatment and, therefore, it took more effort. He became increasingly tired and prone to making errors as the day wore on. As a result, during the latter part of the third year of his clinic visits, we were told that Henry was being given menial assignments at work and eventually was given a half-day work schedule.

Even though Henry was in clinical remission without evidence of tumor growth, I remembered with sadness watching him deteriorate each time I saw him. He and his wife told me he was slow at forming new memories and completing a task in a timely and efficient manner. Mary said this was true both at work and at home. Eventually, maybe late in the third year of clinic visits, Henry was laid off. He stayed home with the children so Mary could go to work to support the family. Henry continued to have problems with executive function and fatigue during the day, so when Mary worked, Henry's parents and friends checked on him regularly to make sure everyone was safe, and the children were getting to and from school on time.

When I saw Henry in the hotel foyer in 2015, I realized that I had lost track of him. I wondered whether it was because his family stopped driving the 200 miles from his hometown near San Antonio to Houston to see me at the MDACC clinic or because I left MDACC in December 2009, or both. In any case, here he was. He clearly retained his memory of us and the fact that I had cared for him for many years.

"Henry," I said, greeting him. "I haven't seen you in years. How are you doing?" Henry told me he was okay, but that he lived with his parents. "Mary divorced me," he said. Both statements were offered to me as facts with little emotion.

"Sorry to hear that," I said. I remembered he had gone into a remission and probably was still in remission, maybe twelve years now as it had to be at least seven years since I had last seen him in clinic.

I thought of his impacted quality of life, his divorce. Divorce can have different causes. I had seen couples divorce to access health insurance like Medicaid without losing a family house and resources. Other times, the impact of the brain tumor and its treatment was too much for a spouse. Maybe his wife, who would have been in her late thirties, found it too much to care for Henry, whose behaviors and dependency were more like having another child in the family. Maybe it was mutually agreed on if his parents had the strength and resources to bring Henry to live with them, then Mary could move on with her life. Most of the time marriages hold together under these circumstances, but sometimes not. For some spouses, seeing the loss of the person they married and watching them neurocognitively decline become increasingly difficult, causes some spouses to move on alone.

"What brings you here today?" I asked. I was curious as this was not a patient conference.

"I live in the city with my parents," Henry said, "and heard about this meeting from friends I made in my support group, so I wanted to look around."

As Henry stood smiling in front of me making small talk about his children, I tried to imagine what his life must be like, now. His children were living with his ex-wife; maybe she was remarried or dating. I did not ask; he did not say. He told me he did some chores around his parents' home, but he was not gainfully employed; he probably never would be.

While I could have spent hours talking to Henry, I didn't. I spent half an hour talking with him, and not because Henry didn't want to talk more. I was uncomfortable seeing his life ruined by the treatment of his astrocytoma. As we parted, by the smile of his face, I could see that Henry was not sad, rather, he seemed upbeat to have come to this meeting with no apparent goal in mind and yet by random chance, we had met and become reacquainted. I hoped that Henry would view this random meeting as the unexpected and happy event it was and a story he could tell his family and friends about for some time. For me, it was gratifying on one level, but on another, it was a painful reminder of how slowly we have progressed in our quest for safe therapies that do not harm normal brain function of CNS tumor patients.

———

In the early years of my career, I was convinced that future chemotherapy would be so effective that we would be able to do away with irradiating CNS tumors. Unfortunately, progress in new drug development for CNS tumors was not moving forward, so I concluded that if we could not eliminate the risk of radiation necrosis, at least we could try and bring forward better treatments for radiation damage to the CNS. As mentioned earlier, late-delayed radiation damage or radiation necrosis has always been difficult to contain and limit and a source of fear for many patients and their caregivers. Over the years, colleagues and I had used many different vitamins and drugs to try and control radiotherapy necrosis in our patients. It ranged from glucocorticoids like dexamethasone or methyl prednisone to pentoxifylline, warfarin, heparin, high-dose vitamin E, COX-2 inhibitors, hyperbaric oxygen, and surgery. None of these agents and approaches, however, provided the statistically strong level 1 proof of benefit for the treatment of radiation necrosis.

In 2007, we finally had purchase on the problem with bevacizumab (Avastin), a humanized antibody developed by Genentech to bind circulating VEGF, a growth factor. Unfortunately, it took until 2011 before I was able to publish on the first placebo-controlled randomized trial of bevacizumab in neurologically symptomatic patients that provided level 1 evidence as an effective treatment of radiation necrosis. Sadly, proof of bevacizumab's value in the treatment of radiation necrosis should have been available about two to three years earlier since we had a strong signal of its value from an earlier study. We were, however, unable to obtain drug from Genentech for a randomized trial as the company was in the process of seeking approval of bevacizumab for recurrent/progressive GBM, and they were disinclined to risk not getting FDA approval. As a result, we had to conduct our study through an NCI Cancer Therapy Evaluation Program (CTEP) grant and were forced to do a randomized trial in people who were symptomatic from radiation necrosis. As a result, the study accrued slowly, but fortunately, it worked so well that we were able to close the study with only fourteen patients because of a p-value of 0.001 for symptom improvement and reduction in T2 FLAIR edema (p = 0.015) and normalized Ktrans (p = 0.02), a measure of the rate at which Gd-contrast crosses brain capillaries.

Over the years I have treated or directed treatment of many adults and children with bevacizumab who had various irradiated tumors that resulted in radiation necrosis. Examples include losing vision from meningioma because radiation caused local edema, putting pressure on the optic chiasm; hemangiopericytoma in the cerebellum; mid- and high-grade glioma of the brain and brainstem; irradiated head and neck tumor patients; and patients with tumors metastatic to the brain previously irradiated with whole brain irradiation and/or stereotactic radiosurgery. The therapy was typically given every three weeks for four to six cycles. Of the therapies with which I have been involved, treating radiation necrosis with bevacizumab is among the more gratifying as it frequently stops and reverses progressive radiation necrosis and, in the process, frequently prevents more neurological symptoms and signs and thereby helps preserve quality of life. It also makes unnecessary high-dose long-term glucocorticoid (e.g., dexamethasone) treatment and its multitude of toxic symptoms and neurological signs. Even with this breakthrough, I have been surprised how few clinicians who, when faced with a patient with serious radiation treatment damage, are willing to treat with dexamethasone for weeks or months hoping to mitigate CNS damage even though bevacizumab is the only therapy with class 1 evidence of efficacy against CNS radiation necrosis. They take the position of waiting to see if it gets worse before starting bevacizumab while I would argue that they should use it early to prevent CNS damage, damage that is generally irreversible and may compromise neurocognitive function and the patient's future quality of life.

18

The National Cooperative Drug Discovery Group Grant

As I have made apparent in the past, my research and clinical career were guided and driven by the goal to create new and better therapies for brain tumor patients. By 1980, only eight years after joining the UCSF and the Brain Tumor Research Center, I was frustrated with our lack of clinical and laboratory research progress at multiple levels and frustrated with our failure to significantly impact patient survival despite our aggressive and focused clinical and laboratory efforts. My most ambitious clinical trials did not show a way forward and no progress was being made by academic and pharmaceutical scientists to develop new drugs to replace alkylating agents. In addition, I had just completed, with Herb Landahl and Cliff Patlak, what I felt was the seminal paper on mathematical modeling of regional brain and CNS tumor drug delivery. For me, this paper defined the end of the road for cytotoxic drugs as we knew them in 1980. We published this work in The Journal of Pharmacokinetics and Biopharmaceutics, which was a prestigious, but esoteric journal for those working in cancer, let alone CNS tumors, so it probably was not read as extensively as I had hoped.

Looking inward at the time and without any clear path forward, I gave part of my laboratory space to Bill Bodell, who was doing research into DNA repair mechanisms associated with alkylating agents. And, for the second time in my life, I turned to art to soothe my soul and, hopefully, reinvigorate my creative juices. I registered at College of Marin for a credit course in sculpture that met for three hours twice weekly. Over the next three semesters I learned how to sculpt in clay, wax, and stone. I also learned how to make molds from clay-and wax-sculptured pieces, pour bronze into the molds, and patina the bronze. I found great enjoyment creating sculpture and a great diversion from my laboratory and clinical work. At College of Marin, I was very lucky to work among artists of considerable skill. These classroom friends, with extensive backgrounds in painting and visual arts, offered simple comments on my work like "the piece is very nice, but maybe a little movement here," pointing to a specific location on a piece I was working on. The peer feedback made enormous difference to me in my quest to sculpt pieces I could take pride in and be satisfied with. I still have six pieces that I like to look at from my three semesters at the College of Marin.

By the end of my third semester of sculpture, I was starting to consider new research in areas that were foreign to me but intellectually interesting and potentially game-changing for the cancer field. Following my period of introspection and the convergence of my efforts as Scientific Director of the Northern California Cancer Program, my professional life entered a new phase. With emergence of a new National Cancer Institute (NCI) initiative, the National Cooperative Drug/Device Discovery Group (NCDDG) program, I was encouraged to lead a prestigious science group from the UCSF School of Medicine, UCSF School of Pharmacy, and The University of Berkeley. Joining on this grant were J. Michael Bishop, MD (School of Medicine), George Kenyon, PhD, C. Ramachandran, PhD, and Al Burlingame, PhD (UCSF School of Pharmacy), and Paul Bartlett, PhD (UC Berkeley). Our goal was to develop selective inhibitors of the c-Src catalytic site. At the time, the only protein tyrosine kinase we knew enough about to study was c-Src, but we assumed other protein tyrosine kinases would be discovered over time and/or made available to study as cancer targets. Our expectation was that if we would succeed it would allow us and others to develop selective inhibitors of other protein tyrosine kinases and usher in a new era for cancer chemotherapy. Operationally, our research was predicated on being able to define the peptide substrate for the catalytic site of c-Src. We felt this would then allow us to add reactive groups, a warhead of sorts, and, presto, we would create a drug to stop the enzymatic activity of c-Src through binding to its catalytic site.

Prior to receiving NCDDG grant approval and funding, I initiated our research program in 1981 with private philanthropic funding from a patient and entrepreneur from the Chicago area. Shortly afterwards, in 1982, we learned that we would be awarded the first NCDDG grant from this new program. The grant was funded in 1983. I continued this NCDDG research through 1988 at UCSF and, after I moved to The University of Texas MD Anderson Cancer Center in Houston, until about 2000. In total, the grant was renewed three times over a seventeen-year period.

In addition to NCI funding for the NCCDG, I received funding from Bristol Myers Research. Between 1982 and 1988, I was a consultant to the Bristol-Myers cancer research program. One winter night in 1985, after a full day of consulting at Bristol Myers Research in Wallingford, Connecticut, followed by a group dinner, Giulio Vita, PhD, President of Bristol-Myers Research and Development at that time, invited me for a walk outside in the snow to talk. It was a nice winter night with snow flurries and reasonable temperatures. During the walk he asked me about my c-Src research at UCSF and what my ambitions were for the program. He wanted to know how it might lead to new anticancer therapies and how additional funding would help to move it forward faster. The walk ended with Giulio offering me a multi-year $2.4 million grant from

Bristol-Myers Research to supplement and expand our program to develop c-Src catalytic-site inhibitors if we would give Bristol-Myers right of first refusal for patented new drugs. I agreed since at the time few of us were focusing on the profitability of a new anticancer drug. Instead, our goal was to create drugs to help people and we were happy to allow pharmaceutical companies to support the later clinical trials and market the drug(s) if we were successful. We were convinced that our research would lead to a revolution in anticancer drug discovery and development and any help we could get to make that happen was welcome.

By far, the most complex research I had been associated with, let alone lead, was the NCDDG grant to develop drug inhibitors of the c-Src. Its size, multidisciplinary nature, multi-institutional participants, and financial requirements topped anything I been associated with in the past. The inception of this NCDDG was coincident with the establishment of all laboratories and research efforts as none of that laboratory research existed on the West Coast before the NCDDG agreement was approved. In our research we were able to take a new and unique concept for anticancer drug development and to create the programs to support its feasibility. Research was simultaneously focused on the discovery and synthesis of peptidic substrates and inhibitors of pp60v-src, the search for a purer protein tyrosine kinase, and the development of means to quantitate in vivo (cell culture) effects of inhibitors on cell phenotype, protein tyrosine kinase expression, and the production of protein tyrosine protein production.

By 1988, we had 22 scientists and technicians working in five research groups. There was a Chemistry Group headed by George Kenyon, PhD from the UCSF School of Pharmacy and Paul Bartlett, PhD from The University of California Berkeley; an Enzyme Group headed by Susan Whitehouse, PhD, and me taking a supportive roll; a Peptide Group headed by Laszlo Nadasdi with my wife, Ellen, in charge of peptide purification; a Biochemistry and Genetics Group headed by Michael Bishop, MD; and a Pharmacology and *in vivo* Group that I headed.

During this period up to 1988, the group was very productive making hundreds of peptides and drug analogs for testing. It also was a time of group frustration in that the goal of making a drug(s) to inhibit the catalytic site of c-Src was turning out to be more difficult than we expected as we could not find a specific peptide or chemical to selectively block the catalytic site. Expanding this research program with limited research space and faculty salaries at UCSF was one of my major considerations to move to The University of Texas MD Anderson Cancer Center.

19

The Move to The University of Texas and my Vision for the Department of Neuro-Oncology

Academic moves can be both fulfilling and a risk to one's career. For me and for my family moving to Houston and The University of Texas MD Anderson Cancer Center (MDACC) in the summer of 1988 was a gamble that some colleagues and family thought was unnecessary.

While I was happy and productive as a faculty member at UCSF in the Departments of Neurological Surgery in the School of Medicine and Pharmaceutical Chemistry in the School of Pharmacy, my research to develop protein kinase inhibitors of c-Src funded by the NCDDG Grant that I first obtained in 1983, and a large grant from Bristol-Myers Research in 1985, was expanding while my research space was contracting. Years before, when short of laboratory space, Ted Phillips, the Chairman of the Department of Radiation Oncology, loaned me laboratory space two floors above my existing lab. This was a very gracious loan of space at the time, however, as Ted's department expanded its research program, he needed me to find other space so that his faculty could occupy the lab space I had borrowed. With no alternative for me at the time, I returned the space so he could reassign it to his faculty, and I moved my lab equipment and people into our already crowded space on the seventh floor of the Health Science East building.

In the Spring of 1987, about three months after consolidating my laboratories, I received a call from Irv Krakoff, MD, chair of the Division of Medicine at MDACC. He asked whether I might consider moving to MDACC to chair the Department of Neuro-Oncology. Irv told me that the position was not being advertised and was meant only for me if I was interested.

Irv had recently been recruited to head the Division of Medicine at the MDACC and was relatively new to the institution. Unlike medical schools where divisions are subunits in a department, divisions were the top of multi-department units with multiple departments under each division at MDACC. For instance, there was a Division of Surgery, Division of Medicine, and a Division of Radiology, as well as other divisions. In Irv's fiefdom were the Departments of Internal Medicine, Medical Oncology, Leukemia, and Neuro-Oncology. I believe that the administration believed that this structure was easier to manage when the number of faculty in each were so large.

So, out of curiosity, I agreed to fly to Houston to learn more about what Irv had in mind and to see the facilities. I had not been back to MDACC since I had participated in a site visit of a PO1 grant of Emil J. Freireich some years earlier. I had heard that MDACC was in the process of change, and I wondered how much it had changed and what changes were being considered for the future. Even though my labs at UCSF were facing a space crunch and my neuro-oncology clinic was inconveniently now across the street from the hospital in a medical office building, I was not actively searching for a new job.

The visit to MDACC was memorable on several counts, not the least of which was the climate I encountered arriving in Houston in mid-August 1987. At the time, I was living in Mill Valley and working in San Francisco, where August can be pleasantly cool. The morning after arriving in Houston, I walked outside of the hotel into the heat and humidity, intending to walk to the building of my first appointment that was only a few blocks away. As an intern I had worked much of the year at St. Louis City Hospital without

air-conditioning and had adjusted to the heat and humidity there,
but then I was 25 years old. Now, I was 46 years old, and the
temperature in Houston that August easily reached 100° F with
humidity in the high 90's. I had a quick decision to make as I
realized that just walking the two blocks to the appointment
wearing a sport jacket could leave me sweating profusely. I knew
that if I lived in that environment for several months, my autonomic
nervous system would one day adapt and I would be able to walk
in the heat and humidity with minimal sweating, but this was not
that day, and I asked the doorman to arrange a ride for me to the
medical center.

Meeting Irv Krakoff was to meet a man who had a vision of a
future MDACC that I could not initially comprehend. What I saw
on my first visit was that most hospital buildings were constructed
of a common pink granite from a Texas quarry. Inside the buildings
I met people who felt strongly about their jobs to provide the best
cancer care possible to the patients who entered their doors. This
seemed to be a shared vision, palpable among the faculty and staff
I met, including a janitor I questioned in the stairway I used to go
between floors. Initially, I thought the facilities were small for the
ambitions of the people I met inside, but this too would change and
over the years grow to be the largest and the most famous cancer
center in the world. The Department of Neuro-Oncology at the time
I interviewed in August 1987 included, in addition to three neurologists, one neuro-oncology fellow, one medical pain physician, and
one part-time psychiatrist.

On this first visit I met physicians, scientists, administrators,
and Charles A. LeMaistre, MD, the President of MDACC and past
Chancellor of The University of Texas System. All were supportive
and wanted me to join them and create a large and vibrant Neuro-
Oncology Department and Brain Tumor Center. I told them that in
addition to expanding the Department of Neuro-Oncology they

would have to expand other departments and programs. These would include neurosurgery, neuroradiology, and pathology (neuropathology) if they wanted to create the multidisciplinary neuro-oncology programs I envisaged in a large hospital. Both Irv and Charles listened to my formulation of a suitable neuro-oncology program for MDACC, but never talked about limits or things that could not be done. Instead, they agreed on a shared vision of what I could create at the MDACC if I took the position. It was more about what I thought I could build than what they wanted me to build. It would be a blank slate with resources that were invisible to me at the time.

After a couple of days in Houston, I returned to my Mill Valley home to talk about my visit to Houston with Ellen, our children, Lisa, and Jason, and with my UCSF colleagues. I was adamant during my visit to MDACC that they would have to build other departments and programs if they wanted to create the multidisciplinary neuro-oncology programs I envisaged. I assumed they would back off on their offer as being too much for the institution to handle and I would not be invited back by Irv Krakoff. At the time, no one, including me, thought there was any chance I would leave UCSF for Houston.

Over the next weeks, I received a couple of letters and calls from Houston. They wanted me to return with my wife for another visit. In addition, I was lobbied hard by two UCSF colleagues who had moved to MDACC and encouraged me to visit again and look seriously at the new opportunities there and consider living in Houston. They were Albert Deisseroth, MD, PhD, recruited to Head the Bone Marrow Transplant Service, and David C. Hohn, MD, recruited to the General Surgery Department. My lack of laboratory space at UCSF and my curiosity about new possibilities at MDACC led me to ask Ellen to go with me to Houston. She agreed and I decided that taking her to Houston in October, when I thought the weather would be better and not as hot, was a good idea. At the second visit, it became clear that Houston and the MDACC were friendly places.

On this second visit, we were wined and dined. While I was busy meeting with faculty, Ellen was being driven around Houston, visiting the downtown area, the Galleria, and some of the faculty-preferred residential areas. While it was quite hot that day, nevertheless, Ellen was surprised to see so few people walking around downtown. She was told pedestrians used underground tunnels downtown to access the various buildings because of the heat. All in all, she was not impressed with Houston compared to the beautiful San Francisco Bay area and Mill Valley. Ellen was disappointed with the visit to Houston but knowing my passion to find new therapies to treat people with CNS tumors, she agreed to consider the move.

After returning to San Francisco, I met with my laboratory people over a period of months to see how many would be interested in a move to MDACC and found that several would consider moving with me. I discussed the move with my UCSF faculty colleagues and my clinical department chair, Charlie Wilson. Charlie offered me a higher salary to stay, and the Dean offered off-campus space for my research. Notwithstanding these sincere offers, I felt the MDACC offer provided an opportunity in neuro-oncology that was not likely to be replicated or offered by any institution in the next ten years. Out of that belief and the anticipation that I might be able to leverage my position and expand my tyrosine kinase research to develop new therapies faster in Houston with added resources, I decided to accept their offer. Thus, in early 1988, I accepted their offer and opportunity to build and develop a multidisciplinary neuro-oncology program at The University of Texas MD Anderson Cancer Center as Professor and Chairman of the Department of Neuro-Oncology and the Bernard W. Biedenharn

Chair for Cancer Research.

In mid-July 1988, two months before Ellen would join me and a month before my laboratory team who had agreed to move with me would arrive from San Francisco, I moved to Houston. In addition to getting our house and belongings ready for the move to Houston, Ellen was also coordinating the move of my laboratory equipment and supplies to MDACC. Joining my laboratory research group at MDACC were, in addition to Ellen, three members of my UCSF laboratory, Hideyuki Saya, MD, PhD, Donald Tinker, PhD, and Boon Hoshino, MS. I was grateful that they were willing to join me on this adventure as I am not sure I would have made the move without them.

The move was hard for my family since we had bought our dream house in Mill Valley less than two years before. The house in Mill Valley overlooked open space that was called "Horse Hill," because a small number of riding horses were kept there; some of the horses were owned by people in the area and others were rented for the year to accommodate young aspiring riders. Our house was on the upslope of an opposing hill with a good view of Horse Hill and Mt. Tamalpais. The sale of that house is one our family regrets to this day. Still, with both children off to college and not knowing if they would return to the Bay Area, Ellen agreed to sell and relocate to Houston in September, after our son, Jason, left for the University of California, San Diego for his freshman year. At the time our daughter, Lisa, was starting her senior year at the University of Colorado at Boulder.

The UCSF School of Medicine and the Department of Neurological Surgery were more than generous to me in that move. Charlie Wilson and the Dean of the UCSF Medical School allowed me to move my entire laboratory and the remaining and substantial Bristol-Myers research funds to MDACC. They gave me a spectacular going-away party attended by people I had worked with at UCSF and in Northern California, including members of the

Northern California Oncology Program and many friends that we
made during the 16 years we lived in San Francisco. While it was
sad to part with my UCSF colleagues and friends, I truly believed I
had a responsibility to take the MDACC job

My original vision of what I wanted to accomplish at the
MDACC was to create a world-class multidisciplinary clinical
neuro-oncology program that would serve the people of Texas and
surrounding states and attract patients and trainees and to lead a
research program to bring new therapies to the clinic much like the
Brain Tumor Research Center had done at UCSF. While this vision
was bold for the department I would inherit, I believed I knew how
to do it and would succeed over a period of years. I did not know
in 1988, when I joined the MDACC, that my vision would need to
expand beyond neuro-oncology to meet institutional challenges in
psychiatry, pain management, rehabilitation, and palliative care.

The first three to four years as Chair of the Department of
Neuro-Oncology were consumed with building the clinical and
laboratory programs in the Department, recruiting a Chair for the
Department of Neurosurgery, and helping to strengthen neuropathology and neuroradiology by encouraging the hiring of more
faculty and the purchase of more MRI machines and neuroradiologists. Prior to my joining the Department, William Fields, a
neurologist was its chair. He retired from the department upon my
arrival making it easy for me to make the changes I envisioned.
Already in the department were W. K. Alfred Yung, MD, who had
completed a Neurology Fellowship program at Sloan-Kettering with
Jerry Posner and Bill Shapiro and was an assistant professor at
MDACC. In addition, Leslie Newton, MD, a UTHSC-trained neurologist, had completed her a fellowship at MDACC just before I
arrived and had been kept on as an assistant professor.

I was fortunate that the Department and fellowship program
existed so programmatic changes and faculty additions could be
made while a level of patient coverage was in place to meet the basic

needs of the hospital and clinics. This allowed me to move forward in several directions at a measured pace. As Ellen will tell you, my measured pace was basically as fast you can go forward. Prior to starting at MDACC, I had assumed my primary task would be to replicate and expand the operation of the UCSF multidisciplinary neuro-oncology program and expand the scope of laboratory research with the help of two faculty that moved with me from UCSF and a new hire, John MacMurray, PhD, a peptide chemist. It was a simple strategy that I had no doubt would be successful at MDACC. Little did I know at the time, the administrative responsibilities and scope of clinical needs that were required of the Department of Neuro-Oncology over the next years would curtail much of my personal laboratory research, research I enjoyed doing and always felt to be important to who I was.

Early on I anticipated we would need two sections, one for clinical consultative neurology and the other for therapeutic neuro-oncology. Other sections would follow. My first physician hire was Arthur Forman, a neurologist and recent graduate of the Sloan-Kettering Neurology Fellowship Program. Hiring Art proved to be a good choice as he was a consummate clinician and excellent teacher. I needed someone like Art to anchor the consultative neurology efforts of the Department as I would have to stay focused on expanding and further developing neuro-oncology and therapeutic programs as well as administration of the department. He also became the de facto prime instructor for medical students and neurology residents rotating from the UT Health Science Center across the street. Art took the responsibility offered and did an excellent job over the years.

When I took the MDACC position in 1988, I realized that recruiting established academic neuro-oncologists would be difficult given the small pool of physicians trained in neuro-oncology and because our department needed our neuro-oncologists to be neurologists given the size of our consultative neurology program. Therefore, to meet our needs, I anticipated that, over the years, we would have to hire from our Neuro-Oncology fellowship program. Fortunately, our program attracted very well trained and hard-working neurologists. In 1989, we accepted three neuro-oncology fellows; in 1990, we added one more, and by 1991, we accepted four fellows. During my years as Chair, we had no problems attracting candidates for our neuro-oncology fellowship program.

My goal for the neuro-oncology faculty was to hire physician-scientists who would be able to advance the field through clinical trials and laboratory research. This had been the route I had taken at UCSF and, I felt, these medical-scientists were critical to move the field of therapeutic neuro-oncology forward. My first such hire was Athanasios "Thanos" P. Kyritsis, a recent graduate of the University of Wisconsin Neurology program who had been writing to me about his interest in neuro-oncology before I took the job at the MDACC. Not only was Thanos an outstanding fellow in our program between 1990-92 but, after completing his fellowship, he became an important faculty member who contributed to our clinical excellence and to our important laboratory research program. He rose quickly to Associate Professor and was being considered for promotion to Professor in our Department in 1999, when he decided to return to Greece as Professor and Chairman of Neurology at the University Hospital of Ioannina and Director of the Neurosurgical Research Institute of the University of Ioannina. Thanos was a great colleague to work with, a good teacher, and a productive and creative scientist in the laboratory whose return to Greece was a tough loss for the Department.

Another neurologist I recruited to the Department was Kurt Jaeckle, who had done his neuro-oncology fellowship at Sloan-Kettering and was, at the time of recruitment, an Associate Professor of Neurology at the University of Utah Health Sciences Center. I recall arranging to meet Kurt in Salt Lake City on the way back to Houston from a West Coast meeting. While we skied together at Park City, I tried to convince Kurt and his wife to join us at MDACC. One of the things I remember about that trip was feeling a little under the weather before skiing and then during skiing having the seams on my ski boots tear, ruining an otherwise beautiful ski day for both of us. The trip was memorable for the wrong reasons, but Kurt did join our department in 1993, and prospered. Kurt was recruited as an Associate Professor and he rose to Professor before he left in 2000, for personal reasons and went to Jacksonville, Florida as a neurologist/neuro-oncologist at the Mayo Clinic. He was a fine clinician who carefully tended to his patients, participated in resident and fellow training, and was an active clinical trialist. Kurt had good clinical acumen and clinical trials judgment as well as solid procedural ideas and administrative skills.

Some of the other faculty members, were also trainees who had completed their neurology residencies in the University of Texas Health Science Center Department of Neurology and two-years in our Neuro-Oncology Fellowship Program. One of the early in-house hires was Charles "Chuck" A. Conrad, who finished his fellowship in 1994, but did not join our faculty until 2000. Chuck was a Neuro-Oncology Fellow between 1992 and 1994. Following his fellowship, he briefly joined the faculty at MDACC, but wanted a change, so moved his family to Oklahoma City where he took a position with the University of Oklahoma Medical Center. Fortunately for us, he returned to MDACC in 2000, as an Associate Professor in the Department of Neuro-Oncology and rose to the rank of Professor. At one time, he served as Medical Director of the Brain and Spine Center and Director of Clinical Operations for the Neuro-Oncology Department. Chuck was noted for his care of patients, thinking outside the box for therapeutic options, and for laboratory research with a medicinal chemist at the MDACC,

Waldemar Priebe. Together they tried to develop new drugs for the treatment of high-grade gliomas. One of the drugs they worked on was Berubicin (CNS Pharmaceuticals, Inc) that is in clinical trials for glioblastoma today. In 2015, Chuck left MDACC to further his clinical work and research at the Austin Brain Tumor Center, the brain tumor hub for Texas Oncology. Unfortunately, Chuck died unexpectedly following a fall in May 2016.

Another Neuro-Oncology Fellow I recruited was Vinay Puduvalli. He was a Neuro-Oncology Fellow between 1996-98. Vinay was a very good clinician and had done laboratory research in our department prior to joining as Assistant Professor. Vinay combined clinical trials research of new drugs and drug combinations and pursued laboratory research looking at drug effects on apoptosis, topoisomerases, retinoids, and epigenetic effects. Because of his clinical and laboratory research and administration of our fellowship program, he advanced to Professor prior to moving to Ohio State University in 2013, where he was awarded the title of Professor and Director of the Division of Neuro-Oncology. In September 2020, Vinay returned to MDACC as the Chairman of the Department of Neuro-Oncology.

The other neuro-oncology fellow from 1996-98 was Morris "Morry" D. Groves. Morry and Vinay trained in neurology together at UT Health Science Center and both were neuro-oncology fellows in our MDACC programs in 1996-98. Morry did not do laboratory research like Vinay but wanted to focus on clinical trials and take care of patients with primary and metastatic CNS tumors. He developed into an outstanding clinician, teacher, and leader while at MDACC. He eventually left MDACC at the end of 2011, to head the Neuro-Oncology program at Texas Oncology. In addition to these neuro-oncology trainees that I recruited during the tenure of my chair, I helped mentor about forty neuro-oncology fellows between 1989 and 2007. Of these, two others, Howard Colman,

MD, PhD, and Sudakar Tummala, MD, joined the Department after completion of their fellowships in 2002. Sudhakar was hired to the Neurology Section of our Department and oversaw its neurophysiology programs and is currently a Professor in the Department. Howard was hired as a physician-scientist and Assistant Professor in the Department and based on his clinical and laboratory research, was promoted to Associate Professor before being hired by the University of Utah in 2010 to be Director of Medical Neuro-Oncology at the Huntsman Cancer Center and a Professor in the Department of Neurosurgery.

During my many years supervising neuro-oncology fellows I have found that some fellows will continue on the neuro-oncology path while others seek different paths. Some of our fellows went to academic institutions, some into private neurology practice, some into palliative care, and a few went into industry. I do not think this is the place to curate the destination of all MDACC fellows from my active years there, but I do want to mention some who are still doing neuro-oncology and contributing to the field.

From 1995 to 2007, the following neuro-oncology fellows joined academia. Eric T. Wong, MD, a 1995 graduate, is currently Professor of Neurology at Brown Biology and Medical School (Providence, Rhode Island). Joon Uhm, MD, PhD, a 1999 graduate, is a Professor of Neurology at Mayo Clinic and Division Chair of the Section of Neuro-Oncology in the Department of Neurology, as well as Fellowship Director of the Neuro-Oncology Program at the Mayo Clinic (Rochester, MN). Sigmund Hsu, MD, also a 1999 graduate, was an assistant professor in our department for several years after his fellowship and is now an Assistant Professor in Department of Neurosurgery, McGovern Medical School, and neuro-oncologist at the Mischer Neuroscience Institute of Memorial Hermann Hospital (Houston, TX). Monica Loghin, MD, a 2005 graduate, is a Professor in the Department of Neuro-Oncology at

the MDACC. Marta Penas-Prado, MD, a 2007 graduate, moved to
Spain to try and establish a neuro-oncology program, but found too
many roadblocks in her way, so returned as an assistant professor
in the MDACC Department of Neuro-Oncology, and later was
recruited by Mark Gilbert as an Associate Research Physician in the
Neuro-Oncology Branch, NCI. Stan Xiaosi Han, MD, PhD, a 2009
graduate, is currently Associate Professor of Neurology and a
laboratory scientist in the O'Neill Comprehensive Cancer Center
of the University of Alabama (Birmingham, AL). Tobias Walbert,
MD, PhD, a 2010 graduate, is an Associate Professor in the
Department of Neurology at Wayne State University School of
Medicine and Director of Neuro-Oncology and Neuro-Oncology
Fellowship Director of the Hermelin Brain Tumor at the Henry Ford
Hospital (Detroit MI).

While the fellowship program at the MDACC was not as
dependent on me for training as was the UCSF program while I was
there, nevertheless, I do believe that I added value to the training of
many of the neuro-oncology fellows during my 21 years at the
MDACC and rejoice in their accomplishments.

20

Clinical Challenges at the MD Anderson Cancer Center

The major driver of my move to MDACC was laboratory research that focused on increasing drug discovery and development with the goal of bringing new protein tyrosine kinase drugs to the clinic through my NCDDG grant. Once ensconced at the MDACC, however, I realized that if MDACC was to grow its hospital and clinic activities to achieve the potential envisaged by the MDACC leadership, my neuro-oncology department was going to have to do more than just be the home to neurology and neuro-oncology. While being department chair and building clinical neuro-oncology and neurology programs and a Brain Tumor Center that I hoped would become an equal to the Brain Tumor Research Center at UCSF in terms of laboratory research, I had to contend with building three other clinical disciplines while maintaining my own clinical and laboratory research programs. These two separate, and, at times, competing departmental directions created a heavier lift than I had originally been prepared for. The effort required resources and a buy-in from clinicians, scientists, and administrators that was at times problematic. As I sometimes am too impatient to get the job done and less tactful than a gentleman should be in the South, I ruffled feathers over the years.

Since my arrival in mid-1988, the Department experienced nonstop growth to accommodate an enormous increase in CNS tumor patients. This was further driven by the recruitment of Raymond Sawaya, MD to chair the Department of Neurosurgery in 1990. Ray was a superb neurosurgeon and teacher who attracted a talented neurosurgical faculty and grew tumor surgery at the MDACC. Our two departments grew CNS tumor referrals and new patients by three-fold during the 1990s.

In addition, patient numbers at MDACC were also growing requiring more services. This demand required that psychiatry, neuropsychology, pain and symptom management and rehabilitation also increase purpose and staff. This growth and increased referral of patients to our department, led to a commensurate need for more personnel, space to house them, and money to run the department. These needs produced some animosity within the Division of Medicine, where our department resided, because of my pressure for additional people and resources to develop these programs.

When I first assumed the Chairmanship of the Department of Neuro-Oncology I lacked the foresight to fully anticipate the large and diverse neuro-oncology department I would build and lead in the mid-1990s. Early in my tenure I saw multiple institutional clinical shortcomings, understood what was needed, and felt a responsibility to try and develop and expand the programs that would be needed in the ensuing years. I was encouraged and supported in my efforts by Irv Krakoff and Charles LeMaistre while they were at the MDACC. Unfortunately, in the mid-1990s, with the retirement of my advocate, Irv Krakoff, and installation of the new Division Head, Robert Bast, I received less financial, administrative, and personal support leading me to conclude that having separate physical therapy/physiatry, pain management/palliative care, and psychiatry programs was going to be problematic to achieve quickly.

—∞—

From the outset of my chairmanship, I knew that institutional needs intersected with our departmental needs to an extent. I already had in my new department a part-time psychiatrist, a full-time clinical neuropsychologist, and an endocrinologist who also did medical pain management. When I first took the position, I believed my clinical training as a neurologist and my experience as a neuro-oncologist provided some comfort that I "knew these fields." The more I became involved with the operation, philosophy, and ambitions of the MDACC the more responsibility I felt to nurture and grow these programs to fulfill the larger institutional vision. I felt that a rapidly expanding MDACC needed these programs more than they understood in the early 1990s. To achieve my goal to build the non-neurology programs in the Department, I needed the support and advice of Irv Krakoff as I sometimes wanted to move faster than Southern sensibilities were used to. I sometimes needed Irv to smooth the path for me among the leaders in the MDACC and those colleagues in other Division of Medicine departments who also needed institutional resources to grow their own programs. In the sections below I would like to expand on the programs that we created in the Department and the external and internal forces that shaped their development and their final academic homes at the MDACC.

Neuropsychology

When I got to the MDACC, I learned that Christine Myers, a PhD clinical psychologist, and assistant professor, had created the foundation for an important program within the Department of Neuro-Oncology that would, if successful, have ramifications for the clinical fields of neuro-oncology and cancer medicine.

Chris's forte was neuropsychological testing to better understand the impact of cancer treatments and surgery on our CNS tumor patients. She developed testing programs and interventions that she and I hoped might help patients maximize their neuro-cognitive functions to improve, in a very specific way, their quality of life.

At UCSF, neuropsychology was not prominent; we had only one part-time private practice psychologist we could call on and, as a result, I had almost no experience with neuropsychology testing before arriving at MDACC. It did not take long, before I realized the importance of Chris's program and the ramifications it could have on the field of neuro-oncology. I interacted a good deal with Chris in the early years since I had always liked the field of clinical psychology and would have completed a major as an undergraduate at the University of Wisconsin had I not been a three-year premed student.

Importantly, I encouraged Chris, supported her fellowship programs, and helped her integrate the clinical brain tumor program with her neuropsychology and testing program. In addition, given the increasing numbers of cancer patients coming to the MDACC, it became clear that we needed a larger neuropsychology program, so I pushed for two additional faculty and establishment of a Section of Neuropsychology in our Department. Meeting more patient needs in our department led to the use of neuropsychology services for patients. The services helped counter the neurocognitive effects of whole brain irradiation in lung and breast cancer patients, as well as unexpected adverse effects of some chemotherapy treatments. These effects led to neurocognitive problems now known as "chemo brain".

Chris was an active academic faculty member who did clinical research and published extensively and advanced easily up the academic ladder to become professor in the department. She became a popular speaker at medical and neuro-oncology meetings.

Psychiatry

When I first interviewed for the Chairmanship of the Department. I realized that one half-time psychiatrist was insufficient to help patients and a legitimate psychiatry program and section within the department was needed. Helping to ensure a strong neuro-psychology program at MDACC turned out to be easy in comparison to building the psychiatry program. It was clear to me and some other faculty, but not all MDACC faculty, that we needed much more coverage, especially if we were going to be able to accommodate larger medical oncology and surgery programs at the MDACC. Initially, I thought it would be straightforward to recruit a couple of full-time psychiatrists. How wrong I was. This turned out to be more difficult than I imagined. In the 1980s, psychiatry was in a national downturn and consult liaison psychiatrists working in cancer centers was a rarity except for Sloan-Kettering.

Because of time constraints and the need to obtain psychiatric coverage, I contracted psychiatry help from the University of Texas Health Science Center. The chairman, Robert Guynn, agreed to come over to the MDACC one day a week to help John Griffith, our half-time psychiatrist. Fortunately, in 1989, one of Guynn's psychiatry residents, Alan Valentine, decided that he wanted to become a consult-liaison psychiatrist to fill out his training and elected to take a postgraduate year four (PGY-4) in our department, splitting his time between neurology and psychiatry. Alan liked the MDACC PGY-4 rotations and the people in our department, and I offered him an assistant professor position in 1990. Not only did Alan become the first full-time psychiatrist during my time as chairman, but eventually became the Head of the Section and eventually the Chairman of the Psychiatry Department when it was created in 2006.

My initial efforts to recruit a Head for the Psychiatry Section was very difficult. Calling psychiatry departments around the county yielded about 5-6 candidates. While I advertised nationally for the Head position, the MDACC leadership severely limited what I could offer in way of enticements such as office space, support staff, and number of academic clinical positions. Eventually, I was able to hire Karen Ritchie, MD, as acting Section Head of Psychiatry in 1991. She was not far removed from her psychiatry residency at the University of Kansas Medical Center at the time, so I was not sure if it would work out well for the Section. Initially, Karen was successful as we increased psychiatry services in the hospitals and clinics. In 1994, we were able to recruit Michael Weitzner, a prior UT Health Science Center resident, following his cancer psychiatry fellowship at the Tampa Cancer Center.

In the early 1990s I was optimistic that we were developing a functioning psychiatry program and departmental section. To address the growing number of patients needing psychiatric expertise, we also hired three specially trained psychiatric nurses in the early 1990s: Mary Hughes, Sharon Van Vleet, and Debra Sivesind. Within a couple of years of hiring Karen, she tired of the constant need to see patients and the responsibility of running the psychiatry program and wanted a 6-month sabbatical to take off time from clinic duties to write a book. Unfortunately, I could not accommodate her wish for a sabbatical because of MDACC faculty guidelines. One unforeseen weekend she cleared out her office and left a note on my desk explaining that she really wanted to write the book. While surprised by the quickness of her decision and lack of forewarning, she was decisive and that was that. At least that is what I thought.

Later that day, it became clear I was not the only one who thought Karen's departure was too abrupt. The MDACC administration refused to accept her resignation for a month while they investigated whether I was the cause of her departure. Within the month, after the faculty review was completed and her resignation accepted, I was formally vindicated. Nonetheless, during that period and for years afterwards, I faced a plethora of innuendos outside the department. Faculty and administrators outside the department behaved as if they were sure that she left the department because of me. While none of the accusers ever confronted me directly and certainly never apologized for their misdirected behavior it remains frustrating that the formal vindication was accepted as recognition that perhaps it was not my fault that Karen left. While Karen and I did not communicate after she left the MDACC, I recently discovered that Karen became a published nonfiction author, obtained a master's degree from Georgetown University's Kennedy School of Ethics, was founder and president of the Midwest Bioethics Center, and continued to practice community psychiatry.

It was not until 1994, that I was able to recruit Walter Baile, MD, from the University of Tampa Cancer Center to head the Section. Additionally, in 1994, Estela Beale, a pediatric psychiatrist joined us. She was on contract because we did not have enough institutional positions at the time. Obtaining institutional resources to meet the needs of the Section to serve the hospital and clinics remained difficult. The hospital businesspeople did not understand why they should provide support for a program like psychiatry, which was considered a "loss leader" in business terms. To counter that perception, we encouraged many of our psychiatry patients and families to write letters and contact the hospital administration. In addition, I asked some of the oncology surgeons how they would handle postsurgical delirium without psychiatric support. It took no time to get the support of the surgeons to help the hospital administration understand that they might be open to legal suits if there was no psychiatric coverage for the treatment of post-surgery delirium and depression. Psychiatry was not an option for the MDACC. It was a necessity, so the powers that be acquiesced with more positions and less hassle for several years, but it seemed that they were always looking over our shoulder seeking to save money, sometimes at the expense of the patients.

Medical Pain Management

When I started at the MDACC, the entire medical pain program rested on the shoulders of one man, C. Stratton Hill, an endocrinologist turned pain management physician. He was also busy with the Texas State Medical Society and outside organizations. His speaking engagements were an effort to change the state law to allow physicians to write repeat prescriptions to manage pain in cancer patients. Before enacting a new law, it was a criminal offense to prescribe controlled substances in the quantities and frequency needed for some cancer patients. As a result of his clinical experience and political connections, Stratton traveled a good deal to speak at state medical society meetings and pain conferences and to consult on state laws being considered to improve the prescription of opioids for the treatment of pain in terminal cancer patients. As a result, I pulled together institutional resources to add staff and grow the program. Meanwhile, outside consultants from the West Coast were telling MDACC leadership and management that, because of the emergence of managed care in the United States, they should plan on having a smaller MDACC footprint. In building my clinical programs, like many of my colleagues at the time, I also had to fight the fallibility of outside hospital consultants.

My first hire in the pain section was Sharon M. Weinstein, a neurologist-trained pain expert from MSKCC who I had hired in 1991. She and Stratton carried the clinical load until we were able to recruit a more senior academic pain specialist in 1992. Sharon was an outstanding clinician and added enormous value to the section, but I and other Division of Medicine faculty thought she was too junior to be head of the section, even though that was the role Sharon saw for herself.

I was fortunate to recruit Richard Payne, MD, from MSKCC to head the Department's Pain and Symptom Management Section in 1992. Within a short time, Richard proposed that we recruit to expand pain research in the department. This led to creation of the Pain Section and Symptom Management Section. Richard headed up the pain effort while Charles "Charlie" S. Cleeland, PhD, was in

1996, recruited from the University of Wisconsin Comprehensive Cancer Program to head the symptom management team. Charlie was interested in the psychological drivers of patient symptoms. When I retired as Chair, Charlie become Chair of the Department of Symptom Research in the Division of Medicine. Within a couple of years, Richard and a hospice physician, Porter Storey, created a clinical Hospice and Palliative Care Fellowship in conjunction with the Hospice at the Medical Center. My recollection is that this was the first fellowship of this type in the United States. The first fellow to complete the fellowship was Elizabeth Strauch who remained with the Hospice at the Medical Center after her fellowship to become Vice President for Medical Affairs.

Of the various department sections, the pain section was the most fraught with politics from within and from outside. Inside the section, Richard had hired an anesthesiologist to perform nerve blocks to alleviate severe pain in some cancer patients, but this put him at odds with some of the anesthesiology faculty as he did not have to do surgical anesthesiology cases. He also had prescription problems that eventually led to him leaving the pain section. In addition, Richard and Sharon did not get along well. Sharon believed he was holding back her promotion. As Chair of the Department, I had hired Richard to head the section and had confidence in his ability so tried to stay out of his way in this matter. In retrospect, it was probably not my best decision, as Sharon may have had glass ceiling issues that I neglected to address. This was brought to my attention when Chris Myers came to my office to tell me that she was approached by Sharon and Leslie Newton to "help them bring me down." Sadly, during my years as chair, this section had political undercurrents that undercut department unity and ambiance.

Richard and Sharon both left our department in 1998; Richard returned to MSKCC to lead the Pain and Palliative Care Service and

Sharon was recruited by the University of Utah and the Huntsman Cancer Center as a pain management and palliative care consultant. Sharon eventually became a professor in the Department of Anesthesiology and Chief of Holistic Medicine at the Veterans Hospital in Salt Lake City.

In my mind, there was only one person to recruit to head the medical pain program as it transitioned from section to department and that was Eduardo Bruera. At the time, Eduardo was Chair of Palliative Medicine at the Alberta Cancer Foundation. When Eduardo interviewed, he clearly wanted to consolidate medical pain and rehabilitation into one department to be called the Department of Palliative Care and Rehabilitation and Integrative Medicine. The program focused on medical pain control, palliative care, and end of life issues. An interesting aside is that I had tried to recruit Eduardo to head the Section on Pain in our department in the early 1990s, but after coming to the MDACC to interview, he told me the faculty and administration would not be supportive of his vision of medical pain control, palliative care, and end of life issues as their mindset was directed to cancer treatment and cure. Establishing a palliative care program was viewed as a defeat. The second time he interviewed, the MDACC faculty and administration were ready and willing to embrace his program and MDACC leadership bought into his dream, leading to the creation of the Department of Palliative Care, Rehabilitation, and Integrative Medicine.

Rehabilitation

Within my first year at MDACC, I realized we had only physical therapists, but no occupational therapists for our patients. While I heard that at one time, we had a program that included a physiatrist, those days were past and no one seemed to be taking responsibility to improve that situation for our neurosurgery, neurology, or neuro-oncology patients, let alone the many cancer surgery patients at the MDACC. Thus, I took on the responsibility to improve that situation through our Division of Medicine.

Like the pain and psychiatry programs, I could not imagine how the clinical medical oncology and general surgery programs were to safely grow and meet patient needs without proper physiatry, so I also went about creating a physiatry presence within the Department. This was initially done by contract with Baylor Medical School and the Texas Institute for Rehabilitation Research (TIRR) since hospital administration assumed this would be a financial drain, negatively impacting the finances of my department. Eventually, I convinced MDACC administration to hire faculty and create space to expand physical and occupational therapy to accommodate the program. Our initial hire was by contract with TIRR to have Theresa Gillis, MD, work in our department. Our hospital administration and some faculty wanted to limit the hospital's financial exposure and did not believe there was an unmet medical need at the MDACC. They were so wrong. By the time I retired from the MDACC in 2009, the cancer patient-specific rehabilitation program was the largest such program in North America and a source of income for the hospital. Terry Gillis remained Head of the Rehabilitation Section for a couple of years before moving to the East Coast. Others appreciated her medical and administrative skills and today she is the Chief of Rehabilitation Medicine Services at MSKCC where she also holds an endowed chair.

Neuro-oncology and neurology

Initially, we had only the section of neuro-oncology. In it, were two groups of faculty, one doing neuro-oncology and one doing neurology, with the former group accounting for the major focus of the department. Nonetheless, since all these faculty were neurologists, most also rotated night and weekend coverage to back up neuro-oncology fellows from our program and neurology residents rotating from the UTHSC Department of Neurology to meet the neurology needs of the hospital. Our clinic coverage was a different matter with the majority of neurology-trained faculty seeing neuro-oncology patients in clinic and two to three faculty seeing only neurology patients referred from MDACC physicians.

Our neuro-oncology program was protocol driven and a source of referrals to the Department of Neurosurgery and the Department of Radiation Oncology. By June 1996, we had thirteen open protocols that accrued 121 patients and by June 1997, eighteen open protocols accrued 142 patients. Our patients were treated in a holistic manner as we assumed full responsibility for their care and encouraged them to call us with new symptoms, including the emergence of other medical conditions. Our patients were as loyal to us as we were to them and made clinic visits even if it meant driving 200 miles or flying from out of state. We primarily treated patients by referral in the 1980s and 1990s. They came mostly from Texas and the surroundings southern states of Oklahoma, Arkansas, Mississippi, Louisiana, Alabama, and Tennessee. We also had patients that sought our care and protocols from Colorado, Florida, New Mexico, Illinois, and Wisconsin.

These were heady and gratifying times for our neuro-oncology section and for me. All the neuro-oncology faculty were developing clinical trials, many with pharmaceutical or NIH grant support. My clinical activities focused on drug therapies during accelerated fractionated EBRT combinations and phase II and phase III clinical trials of DFMO and DFMO combinations. I also studied and advocated for the use of Ritalin® (methylphenidate) and Concerta® (controlled delivery of methylphenidate) treatment of our patients with neurocognitive slowing, working with Chris Myers in our Neuropsychology Section and Alan Valentine in our Psychiatry Section. Our experience suggested many of our patients suffered from neurocognitive slowing and very few with true depression. At times, I was prescribing more of these agents than anticonvulsants.

—w—

One of the joys of our department was that it was easy and gratifying interacting with colleagues in psychiatry about medication and treatment and with clinical neuropsychologists about understanding and trying to alleviate the neurocognitive impact of irradiation and chemotherapy treatments on our patients. We agreed on and evaluated different strategies to minimize the impact of tumor location and treatment on neurocognitive function, a good surrogate for quality of life in our patients and their families. It was in this atmosphere that we first starting using methylphenidate in the early 1990s.

In retrospect, my years at the MDACC were mixed with respect for my accomplishments along with frustrations and disappointments. The programs and sections I advocated for and enabled, grew, and today are internationally known. Among my frustrations and disappointments, there is one that I wish I could reverse. Prior to retiring as Head of the Division of Cancer Medicine in 1994, Irv Krakoff asked if he and Charles LeMaistre should pursue creating a Neuroscience Division for me within the MDACC. Irv thought it would be a good idea as a Division of Neuroscience, or some similarly named Division, would serve to house, as departments, the sections of neurology, neuro-oncology, neuropsychology, psychiatry, pain medicine, and symptom management that currently existed within the Department of Neuro-Oncology. Without much thought or guidance, I declined the offer primarily because I was exhausted at the time, trying to juggle so many clinical, research, internal political, and administrative balls in the air with so little administrative help and advice. I had about 110 faculty, technicians, and administrative people but did not have an Executive Administrator to help me. As a result, I declined the offer, a decision I rue to this day as the years after Irv's retirement were not easy for me and ultimately led to my forced retirement in late 1997.

21

The Irony of the Guiding Premise to Move to the MD Anderson

In my mind, the move to the MDACC to accept the Chairmanship of the Department of Neuro-Oncology was premised on my ability to secure and expand the protein tyrosine kinase inhibitor research already funded by NCDDG and Bristol Myers Research grants and also a response to the opportunity and challenge of building a world-class neuro-oncology department. The reality is that our research group failed to produce the drugs we sought to discover, but I did build a Neuro-Oncology Department I could be proud of. Our NCDDG research group at MDACC, UCSF, and UC Berkeley expected to successfully define a peptide substrate for the catalytic site of c-Src so we could add reactive groups to create irreversible inhibitors of the Src protein tyrosine kinase catalytic domain. Unfortunately, after about ten years, and while I was at the MD Anderson Cancer Center, we gave up on our goal to create a c-Src catalytic-site inhibitor after John McMurray, PhD, an assistant professor in my Neuro-Oncology Department at the time and a project leader in our NCDDG program, determined that a cyclic peptide was the only specific substrate of the c-Src catalytic site. Cyclic peptides occupy a unique 3-dimensional space and are unstable in the body. If the cyclic peptide were to be "weaponized" with a reactive warhead chemical group, it would most certainly be destroyed in the body long before it reached c-Src in the tumor cell.

Unfortunately, I do not think chemistry exists even today, to allow us to develop a selective inhibitor of protein tyrosine kinase of c-Src based on the structure of this unique cyclic peptide. Thus, like all of the pharmaceutical industry at the time, we ended up developing ATPase inhibitors of the c-Src protein tyrosine kinase that were far easier to make than trying to inhibit the true catalytic site of the enzyme using combinatorial chemistry approaches. Of necessity, we then started our own combinatorial chemistry program at MDACC. We used a grant from a MDACC philanthropic supporter to purchase robotic equipment for the large-scale synthetic program we needed. Initially, John McMurray ran the combinatorial chemistry effort, but the magnitude of the program required adding medicinal chemists to our program over time. In addition, Ray Budde, who had a PhD in Plant Biochemistry, joined our program as a post-doc and quickly became a project leader when the project leader, Don Tinker, PhD, left the NCDDG program at MDACC. While Don had moved with me from UCSF, he eventually decided to leave academia and moved to Seattle to work for the King County Water District.

Looking for an edge in our combinatorial chemistry program, we decided to collaborate with Tripos, a St. Louis company engaged in high-level three-dimensional drug modeling. Together with our scientists, we chose a new chemical backbone for our chemistry program that was not being used by the industry, a chemical family called thienopyridines. In the third five-year renewal of our NCDDG grant, we realized we could not put enough resources into drug development and the expensive isolated c-Src enzyme testing that Ray had developed. The NCDDG grants were not scalable, and we were encouraged by the NCI to seek an industrial partner for the next steps.

To this end, Ray and I traveled coast to coast in 1996, seeking a partner from either large or small pharma. We approached Bristol-Myers Squibb, but Giulio Vita, PhD had long retired, and the new, young head of cancer research told us that the future for anticancer drug development at Bristol-Myers Squibb would not be with protein tyrosine kinase inhibitors but with K-Ras inhibitors. While K-Ras, a signaling protein that functions to instruct the cell to proliferate or to mature, is at least partially responsible for nearly 20% of human cancers through driver mutations of the KRAS gene. Thus, K-Ras was an attractive drug target, but the lack of obvious binding sites hindered pharmaceutical development until recently. The young Bristol-Myers scientist was wrong in his prediction as drugs to inhibit the activity of protein tyrosine kinases to treat cancer became available in 2001 when Novartis Pharma (Basel, Switzerland) gained FDA approval for the first protein tyrosine kinase inhibitor, imatinib (Gleevec®), to treat chronic myelogenous leukemia (CML) and acute lymphocytic leukemia (ALL) that are Philadelphia chromosome-positive (Ph+) as well as gastrointestinal stromal tumors (GIST). Eventually, Bristol-Myers Squibb developed and marketed dasatinib (Sprycel®), a Src inhibitor, for Philadelphia chromosome-positive (Ph+) CML and ALL, with others in the pipeline. Today, there are at least a dozen protein tyrosine kinase inhibitor drugs in use for the treatment of a variety of cancers.

While Ray Budde and I got quite close to finding a partner, we could not overcome the misfortune of being in Houston instead of being in the San Francisco Bay Area, San Diego, or Boston, where venture capital was easier to obtain. As a result, we started our own company in Houston in 1997, SIGNASE, primarily to expand our combinatorial chemistry library. We attracted first-round funding of about $2 million. However, we were unable to attract a CEO to our Houston-based company and were, therefore, unable to obtain second-round venture capital funding. Sadly, SIGNASE closed its doors in 2005. The patent assets of SIGNASE were acquired by a Phoenix company that did not pursue our research to its completion.

I learned many valuable lessons from this activity, some related to how people in companies and venture capitalists behave and some related to the protein tyrosine kinase (PTK) inhibitors being developed by pharma at the time. Once incorporated and funded, almost predictably, SIGNASE ran into problems with leadership and faculty at the MDACC. Incubator space that had been promised to allow our synthetic chemistry group to expand was canceled for various internal MDACC reasons. As a result, we had to rent and modify space in a private office building to house SIGNASE. Unfortunately, the move also catalyzed a fundamental change in how research was conducted, and the company morphed into a structure that made second round venture funding impossible to achieve.

Initially, MDACC leadership had agreed to allow me to be the non-executive President of SIGNASE while at the same time, Chairman of the Department of Neuro-Oncology while we were seeking venture funding to expand our NCDDG research to become an early-stage pharmaceutical company. Once we had secured outside funding, this approach started to become tenuous. Staying too far in the background as I was forced to do by my MDACC position, provided Ray with an opening he thought he could fill. At the outset of SIGNASE, Ray was the de facto Chief Scientific Officer. This too did not last long as Ray, aided by my absence at the new company site, started making decisions I thought were incorrect. I believed he had assumed a mantle outside his skill set, skills not so easily learned without serious internal mentorship.

In retrospect, a perfect storm was brewing that I failed to see right away. Since I was Chair of a department, I was constrained by the MDACC administration from taking on a larger role in SIGNASE. Second, of the two initial venture groups that funded SIGNASE, only one remained, AM Pappas. The remaining board member who represented AM Pappas was Eric Linsley, who was relatively new to this type of early-stage pharmaceutical company.

The company was embedded in a complex state-funded cancer center with degree-granting university rights. While we desperately needed a CEO, we and AM Pappas lacked the wherewithal to create a viable management structure in the company or to attract a CEO. I learned the hard way transitioning academic research into a viable pharmaceutical business and a company takes more than money; it takes leadership and business acumen. Unfortunately, over time it was clear that both were missing from the nascent company. I think part of that failure was my unwillingness to take the role of CEO in SIGNASE as my position and security at the MDACC were being challenged because of SIGNASE and internal MDACC politics. The whole fiasco was a tremendous disappointment to me as prior to obtaining venture funding we were in the process of talking about being acquired by a West Coast pharmaceutical company that has been reasonably successful over the years.

During my 17 years directing the NCCDG grant and 8 years of laboratory research after the grant and during the short lifetime of SIGNASE, I learned quite a bit about inhibiting protein tyrosine kinases and the impact of reversible compared to irreversible inhibitors of these enzymes. One pharmacokinetic-pharmacodynamic dogma I still hold onto is that binding to enzyme targets such as protein tyrosine kinases should be irreversible or, at the very least, if binding was reversible, it should be very tightly bound to permit optimal regional tumor pharmacokinetics for the treatment of infiltrative gliomas. I also had another bias based on some unpublished research I had done with c-Src inhibitors we had developed. I found that too much exposure to a c-Src inhibitor could lead tumor cells, grown in three-dimensional culture, to generate genetic changes and phenotypic growth enhancement whereas lower doses of the same c-Src kinase inhibitors appeared to only slow tumor cell growth and invasion. To this day, I still harbor an affinity for c-Src inhibitors and continue to think they would be great supporting drugs for a significant number of different lead signal transduction inhibitor drugs in the treatment of cancer.

Thus, while I moved to the MDACC to expand and, hopefully, strengthen my NCDDG drug discovery and development program, at the end that outcome was not realized for various scientific reasons as well as MDACC and SIGNASE political reasons. In my mind, the fact that SIGNASE was unable to bring a drug forward to the clinic for even phase I testing remains, in my mind, one of my great disappointments.

22

The MD Anderson Brain Tumor Center and the Society for Neuro-Oncology

One of the key elements and successes of the MDACC neuro-oncology program was that it was, from the outset, developed as a multidisciplinary team effort that included neurosurgeons, neuro-oncologists, neurologists, neuroradiologists, radiation oncologists, neuropathologists, neuropsychologists, research and clinical nurses, social workers, and data managers. Of this group, all but neuro-pathology and the data manager had a presence in the clinic. Initially, a neuroradiologist came to clinic if called. After several years it became more efficient to have a neuroradiologist assigned to the clinic where she/he would read MRIs and provide unofficial readings and consultations when asked. Our multidisciplinary clinics were so successful that most solid tumor clinics in the MDACC copied our approach. Over the course of several years, our combined neuro-oncology, neurosurgery, neuropsychology, and psychiatry clinic grew in capacity such that we accommodated more than 16,000 patient visits per year. By the mid-1990s, we were running clinics five days a week with at least one neurosurgeon, neuro-oncologist, and neurologist present most of each day and sometimes three to four neurosurgeons and neuro-oncologists in the clinic at the same time.

During those years, our hospital and clinical practices grew rapidly. At the same rate or maybe even faster, the Department of Neurosurgery under the leadership of Ray Sawaya grew in faculty, prominence, and tumor cases operated on to exceed the numbers at UCSF (if you exclude the pituitary cases of Charlie Wilson). In parallel, our clinical neurology and neuro-oncology programs grew to accommodate a volume of patients I could never have predicted and, at one time, was twice the size of any other such program in the United States.

Unfortunately, the magnitude of the job and the rapid growth of our clinical programs at the MDACC made it impossible for me to continue my own laboratory research at the scale I would have liked. Life is like that. Institutional moves allow some things to happen and cause others to contract or suffer. As an optimist, I tend to remember the positive more than the negative aspects of my time at the MDACC. While it is a truism that success begets success, in research I found that failure can beget success as well. In fact, I believe that a medical scientist's career requires both failure and success. It was this approach to research that I encouraged in students, doctoral candidates, post-doctoral students, residents, and fellows that came through my laboratory. I would tell them that sometimes failure can open a new door in research and if you are always right then you are not asking important enough research questions.

Failure frequently, if not always, resides around the corner from success. We attempt something new, test a hypothesis that resides in our mind, or seek a relationship with someone. In academia, failure can assume a specific purpose. For instance, one must con-tribute to and advance the scholarship in a field to advance in rank to professor. For me, I had laboratory programs to test hypotheses that I felt would guide the progress of research and eventually the improvement in outcomes for people with CNS tumors. I also had clinical programs that tried to build on laboratory research that I and others had done to improve clinical outcomes. All these endeavors, could, if put to the test, be considered hypothesis-testing experiments in that knowledge would be gained. Unfortunately, some research outcomes failed to improve outcomes. Much of my research life revolved around the pharmacological reasons that drug therapies failed to achieve the improvement in outcomes we all sought. In many of these instances, the experiment was successful, but the outcome yielded no alternative to build success upon, so the line of research was terminated. I know that many colleagues, over the years, continued their lines of research, making minor changes to their research and grants to obtain year after year of NIH funding. I could not play that game and would try to understand and develop new research areas hoping that I would find something to change the course of CNS tumors and improve the lives of people who develop these tumors. In essence, I spent much of my early academic life living with constant failure. This reality drove me to educate others and create programs and organizations that might break this cycle.

Being a driving force in these efforts and a reliable observer of the changes occurring in this field of medicine led me to two actions: create a new textbook to exemplify the broadness and diversity of neuro-oncology clinical practice and create a new multidisciplinary organization to bring together the many clinical specialties and laboratory research scientists working in and needed, to move the treatment and care of patients with CNS tumors forward.

First, let me make the case for a new textbook. After arriving at the MDACC, I began to appreciate the enormous complexity of the field of neuro-oncology. It was far more complex than chemo-therapy and the coordination of care for CNS tumor patients. As a result, I set a goal to create a new and inclusive textbook drawing on the knowledge of colleagues at the MDACC and other institutions in the United States. The first addition of the new textbook, *Cancer in the Nervous System*, was published by Churchill Livingstone in 1995. Our goal was to produce a textbook to help physicians better cope with and treat people afflicted with cancer of the CNS and to serve as a guide for aspiring neuro-oncology trainees. The book, which included nineteen chapters by fifty-two professionals in the field, required a great deal of my time, yet it was well worth the effort. I thought the book would be popular and useful, like many medical oncology textbooks had become.

When it came to producing a second edition, I had more problems than I expected getting authors to upgrade and edit their chapters for many different reasons. Some chapters were multi-authored, and the primary author was unwilling to cajole the other authors; some authors did new academic pursuits that limited the time they could commit to the textbook; and some felt that they had nothing new to write about. As a result, for many chapters our department editor, Joann Aaron, and I ended up doing much of the chapter updating ourselves. Nonetheless, the second edition of the textbook was published by Oxford University Press in 2002. To make the book more available we put the book online on the Society for Neuro-Oncology (SNO) website in 2004 so neuro-oncology physicians, trainees, nurses, and caregivers around the world would have free access to it. While some of the material is out of date today, some chapters and concepts surrounding rehabilitation, neuropsychology and pain remain relevant.

The second need I foresaw during the early 1990s was based on the reality that most clinical and research activities in neuro-oncology were concentrated in a few major medical centers, but the growing and diverse scientific needs of the existing and emerging scientific community had expanded beyond the scope of those organizations. An organized effort to fill this gap and coordinate the activities in neuro-oncology was needed to foster education for everyone in the field and to provide a home for a varied member-ship. Neuro-oncology has always been a team sport involving many diverse disciplines. I believed providing an organizational home that brought these groups together would be good for everyone involved.

Much like I envisioned the value for Asilomar meetings in 1975 to bring researchers together to talk about their research and plans for new research that might lead to better treatments for our patients with CNS tumors, I felt a national neuro-oncology organization would achieve that goal. It could help improve care for our patients by teaching about patient needs such as neuropsychology, radiology, nursing, pain management, rehabilitation, and end-of-life issues. I envisioned an organization that would promote multidisciplinary interactions and provide balanced representation for all specialties interested in advancing research and treatment of central and peripheral nervous system tumors. I also hoped that such an organization would help reduce physician burnout by expanding the network of friends and colleagues who could be accessed when the going got tough for some of my fellow clinicians.

This realization led me to discuss options for various paths forward to achieve this goal with colleagues in the CNS Section on Tumors of the American Academy of Neurological Surgeons and with Margaret Foti, the Chief Executive Officer of the American Association for Cancer Research (AACR). I made my case to these groups but concluded there was no organization that could accommodate the needs I foresaw. The AANS bylaws did not allow for non-neurosurgeons to hold office in their organization or spinoffs. The AACR did not think another organization was needed as Margaret felt all activities could be subsumed in the AACR. To me, the need was clear, and I believed having an independent organization was paramount.

Fortunately, at the MDACC I had resources available to help develop a plan for a new organization. Linda Greer and Jan Esenwein were working for me in the Department of Neuro-Oncology at the time. Linda was my administrative assistant and Jan was helping with strategic planning for our Brain Tumor Center that I co-directed with Ray Sawaya. Linda and Jan were willing to help me and put in extra time to help create a new multidisciplinary organization to bring my dream to fruition. In 1994, the three of us moved ahead to develop an organizational structure and create bylaws that would guarantee the success of this new organization.

My vision was to establish an organization to promote multi-disciplinary interactions and provide balanced representation for all specialties interested in advancing research and treatment of central and peripheral nervous system tumors. Key to this vision was the realization that we needed a carefully crafted set of bylaws to ensure that no one group (e.g., neurology, neurosurgery, medical oncology, pathology) would be able to take control of the organization. I contacted friends and colleagues involved with other nonprofit organizations to see how bylaws were constructed. Of the colleagues I contacted, Jay S. Loeffler, MD, was the most helpful.

At the time, Jay was a radiation oncologist and attending physician at the Brigham and Women's Hospital and Dana–Farber Cancer Institute. He specialized in neuro-oncology and was the founding director of their Brain Tumor Center. He was also a member of the International Stereotactic Radiosurgery Society and its president from 1997 to 1999. My call to Jay in June 1994 was prescient as that Society, under the leadership of its president, L. Dade Lunsford, MD, had recently completed a new set of bylaws that Jay sent me. Their bylaws together with input from colleagues in the Joint Tumor Section of the American Association of Neuro-logical Surgeons, a dozen or so colleagues around the country and a Houston lawyer friend enabled me to draft an organizational template and bylaws for The North American Neuro-Oncology Society. Fortunately, some of the forty-four colleagues who vetted the first set of bylaws believed that Society for Neuro-Oncology (SNO) would be a better name and less restrictive of membership, so we changed the name on the bylaws and moved ahead to incorporation in the State of Texas.

Initially, we had thirty-eight paid members who had contributed $25. Membership quickly grew among interested physicians and scientists as we obtained membership commitments from additional people around the country and quickly grew to eighty-eight members in the United States and Canada. A nominating committee was formed consisting of Drs. Mitchel Berger, Patricia Duffner, Stuart Grossman, Philip Gutin, Nicholas Vick, Jay Loeffler, Raymond Sawaya, Clifford Schold, and me. Using a slate of officers chosen by the committee, we had an election by mail for the first officers and Board of Directors in 1995. I was honored to be elected to serve as the first President of SNO. Also elected were Michael Prados, MD as the Vice-President and Stuart Grossman, MD as the Secretary-Treasurer. The elected Board of Directors included Drs. Mitchel Berger, Darell Bigner, Jan Buckner, Peter Burger, J. Gregory Cairncross, Steven Leibel and Roger Packer.

In early November 1995, an organizational meeting was held during the Eleventh International Conference on Brain Tumor Research and Therapy (also known as the Asilomar Conference, a nickname that follows it to this day) at the Silverado Resort in Napa, California. At this meeting, the mission of the Society, "a multidisciplinary organization for the advancement of neuro-oncology through research and education," was articulated. The meeting was attended by representatives of the American Brain Tumor Association, the National Brain Tumor Foundation, the Pediatric Brain Tumor Foundation, the Preuss Foundation, and the Brain Tumor Society. The organization continued to expand as the slate of officers put up for election was sent to almost everyone we thought would be interested in the organization. The organization's potential was immediately evident with the membership quickly rising to 163.

I filed for incorporation of SNO as a nonprofit and 501(c)(3) corporation on January 31, 1996. The incorporation paper was notarized by one of our Neuro-Oncology Department highly regarded administrative assistants, Rebecca Reyes. SNO was approved for 501(c)(3) nonprofit organization status by the IRS and the State of Texas in mid-April 1997. Helping me negotiate the legal path for SNO during those years was Attorney Donald Brodsky, who graciously provided advice and services pro bono, providing guidance during the year of bylaws formulation and, later, with incorporation of SNO in Texas and our application for 501(c)(3) status. The organization also benefited from the voluntary efforts of my accountant, William Shields, CPA, who provided accounting and tax filing services at no cost for the first five years of SNO.

The first SNO Annual Meeting was held November 8-10, 1996, in Santa Fe, New Mexico, and attracted 215 attendees who presented 115 abstracts. The meeting was endorsed by the major brain tumor philanthropic organizations, including the American Brain Tumor Association (ABTA), the National Brain Tumor Foundation (NBTF), the Pediatric Brain Tumor Foundation (PBTF), and the Brain Tumor Society (BTS). In addition, the ABTA sponsored the first award for Research Excellence. Compared with SNO's first small meeting, the 2019 SNO Annual Meeting in Phoenix, Arizona attracted nearly 2,600 participants. From the original membership of 163 in 1995, SNO grew to 2,800 members in 59 countries by the end of 2021. Much of this growth is due to the excellent leadership and guidance of Chas Haynes, JD, the SNO Executive Director as well as the many members who served as elected officers and committee chairs. The growth of SNO, in purpose, size, and commitment to the ideals of the founding members, is one of the great joys I have experienced on the neuro-oncology path I embarked on in 1967. SNO has since continued to realize the vision of its founding members, growing rapidly in scope and membership to include a multidisciplinary group of pro-fessionals involved in the study and treatment of tumors of the central nervous system.

23

Memorable Patient Vignettes

Over the decades I have treated and followed thousands of adults and children with CNS tumors. Each person who became my patient was special to me. I was entrusted with their care, and I always felt a responsibility to them, their families, and their close friends to guide them to the best quality of life possible and for the longest time possible. In this quest I was not alone as most, if not all my colleagues and trainees shared that goal.

While writing this memoir I have been reading old cards and letters from patients, families, and colleagues. That effort produced a kaleidoscope of memories of patients and families, the valuable contribution of colleagues, and the resilience and humanity of the physicians, nurses, and caregivers responsible to them.

—ɯ—

Some recollections and stories remain with me in sufficient detail to tell the reader. The following are some of those stories I would like to share.

In the late 1970's, while at UCSF, I cared for a youngster, who was about 6 years of age when I first him and his family. My UCSF colleague, Mike Edwards, had performed a wide resection of this youngster's tumor that was diagnosed as an anaplastic astrocytoma. It was my job to coordinate his post-surgical care which in this child's case would be radiation therapy, chemotherapy, and MRI follow up for as long as he lived. If we were successful, this might be many years. The youngster (who I will call Mark) was the son and youngest of three children of a wonderful Air Force couple stationed at Travis Air Force Base north of San Francisco. His father was a highly regarded captain in the Strategic Air Command (SAC) and was adored by Mark. Unfortunately, over a period of two years, the tumor grew multiple times and required that I come up with multiple different chemotherapy regimens to try and slow tumor growth. During this time, his father was offered a major promotion to the position of Wing Commander if he agreed to move out of state. The offer of advancement was declined as he wanted his son to remain at UCSF so I could treat him.

My approach to informing pediatric patients was to try and convey to them, with parents present, what was going on with their tumor and the therapies we planned to use to a very general extent that they could understand. I did this so that my young patients would have confidence in me and better understand their treatment program. Sometimes this was not possible or appropriate, but most times it was encouraged by parents.

This youngster was bright and had a pleasant disposition and appreciated information about his various treatments and being part of the treatment process. I recall that all his treatments, external beam irradiation and cytotoxic chemotherapy, were given on schedule without complication. Unfortunately, his tumor was hard to keep in remission, I had to treat him with multiple chemotherapy regimens over a period of two years. To this day, I retain the visual memory of his last visit to my UCSF neuro-oncology clinic. It was about two years after I first met him with his family. Because of tumor progression, I had treated him with conventional EBRT and PCV chemotherapy as well as two experimental chemotherapy options I was using in adults at the time. After seeing the MRI and examining him, I tried to carefully convey to him that I did not have any new therapies to offer him. He listened politely to what I had to say and then said, in a clear voice, "I am not ready. You have to come up with another therapy for me." As I am trying to hold back the tears that are forming, I see his parents teary-eyed and standing to my left side. I clearly was not going to let this youngster down, so I told him that I would give him a new therapy and stepped out to think about what I was going do and to have my own cry.

The conundrum I had was that I wanted to come up with a chemotherapy regimen that was not going to ruin his remaining months of life and yet might offer a potential to slow the growth of his anaplastic astrocytoma which by now was behaving as a glioblastoma. I decided to treat him with oral hydroxyurea on an every six-hour dose schedule which would achieve good penetration into his brain tumor and its infiltrative edge in normal brain. I had used this schedule routinely over several years to potentiate EBRT in adults and children with CNS tumors and was very confident that I would not worsen his remaining quality of life and might slow the growth of the tumor.

The story does not end here. Having grown up with a father who flew Air Force jets all over the world, Mark loved airplanes, adored his father, and had always wanted to fly with his father in a jet airplane but had been unable to do so because of his age and size, the limitations the Air Force had set for safety reasons. Through some wizardry, his father got the necessary approval to take him up in a jet trainer for the ride of his life and a memory his father would never forget along with a wonderful photo showing the two of them in the cockpit of the jet on their way to takeoff. Sadly, I have been unable to find the photo that, I believe, was published in a newspaper. I even requested help from the Air Force History Office to obtain a copy of the photo, but to no avail. Too me, the memory of youthful courage lives on.

—⁊⁊—

Over my academic career I have been fortunate to work with some of the best primary CNS tumor neuropathologists in the country. Given the size of the clinical programs at UCSF and MDACC, these neuropathologists had plenty of material and experience to help them attain this competency. My go to neuropathologist at UCSF was Richard Davis and at MDACC, it was Janet Bruner, Greg Fuller, and Lauren Langford. Many patients were referred to me at MDACC after surgery, and in these cases I required a review of the histology by one of our MDACC neuropathologists before I saw the patient in clinic. So efficient was our multidisciplinary neuro-oncology program in the 1990's that I routinely had a careful neuropathology assessment even if the patient brought the slide to clinic two hours before their visit.

The second story begins in the 1990's. It was not uncommon for our MDACC neuropathology reading to differ from the outside interpretation given the wide geographic catchment area serving the MDACC. Sometimes our MDACC tumor pathology review led to a worse tumor grade, but sometimes it led to a much better tumor diagnosis and prognosis. Seeing new patients with CNS tumors in clinic is not generally easy, nonetheless, I used to enjoy seeing a patient in clinic and to be able to tell them that the diagnosis was not nearly as bad as they had been told.

One day, I saw a woman in her 30s who had been referred after an excellent surgical resection of a right frontal tumor. Her referral diagnosis that accompanied her to my clinic was glioblastoma, so when I walked into the outpatient clinic room to meet and exam her, I saw her husband and parents present, and all clearly sad and frightened. In circumstances like this when the true diagnosis is not nearly so bad, I found it best to clear the air and not waste time, so before I took my own history, I told them that her tumor was an ependymoma and the surgeon had done a very good gross total resection of the tumor. I then proceeded to take her history, exam her, and advocate for the therapy I thought best for her. The relief from the patient and her family was palpable after I discussed the possible very long-term survival that was now possible. This does not mean that everything would go smoothly for the patient, but optimism is certainly allowed and expected.

While this patient sailed through EBRT, she was finding it harder to lead the life she had led before the tumor diagnosis. She had been raising four children, ages two to twelve years-of-age, managing a household where her husband sometimes had to travel to Mexico on business, and a busy social schedule that included competitive club tennis. She found multitasking a problem and was getting depressed and worried that she might not be able to meet all the family obligations she had defined for herself. As a result, I spent a good deal of time with her and started her on Ritalin to help her compensate for neurocognitive function that she felt compromised her ability to be the type of mother to her family that she wished. With psychological support and Ritalin, she was able to rise above her problems, organize the Bat Mitzvah of her eldest daughter and later that year, going off Ritalin. Happily, today, 25 years later, she is an active and vibrant, wife, mother and grandmother leading a normal life.

—⁂—

Another recollection I have is of a young Texas State Trooper of about 30-years- old and father of two who had a seizure at work that resulted in an MRI and a diagnosis of left frontal glioblastoma that was treated by a subtotal tumor resection, EBRT, and adjuvant chemotherapy. He did well, but of course would never return to law enforcement as a Texas State Trooper. Once he had recovered from surgery and EBRT, he was given a desk job in the state trooper program. At one of his follow up clinic visits. something unusual happened. One of my neurosurgical colleagues, Fred Lang, who had operated on him initially saw the recent MRI and suggested to me that he would be willing to reoperate and try for a gross total resection since the young man was doing so well clinically and was not suffering from any obvious frontal lobe dysfunction such as diminished executive function or drive to finish tasks.

217

The young man agreed to take the chance on surgery. Fred did what he had promised, and the tumor was removed, and the young man recovered with no frontal lobe dysfunction that we could find. During a post-chemotherapy clinic visit, I enquired about what he was planning to do now that the tumor was in remission; would he stay at the desk job, or did he have other options? He said that he was also a musician and had taught high school band at one time and was looking for a job at a high school or junior high school. At the time, I was surprised at his expectation that he would find a school job teaching music, but he proved me wrong for doubting. Everything worked out well and he, in fact, competed for the position of band director at a West Texas High School and was selected to fill the position. Five years later, he was doing well as father and band director. Sometimes, taking a calculated risk for an outstanding surgical outcome is worth it for the patient, especially when working with a gifted neurosurgeon.

—␣␣—

My last patient story starts in 2001 when I had the privilege of becoming Dr. Marnie Rose's neuro-oncologist. Marnie was a 27-year-old first year resident in pediatrics at Children's Memorial Hermann Hospital in Houston. She had recently been diagnosed with an anaplastic oligodendroglioma at Methodist Hospital in Houston and was referred to me in April 2001 to coordinate the treatment of her tumor. My plan for her was EBRT followed by adjuvant chemotherapy with PCV chemotherapy. She planned to continue being a pediatric resident while undergoing therapy and she told me she had agreed to share her cancer journey, personal life, and professional duties as a medical resident with a TV crew from the ABC reality series, *Houston Medical*, that followed the lives of doctors, nurses, other health care professionals and patients at Memorial Hermann Hospital. *Houston Medical* aired nationally on the ABC Network for six weeks in the summer of 2002.

During the show's debut episode, Marnie stunned viewers by pulling off her wig, revealing that she was both a physician and a patient. Throughout the run of *Houston Medical*, viewers, me included, were awed by her determination to keep working despite her illness, candor about her disease, and positive attitude in the face of adversity. Marnie had agreed to be filmed throughout her ordeal. She wanted to show how cancer can touch the lives of young people and offer strength and optimism for others afflicted with CNS tumors and cancer. Because of her commitment, a film crew followed her around almost daily as she performed her residency duties seeing pediatric patients during the day and when she took night and weekend call. Her courage was apparent even when she began to have left-sided weakness. One TV scene I cannot forget was filmed after night call as she walked with a slow and methodical gait alone in an underground corridor of the hospital, clearly tired and burned out from the day's effort and her weakness.

The impact of caring for Marnie was hard for me as I was filmed with and without Marnie during each return appointment. Sometimes I was interviewed and filmed in my office before I was to see Marnie in the clinic. Each of these encounters and filming were spontaneous without my foreknowledge of questions or directions the movie director, Charles Bangert, was planning to take at the time. The questions had to be answered carefully as I knew that some of the filmed interviews might be aired to the public in the TV program. At other times, the camera would be turned off as the crew would ask questions about Marnie's care so that they could better understand and be sensitive to what her path forward might look like. Since Marnie wanted me to be candid throughout my on-camera interviews, it was a little easier for me to navigate the questions, although I worried how Marnie might take some of my answers.

Aside from making sure my tie was straight and my hair combed

I did not prepare for the interviews as I never really knew what questions would be asked. So, as much as I would have liked to be a little less emotionally involved in Marnie's care, I felt a strong obligation to help Marnie as best as I could with her treatment and to support her emotional roller coaster ride as the tumor grew and transformed to a glioblastoma that required additional surgery.

Setting aside my interactions on camera with Marnie, Marnie was special. She had a beautiful face and smile that would captivate. Like anyone faced with an aggressive CNS tumor, her mood and spirit would fluctuate with each MRI and each challenge we faced. She could fluctuate from optimistic to realistic. When the MRI was good, she was ebullient and optimistic; when the MRI showed tumor growth, she might be tearful and distraught depending on whether I could offer her a logical explanation and/or a new therapeutic option.

For family and friends and for her TV audience she wanted to maintain her appearance as best she could, so when she had tumor and treatment-related brain swelling, I started low-dose dexamethasone. After researching dexamethasone and thinking more about it, she asked if she really had to take dexamethasone tablets since it might cause her to have the common side-effect of a moon face and weight gain. As I had used oral glycerol for patients with pseudotumor cerebri (a condition that caused generalized brain swelling) and in some brain tumor patients like Marnie who disliked the side-effects of steroids like dexamethasone, I offered this to Marnie, and we used it for a while to avoid dexamethasone. The oral glycerol worked for a couple of months and the MDACC pharmacy carried oral glycerol especially for Marnie.

After surgery, EBRT, and eight courses of CCNU (lomustine) and procarbazine (matulane), Marnie was doing well and enjoying her life as a pediatric resident and with her friends. At her birthday celebration in February 2002 at a Vietnamese restaurant, one of her friends presented her with a birthday cake in the shape of the brain to celebrate that her tumor was not growing. Sadly, the good times were going to end sooner than expected. At her next MRI evaluation and clinic visit in mid-March, we both saw the tumor growth on the MRI. I felt that the tumor was now a glioblastoma but Marnie, the independent and thoughtful soul she was, was unwilling to tell her family until after the family Passover Seder the next week. Her family, friends, and members of the *Houston Medical* team were planning to be at the Seder, and she wanted it to remain memorable for all.

Shortly after the Seder, Sam Hassenbusch, an MDACC neurosurgeon I worked with frequently, agreed to operate on Marnie and remove as much tumor as possible. In a fateful irony, Sam was diagnosed with glioblastoma in 2005, and succumbed to the tumor 3 years later. Sam operated in early April 2002. At this second resection we learned that the tumor was now a glioblastoma. Since Marnie's tumor grew through CCNU and procarbazine, I did not have a great deal of confidence that temozolomide (Temodar), a newer alkylating agent, would help, but we tried it for about two months without much success. There were few chemotherapy treatment options for me to draw upon. I recall looking for a new experimental therapy that might offer some tumor control, but I did not think we had a good enough experimental therapy available at the time to offer her a good treatment option. I did, however, think one option might possibly help her. We had recently closed an experimental study of an oral protein tyrosine kinase inhibitor, PTK787, which, when combined with oral temozolomide, seemed to be active against glioblastoma. We did not know if it would be statistically better than temozolomide at the time, but it seemed to me and Marnie worth trying. Since the study was closed, I had to seek compassionate use approval from the pharmaceutical company and the FDA, so I turned the regulatory wheels to obtain the drug.

The therapy worked for several months, but then the tumor started to grow again, and Marnie developed pneumonia. Unfortunately, her pulmonary condition quickly worsened as the brain tumor grew requiring an ICU admission prior to her death in August 2002, just five weeks after the final episode of *Houston Medical* had aired.

—∞—

Following her passing, her family wanted to honor Marnie's spirit, courage, and strength and to fund pediatric initiatives and brain cancer research at the Texas Medical Center. They established the Dr. Marnie Rose Foundation and the Dr. Marnie Rose Professorship in Pediatric Neurosurgery at McGovern Medical School "to spur innovative research and novel treatments for pediatric brain tumors, the second most common cancer in children."

The foundation also started *Run for the Rose*, an annual event that raises funds to support children's health initiatives and brain cancer research. Her brother, Myles Rose, Marnie's twin, put it eloquently in an online communication, "My sister chose to fight cancer with the nation watching. In doing so, she both put a 'face' to brain cancer and offered strength and optimism to many who were ill. Through our annual fundraiser, *Run for the Rose*, we hope to continue Marnie's legacy." The Dr. Marnie Rose Foundation and a yearly *Run for the Rose* fund raising event in Houston began in 2003 and has, over the years provided over $6.5 million dollars for CNS cancer and pediatric research.

Like many patients I have had the privilege to care for as a neuro-oncologist I will never forget Marnie Rose and her infectious smile, personality, spirit, and tremendous sense of purpose and legacy to be a physician to the end and be a beacon of hope for the many children and adults with cancer. Nor will I forget the thousands of other patients I have cared for over my career.

24

Time at the MD Anderson and Life in Houston Come to an End

In addition to my academic life at the MDACC in Houston, Ellen and I enjoyed many aspects of living in Houston such as the Houston Symphony that we attended regularly as members, several different theaters including the famous Alley Theater, various history and art museums, and many good restaurants. There were occasional black tie MDACC fund-raising events such as the gala birthday party for President George H.W. Bush, as well as some unusual MDACC fundraising events such as Polo on the Prairie at the Musselman Brothers' Lazy 3 Ranch in Albany, Texas.

I also enjoyed road biking with friends from the MDACC. Most of our biking was in the many small towns and rural areas bordering Houston. I found biking to be cooler than walking during the Houston summers. I remember formally training with 50- and 100-mile bike rides in 1994 to be able to ride The Oregon Bicycle Ride in the summer of 1995. Without hills to train on in Houston I realized that I might be at a disadvantage biking the hills and mountains in Oregon. When I started riding in Oregon, it quickly became apparent that my low gears were not low enough, so I had to have my derailleur exchanged the night of the first biking day. To this day, I remember the beautiful and challenging 550 mile, seven-day bike ride from Baker City in the far east of Oregon to Reedsport, four miles from the Pacific Ocean. The trip was great fun, especially since I did it with Don Herzog, an old friend from Mill Valley.

While the 1995 Oregon Bicycle Ride was great fun for me, a ride I took in 1996 ended up being just the opposite, a life-changing event. On a 50-mile Leukemia Society fundraising ride to Galveston in March 1996, I suffered a serious bike accident. I sustained five broken ribs on the right side, a broken right clavicle, a right temporal skull fracture, a small cerebral bleed on the left, and a concussion that caused amnesia for about five days. I did not recall everyone who stopped by my hospital room at the time, but I do recall seeing my son, Jason, and his wife, Cynthia, as well as my sisters, Laurie Merel and Deborah Gollin who had flown in from Chicago and Milwaukee, respectively. They had come to see how I was doing and to support Ellen. I also have a vague memory of saying, somewhat flippantly, that my family must have been confident that I was going to recover since my daughter, Lisa, had not flown in from San Francisco. The true reason I had forgotten was that she was pregnant with her first child at the time.

I returned prematurely to work part-time within three weeks of the accident because I felt it was my duty and responsibility to return to lead the department. However, my wife and colleagues thought I returned to work too soon as it took six to nine months for me to get back to my "normal." I do recall that I was more impulsive and disinhibited, for months after the accident. I also did not have sufficient insight into what were likely some neuro-cognitive problems as a result of the concussion and amnesia.

About a year after the bike accident, Andrew von Eschenbach, then Executive Vice President and Chief Academic Officer of the MDACC, began to pressure me to retire as Chair of the Department of Neuro-Oncology. No one in the MDACC administration ever told me why they wanted to me to retire as Chair of the Department of Neuro-Oncology. To this day, I remain uncertain why I was asked to resign the chairmanship. In my mind I assumed the accident and head injury and perhaps my inherent lack of patience was the reason

Andy pushed me to resign. Another hypothesis some colleagues and I considered was that internal department and institutional politics may have been at work to push me out for their own gain or because of some perceived and unsupported gender bias reasons. For whatever reason, the process left a bad memory for me and others in the Department. The hardest part, then and now, was giving up leadership of the largest and one of the most productive neuro-oncology departments in the USA before it was time.

By late 1997, my "retirement" as Chair of the Department of Neuro-Oncology appeared imminent and the wheels within the MDACC began to turn quickly. The sections I had created I expected to become free-standing departments over time. My forced "resignation" as chair of the Neuro-Oncology Department speeded up that process. Over a period of about a year, four new departments were created from my Neuro-Oncology Department. These were the Department of Psychiatry, Department of Symptom Research, Department of Palliative Care, Rehabilitation, and Integrative Medicine in the Division of Internal Medicine, and the Department of Pain Medicine in the Division of Anesthesiology, Critical Care, and Pain Medicine. Al Yung became interim chair of the neuro-oncology department after my resignation and, in several years, the chair.

I am quite proud that the Department of Neuro-Oncology, during my time as chairman and because of my vision, was the womb from which all supportive oncology departments and sections at the MDACC were born. In those years we did a lot more than "just" brain tumors, although we did become the largest clinical CNS tumor program in North America by 1997. Sadly, I felt the forced decision for me to retire had irreversible and detrimental effects on the department and future of neuro-oncology at MDACC as well as the expectations I had had for the the Department and the Brain Tumor Center. I am grateful for the many people I was fortunate to work with during the over 21 years I worked at the MDACC. There were some wonderful and committed administrative people and nurses. Too often, physicians give too little credit to the people who support us and believe in the value of what we can do together. I, for one, understood and appreciated their contributions and importance to the department and to my success as chairman. During my years at the MDACC, my administrative staff were the ones who helped create order and subdued the chaos around us. They figured out how to improve efficiency, ensure record accuracy, and how to navigate institutional bureaucracy and personality differences. When I started at MDACC, I hired Diane Romagnoli-Smith to be our first Department Administrator. Diane stayed with our department until the early 1990s when she left for another position. I then hired Jenella Smith who stayed with us until 1998, when she retired from the Department to bike across the United States, a feat she accomplished in 1998. Following Jenella, I hired Marketta Beneke in 1998, the first Department Administrator with a master's degree. Marketta stayed in this position until sometime after I had left the MDACC.

My personal administrative assistants were, in sequential order, Gail Destin, Linda Weiser, Linda Greer, Melissa McLane, and Kay Hyde. Each of my administrative assistants had a story and each, aside from Kay, left the MDACC well before I retired from the MDACC in December 2009. Each, in their own way, had an impact on me and my career at the MDACC. In addition to my personal administrative assistants there were two woman, Rebecca Reyes, and Mary Moise, who were administrative assistants to other faculty but, nonetheless, held a special place in the Department for their unselfish dedication and willingness to do whatever was needed to support their faculty and the needs of the department even if it required extra hours of work, or taking on an assignment that others were unwilling to do. Eventually, Mary gravitated to the research laboratory as the Laboratory Administrator, where she still works.

The clinical and research nurses I had the pleasure to work with were important to my success and that of the department. The first Advanced Practice Nurse I worked with for a sustained period was Geline J. Tamayo, Clinical Nurse Specialist, from 1998 to 2003. Geline was followed by Laurel Westcarth, APN, who I worked with until I retired from the MDACC at the end of 2009. As the Department grew and our research protocols climbed in numbers, research nurses became an important part of our clinical program. The first research nurse in the Department was Mary Jo Gleason. Over the years we had many research nurses, but Mary Jo became the mainstay of the effort and became the head of research nurses. Other research nurses I worked with over the years include Kathy Hunter, Eva Lu Lee, Sur Ja Min, Carolyn Loch, Vivian Liu, Sherry Waldrum, and Pat Kagy. The clinic nurses I recall working with include Sang Kang, Tran Nguyen, Angie Ames, and Tara Alexander (Mammoser). One nurse, Karen Baumgartner was first a clinic nurse, then research nurse, and eventually, after attaining her MS degree, an APN in the Department. I worked with Karen through all three career iterations. Lastly, our very important neuro-oncology research clinical database has been in the capable hands of Sandra Ictech since its inception in 1990.

Giving up the chairmanship and having no clear position or path forward I continued to do laboratory research with space assigned outside of department research space since my tyrosine kinase research was moving its status as a NIH-funded program to SIGNASE, a company I had founded with Ray Budde. In the last years of my MDACC research career, I developed new research directions with the help of bright research assistants, Jacob Jochec and Patricia Koch, and postdoctoral students, Kenji Tada, MD, Yoshi Kajiwara, MD, and Sonali Panchabhai, MBBS. In one of our research endeavors, we created a semiquantitative fluorescent micro-scopy assay for ODC enzyme activity-levels for the study of human central and peripheral nerve formalin-fixed tumor microarrays. This research helped me better understand the basis for DFMO anti-tumor activity in clinical trials I had conducted and would support the basis for forming a company (Chapter 27) and embarking on a second Phase III clinical trial as a prelude to a market approval application years later.

My research group also developed a new methodology for semi-quantifying three-dimensional tumor growth using new instrumentation and approaches. These could be used to better evaluate and present anticancer drug-drug interactions such as synergism versus additive effects of therapy combinations. In addition, we expanded these three-dimensional culture studies to measure protein levels under stressed conditions of hypoxia and serum starvation using reverse-phase protein microarrays. My research goal was to develop these techniques and show how they could be used so that others might more readily develop new drug combinations for treating CNS tumors. Unfortunately, my optimism for the future use of that technology has not materialized.

In retrospect, I stayed too long after relinquishing the chairmanship of the Department of Neuro-Oncology, but no oppor-tunities came my way to consider. I even contacted colleagues at the University of California Davis (Sacramento), the University of California Irvine, and Stanford for possible opportunities. Near my retirement from MDACC in 2009, colleagues on the East Coast told me that there was a rumor that after my bike accident that I had re-linquished the department chairmanship for medical reasons and that I was, in the words of a friend, damaged goods. This false narrative and information came to me too late to reverse or counter. Sad as this was for me to handle, nonetheless, I believe that I left a legacy of important departments at the MDACC that provide superb care for cancer patients, enabled the training of generations of physicians, clinical psychologists, and nurses that have gained national prominence because of their contributions to cancer medicine.

25

Back to California

At the end of 2009, I retired from the MDACC as an Emeritus Professor in the Department of Neuro-Oncology. Ellen and I moved to a house we bought in Greenbrae (California) to be closer to our daughter, Lisa, and her two children, Rebekah and Josh, and our son, Jason, and his wife, Cynthia.

Before we left Houston, the Department of Neuro-Oncology and the Division of Medicine organized a beautiful and thoughtful retirement party for me at the Petroleum Club in Houston. Prior to the party, Hideyuki Saya, MD, PhD, who had recently flown into Houston from Tokyo, gave a very exciting lecture in the MD Anderson's main auditorium. His lecture, "Mouse Cancer using Induced Cancer Stem Cells," was given in honor of my retirement. Hideyuki had been my postdoctoral research fellow at UCSF and moved with me from UCSF to MDACC in 1988. He is a brilliant and creative laboratory scientist whose research has covered a broad scope of cancer. I was always impressed by his ability to answer a question or develop a methodology to learn more about a biological process without fear that he might not master a new methodology. In 1995, while the MDACC academic promotion committee was deliberating on his application for promotion to professor, he was recruited back to Japan with the rank of professor and given the opportunity to head a new research institute at Kumamoto University. By the time I retired, Hideyuki had moved to the prestigious Keio University School of Medicine in Tokyo where he had been recruited to be professor and Chair of the newly created Division of Gene Regulation. Besides Hideyuki, another dear friend from Japan, Yukitaka Ushio, MD, PhD, an outstanding neuro-surgeon, researcher, and teacher, flew from Kobe, Japan to attend and speak at my retirement party and to present a beautiful photo summary of my many trips to Japan.

In addition to Hideyuki and Yuki, I was honored and grateful that Bill Shapiro, who was Chairman of the Department of Neu-rology, and his wife, Joan Rankin, came from the Barrow Institute in Phoenix. Phil Gutin, who I worked with since his residency in neurosurgery at UCSF and on the faculty upon completion of his residency, flew to Houston from New York City where he was the Chair of the Department of Neurosurgery at the Memorial Sloan-Kettering Cancer Center in New York. In addition, two prior neuro-oncology fellows now living outside Texas, Alexandra Flowers from Hartford, Connecticut, and Joon Uhm from the Mayo Clinic in Rochester, Minnesota made the effort to attend the festivities.

I was also deeply honored and grateful that my sisters, Laurie, and Deborah, had flown in from Chicago and Milwaukee to support me at this time of transition. My sisters had always been supportive and encouraging of me. In addition, my sister-in-law, Louise and her husband, Jerry Stein, also flew in from Milwaukee to be with Ellen and I at this transition. I never expected that so many family and old friends would attend my retirement party.

When I get nostalgic for my twenty-one years at MDACC, I derive great enjoyment looking through a PowerPoint retirement presentation and the hundreds of photos taken by nurses I worked with at the MDACC, which they presented to me at my retirement party. They had photographed me alone and with colleagues and trainees at my neuro-oncology clinics over a three-month period before I left. There was a great deal of appreciation and love among those I worked with over the years. Early in my career I realized it takes many diverse people to build a strong clinical program; people who need to be appreciated, respected, and acknowledged. It is important, too, to make sure the people you work with know, as a daily fact, that what we accomplished is what they accomplished as well and made possible.

Ellen and I moved to Greenbrae in late November 2009. We were quite happy to be so close to our grandchildren to watch them grow up and support their various music and sports activities and accomplishments at school. Problematic for me and Ellen on our return to California was the question of what I was going to do with my time as I was not ready to completely retire from medicine and neuro-oncology. I was willing to do clinical neuro-oncology as I wanted to stay on a clinical path. I was even prepared to help develop a new neuro-oncology program or contribute to an existing program. I considered and interviewed at the University of California Irvine, the University of California Davis, Stanford University, UCSF, and even at the Pacific Medical Center of Sutter Hospital. While optimistic when I started my search, I grew frustrated and concerned that my ambitions exceeded those of the institutions I sought to join.

About two months before we moved back to California, I discovered that Kaiser Permanente Redwood City Hospital had recently hired a young neuro-oncologist, Scott Peak. I decided to investigate this further hoping they might want part-time clinical help. Since I had worked with neurosurgeons at the Redwood City Hospital for fifteen years while at UCSF, I made some calls. One thing led to another, and I was soon interviewing with William Sheridan, Steve Nutik, who I had worked with while I was at UCSF, Scott Peak, and other physicians in the Department of Neurosurgery and Neurosciences at Redwood City Hospital. After the interview Bill Sheridan, the Department of Neurosurgery and Neurosciences Chair, offered me a Pool Physician (part-time) position to work at

Kaiser Permanente's Redwood City Hospital two days/week. It seemed a perfect solution. I could work as a neuro-oncologist doing direct patient care, which I enjoyed, and help a young neuro-oncologist grow his program.

Working for Kaiser Permanente was a new experience. No more did I have an advanced practice nurse (APN), a research nurse, a clinic nurse, and neuro-oncology fellows to work with. I was the sole connection to my patients. I had to learn how to use Epic Hyperspace (Epic Systems), the electronic medical record (eHR) Kaiser used. Over a period of a month or so I became proficient using the eHR and found that I had not lost my skill set for direct patient care. I did miss some of the information that would filter to me from my APN and fellows, so had to work extra hard to anticipate patient and family issues. As I was hired through a regional program within Kaiser, no one complained if I spent an hour or more with a patient; this was often a necessity for new patients and those with neurocognitive problems.

Bill Sheridan and the neurosurgery staff wanted me to work Thursday and Friday so I could attend the weekly Friday morning Stereotactic and CNS Tumor Board between 8:00 a.m. and 9:30 a.m. Initially, I contemplated driving 44 miles each way on Thursday and Friday, but quickly realized that driving from Greenbrae to Redwood City would require driving through San Francisco and a total of three counties with a great deal of traffic. Depending on the time of day and traffic, the one-way trip would take 60 to 90 minutes. As a result, I decided to stay overnight at a nearby Holiday Express Hotel on Thursday nights, which worked out well for six years. A bonus was that I could meet for Thursday dinner with Dennis Brown, an old friend and serial pharmaceutical company entrepreneur who I have known since the 1980s. For years, we cycled through restaurants in Menlo Park and Redwood City, but eventually we settled on Harry's Hofbrau in Redwood City across from the Holiday Inn Express. This location also allowed me the opportunity to have dinner with my son, Jason, and occasionally his wife, Cynthia, if they had the time. At these Thursday night dinners, we frequently talked about new drugs or potential repurposed drugs that might be helpful for treating CNS cancers.

This arrangement worked well for about six years until I tired of staying at the hotel and commuting and I told Bill I was planning to quit. He protested. "Don't quit! Why don't you stay on and do telemedicine with your patients and do second opinion consults for Northern California Kaiser Permanente patients?" Since there were about 4.6 million patients in the Kaiser system at the time and I was following 140 patients, I thought it was worth a try.

Four years later, I still follow about sixty to seventy patients and do second and third opinion consults throughout Northern California from my home office. I have even initiated and overseen chemotherapy via telemedicine for eight to twelve months on about ten patients in the past five years without any problems. If any of my patients need a neurological examination and/or surgery I arrange for them to be seen by a Redwood City Hospital colleague. Some of the patients decided to stay with the physician I referred them to, but many gravitated back to me for telemedicine follow up. So far it has been gratifying caring for my Kaiser patients, and none have complained about the arrangement. I do, however, truly miss having dinner on Thursdays with Dennis and, when possible, with my son, Jason, and his wife Cynthia.

Most Thursday dinners I had, however, were with Dennis over the six years I went to Redwood City Hospital. I found these dinners fun and intellectually stimulating as Dennis has a great sense of humor and we discussed potential new uses for existing drugs or studies that might guide a decision to bring an old drug forward for a new use such as in the treatment of glioblastoma. One such drug was dianhydrogalactitol (DAG), a drug I had studied at UCSF in the laboratory and clinic. Through discussions I had with Dennis I learned that this drug, which I knew quite a bit about, was being the lead program of Del Mar Pharmaceuticals, a Vancouver, Canada company started by Jeffery Bacha and Dennis. I was supportive of the drug being further developed and possibly commercialized, but I thought that a single-day IV injection would be better than a three - to five 5-day delivery approach. The drug known as VAL-083 is in clinical trials for glioblastoma today and may, eventually be approved by the FDA for a subpopulation of glioblastoma patients.

Years earlier, while I was at MDACC, Dennis had encouraged me to start VBL Pharmaceuticals to try and commercialize DFMO and, with a friend of his, Edward Luck, funded the virtual company as we sought a financial and regulatory path to its commercialization for the treatment of anaplastic gliomas. Unfortunately, VBL Pharmaceuticals was unable to bring DFMO forward.

26

CNS Anticancer Drug Discovery and Development Conferences

After "retiring" to Marin, one concern festered in my consciousness: Why was there no progress in new drug development for CNS tumors? Having worked for more than five decades in anticancer therapeutics and drug discovery and development to find that "new" drug, I was disappointed and frustrated that none had come forward to treat CNS tumors and little was on the horizon. To express my concern and prepare a basis for a future conference I was considering, in May 2012, I wrote an essay about healthcare and thoughts on how to optimize new drug discovery/development for uncommon cancers. While never published and maybe a bit out of date today, it, nevertheless, further galvanized me to try and bring together colleagues in academia and the pharmaceutical/biotech industry to organize a specially focused program on the problems that had restricted drug discovery for CNS cancers.

As I started writing the essay, I asked myself why I was writing this essay. To what end? I did not have the conceit to believe I could provide a roadmap for finding better therapies for patients with cancer, but I did and still do believe that we can, as a society, provide inducements and controls to achieve better therapies for uncommon and rare cancers over a period of years in a manner consistent with good science and good business practices. The Orphan Drug Program and Rare Disease initiatives of the FDA seeks to accomplish that goal at a regulatory level. I, however, was more interested in the drug discovery/development process and what people could do in

2012 to influence the FDA to make more effective choices that would help enable the development of new drugs for rare CNS tumors.

The adults and children I treated and cared for over my career who had primary CNS tumors were considered to have rare cancers. These tumors constitute about 1.4 percent of all cancers. Because of my frustration at the lack of effective new drugs for the patients I treat and the toxicity of current treatments (surgery, irradiation, cytotoxic chemotherapy), I have long been concerned with the approach used by pharmaceutical and academic scientists, the pharmaceutical and biotech industry, and their regulators in the FDA.

On one level, I thought the FDA was not sufficiently sensitive to the problems of developing new therapies for gliomas and medulloblastoma tumors, and especially the R&D challenges. On another level, I understand improved treatments for people with CNS cancers (and other cancers) will likely require specifically targeted inhibitors of pathways that support neoplastic transformation and growth. While many scientific articles lead us to believe that we understand these signally pathways and the implications of some target proteins within the pathway, unfortunately, that is not always the case as these pathways are frequently composed of numerous nonlinear interactions that we do not fully understand and that affect the flow of the pathway and the target protein we seek to mitigate by a drug or other effectors. Thus, meaningful drug discovery/development for CNS tumors has been excruciatingly slow compared to other cancers.

Another worry of mine has been an expectation that effective therapy will require multiple targets within the tumor cell being blocked or otherwise mitigated. It has been hoped that since some signaling kinase inhibitors work on several targets in the tumor cell that the drugs will work better to control tumor growth. This has frequently happened because it is sometimes too difficult to make a truly selective inhibitor of one enzyme or protein interaction, or we think that we know what the second target should be. Then, when the drug goes into rodent tumor models, we accumulate information relevant to rapidly growing high-grade tumors but question whether this is less valuable against more slowly growing and more heterogeneous human tumors. Then we are surprised when the new drug only increases overall survival by two to four months. The pharma marketing people look at this modest gain as a positive since it was statistically significant because the p-value in their very large study is less than the magical number 0.05. And soon, we have the next mediocre drug to treat our family and friends who have cancer. In addition, when this new and not truly specific/selective drug is used in a combination with another drug, it produces toxicity in ways we do not understand, and we are stuck with a mediocre drug and little latitude to make large meaningful gains in survival. The good treatment bar stays low and clinicians like me complain to no one in particular.

Another concern is that we may be keeping the bar for treatment efficacy too low. What we need is a path forward that raises the bar for therapeutic achievement and, at the same time, provides a strong financial carrot to industry to make this dream possible. Maybe this requires a new compact with the FDA, pharma, lobbyists, and politicians in Washington.

While cutting the cost of drugs seems to be driving our news media and legislators to gain points with voters, I think we need more incentives for pharma to make better drugs by expanding exclusivity or patent protection to allow pharma to study more old and new drugs available to them in more complex systems and for longer periods of time. Maybe a drug that doubles two-year survival should get twelve years of exclusivity. Besides providing more exclusivity, the FDA needs to make it easier to stage drug approval so that a second randomized study or a long-term toxicity profile required for FDA approval can be studied for orphan agents through an FDA mechanism that allows some early third-party payment to cover part of the cost of clinical trials. This would be done with the full understanding that the cancer patients accept a generally higher risk of toxicity to achieve what has become an ever-elusive benefit of longer and better-quality life.

Another consideration is many glioma trials will require years to decades to complete, based on current FDA guidelines to achieve a statistically significant increase in overall survival (OS) in at least one randomized trial. This endpoint is hard to meet in that it might require a 10-year clinical trial, making it too risky for venture capital support.

Even though I was retired from the MDACC and no longer active in academia, I was optimistic that I could help others to find a path forward for better CNS tumor drug discovery and development. I invited scientists, clinicians, FDA regulators and statisticians from academia, industry, and government to plan the first CNS Anticancer Drug Discovery and Development Conference (CADDDC). In initial deliberations with members of the organizing committee, we concluded that a two-day freestanding meeting would be optimium. While we put together ideas for the conference, I simultaneously started to raise money to defray some of the conference costs and to be sure we had some money to support trainees and postdoctoral students so they could join the conference. I had almost pulled off the conference at a hotel in Bethesda, MD until I discovered that I would have to guarantee the first $10,000 for the conference room and hotel reservations. As I had not yet raised the money, it would have to come from me personally, so I sought advice from a friend, Chas Haynes, the Executive Director of the Society for Neuro-Oncology. As result of that call, he offered to schedule the meeting two days before the start of the November 2014 SNO Annual Meeting at the Loews Miami Beach Hotel. This way, the room risk became the responsibility of SNO, and the meeting would benefit from their professional help to advertise, manage abstracts, organize meals and breaks, hire, and coordinate audiovisual people, pay bills, and have someone on site to manage registration and other functions.

And so, it was that the first CADDDC was held, in November 2014 prior to the 2014 SNO annual meeting. I was happy how well the conference went and how pleased attendees were that we had put the effort in to make it reality. One of the goals of the conference was to create a white paper to summarize the status of the field, provide some guidance going forward, and to admonish those present, whether in academia or industry, to redouble their efforts to create and develop needed drugs for the treatment of CNS tumors.

The 2014 CADDDC was followed by two additional conferences, one held in November 2016, before the SNO Annual Meeting at the Fairmont Princes Hotel in Scottsdale, Arizona. The third conference was was held prior to the November 2018 SNO Annual Meeting at the Marriott Hotel in New Orleans, Louisiana. I was sad realizing there would be no 2020 CADDDC. Interest in a two-day meeting was waning. The educational process I had thought so important before our first conference in 2014 had been met for many by the end of the 2018 conference, based on discussions I had with speakers and attendees. I considered an abbreviated online conference using software such as ZOOM Cloud Meeting but found limited interest and shelved the idea for having another CADDDC and moved on to other challenges and opportunities along the neuro-oncology path, including finishing this book.

Medicine, science, and life are like that. Sometimes needs and progress are coupled and require big steps to move forward; at other times, progress and advances reduce what is perceived as a large need to a small incremental step. So, it was for the CADDDC held in 2014, 2016, and 2018. I believed they were necessary, but not sufficient, to help move the drug discovery/development field forward. From an educational perspective, physicians and scientists in academia and industry who did not fully understand the problems associated with drug distribution to CNS tumors and the importance of drug binding and residence time on tumor cell targets, now understood more if they attended these conferences. In addition, physicians and pharmaceutical scientists were now aligned in their understanding of those factors that affect the risk/benefit ratio that pharmaceutical companies must confront if they are to create the drugs, we need to treat CNS cancers.

After the 2018 conference, I felt I could do no more; it was up to others to forge paths to bring new drugs and therapies forward to help our patients. Nonetheless, I still hoped that some of our ideas would stimulate others to think differently and maybe more creatively to bring new therapies to patients in my lifetime. With each CADDDC we held, entrepreneurial pharmaceutical scientists and chemists came to me during and after the conferences to tell me that they would go back to their companies and develop anticancer therapies that would be brain penetrant to improve the chance of the drug being active against CNS neoplasms. Years later, I am still waiting for these drugs. I keep hoping that maybe these drugs are in a research laboratory somewhere and soon to be studied in the clinic. Such is my eternal optimism.

27

Founding Orbus Therapeutics to Advance Eflornithine Treatment

A major benefit of our move back to California was that my wife and I would see our children and grandchildren who live in the area more frequently. This proximity turned out to have another advantage, too. It led, I believe, to the founding of Orbus Therapeutics, Inc., a virtual late-stage biopharmaceutical company, in February 2012. Orbus Therapeutics had been started in Palo Alto, California by Bob Myers and my son, Jason.

Jason had some hands-on experience in molecular biology laboratories before he graduated from the University of California San Diego (UCSD) in 1993. He had worked summers in a research laboratory in Pharmaceutical Chemistry at UCSF and in Webster "Web" Cavenee's Ludwig Institute for Cancer Research laboratory at the University of California San Diego (UCSD). After graduation from UCSD he was a laboratory technician at a start-up company, Gene Medicine, in Houston. As he approached deciding on graduate studies, either for an MD or PhD, he realized that he would rather get an MBA, with an emphasis on entrepreneurship, and graduated from the McCombs Graduate School of Business at The University of Texas in Austin. His first job out of graduate school was at ALZA Corporation in Mountain View, California where he worked with Bob Myers. Subsequently, after the acquisition of ALZA by Johnson & Johnson, Jason continued working for Johnson & Johnson for a while before moving on to Brain Cells where he was Chief Business Officer; from there Jason moved to Sorbent as Chief Business

Officer. Bob's path was different as he co-founded Jazz Pharmaceuticals and encouraged Jason to join Jazz Pharmaceuticals where Jason eventually became its Vice President of Corporate Development.

After working together successfully at two compaines, Bob and Jason decided to create their own biopharmaceutical company. After evaluating several options around which they could form their company, Jason and Bob contacted me for information about DFMO, a drug Jason knew I had worked with in the laboratory and clinic for decades. As I discussed earlier in this book, my initial interest in DFMO was a result of close laboratory interactions I had with Larry Marton, MD, a colleague in the UCSF Brain Tumor Research Center who worked in an adjacent laboratory studying polyamines and their interplay with cancer, especially CNS tumors. At the time, DFMO was the primary inhibitor of polyamine metabolism that was available for laboratory and clinical study. It had been discovered and developed by the Richardson-Merrell Pharmaceutical Company to treat trypanosomiasis in the 1970s. Interest in DFMO as a treatment for human cancer followed the discovery that the target in the trypanosomes, ornithine decarboxylase (ODC), was the same as in mammals like us. Between 1974 and 1988, Larry and I did *in vitro*, in vivo, rodent tumor model and pharmacokinetic studies that supported clinical trials I started at UCSF and completed at MDACC.

Because of the very good results of my phase III randomized trial of DFMO with the PCV combination versus PCV published in 2003, together with two entrepreneurial colleagues, Ed Luck and Dennis Brown, I started VBL Pharmaceuticals, our goal being to commercialize DFMO. While Ed was able to raise some funding, we never were able to raise enough funds to support a clinical trial, even though we did obtain Orphan Drug Status from the FDA. We even tried to obtain funding from Sanofi-Aventis, who, at the time, was producing DFMO for the WHO-sponsored treatment of sleeping sickness (trypanosomes). But Ed did not think the conditions they offered were sufficient for our startup company. In the end, our effort under VBL failed as we could not obtain sufficient funding to support a phase III clinical trial for eventual FDA market approval.

Fortunately, in early 2012, Jason and Bob took up the challenge. After extensive discussions and spending days reviewing and preparing data from clinical studies I had conducted, they told me they wanted to create a late-stage biopharmaceutical company focused on commercializing DFMO for the treatment of mid-grade cerebral gliomas.

When I started this journey with Jason and Bob, I thought I knew and understood everything about DFMO. Because of their persistent questioning and challenges, I went back further into the clinical trial databases that had been curated from DFMO studies conducted under an FDA Investigational New Drug (IND) application at MDACC and UCSF. I sought updated information from the clinical studies data offices at MDACC and UCSF that retained data on clinical CNS tumor studies and was able to determine the overall survival of patients reported in the 1992 publication. This led to an "aha moment" for Jason and Bob. They realized from our single-agent phase II study that we had a longer survival for recurrent anaplastic astrocytomas than had ever been seen in the literature for more cytotoxic drugs. Based on that knowledge they decided to start a new company.

Orbus Therapeutics was created in 2012, with Bob as Chief Executive Officer (CEO) and Jason as Chief Operating Officer (COO). While I was one of the three co-founders of Orbus, I was pretty much the silent co-founder, brought out for investors when Bob and Jason thought it helpful to raise funds for Orbus. Bob and Jason spent the next three-and-a-half years meeting with more than 100 venture capital firms and pharmaceutical companies to raise funds.

One of my first and very memorable experiences working under my son's supervision occurred at a meeting with potential investors in Palo Alto. Before we went into the meeting, Jason was trying to figure out how to refer to me. Jason asked me, "should I say Dr. Levin, Victor Levin, or Victor?" That afternoon, Jason made a thoughtful and polished presentation to the room full of attendees from the venture firm. After he finished, one of the venture partners asked, "What does your dad think about this?" From that time forward, Jason no longer questioned how to introduce me.

In August 2015, Orbus Therapeutics announced they had raised $32.5 million in series A funds to enable the STELLAR Study, a randomized phase III trial of DFMO combined with lomustine versus lomustine alone for recurrent anaplastic astrocytoma. The year before, Orbus had obtained Breakthrough Therapy Designation from the FDA for DFMO treatment of gliomas based on my earlier clinical trial results and the newly obtained survival data for recurrent anaplastic astrocytomas. This was a milestone, as DFMO became the first drug to receive that designation for the treatment of a CNS neoplasm. We had obtained Orphan Drug Status from the FDA while under VBL Pharmaceuticals.

Using good judgment, even though I was a co-founder of Orbus Therapeutics, Bob and Jason did not offer me a company position but asked that I become the Senior Medical Advisor for Orbus Therapeutics. I happily accepted that responsibility as I wanted to make sure, as best I could, that medical and treatment errors were kept to a minimum as I had seen trials fail before because of poor design and/or execution.

The first patient in the STELLAR Study was enrolled in late September 2016, four and a half years after the company was incorporated, a tribute to the foresight and tenacity of Bob and Jason. At the time of this writing, the STELLAR Study is closed after accruing over 340 patients from eight countries and about

80 clinical sites. Unfortunately, at this time, the study is still blinded so we have not seen the statistical analysis to deteremine whether the eflornithine-lomustine arm is superior to the lomustine arm, nonetheless, I remain hopeful and confident that the study will show a significant benefit of eflornithine to lomustine therapy.

—⁓—

Over the past 20 years, I have been asked by potential investors and neuro-oncology colleagues the same question, "How come the drug was never approved for cancer treatment?" I always thought this would be a good article for someone in the Harvard Business School to write about, but since they have not, I would like to offer my explanation.

Between 1981 and 1999, DFMO was evaluated in nine NCI-sponsored and published phase II trials exclusive of my brain tumor trials. In my review of these other cancer studies, I found clear clinical efficacy against childhood leukemia, acute myeloid leukemia, metastatic melanoma, and cervical cancer.

In my opinion, the reason DFMO was never approved by the FDA for a cancer therapy was because of the lack of an FDA NDA-focused clinical trial over that twenty-year period due to the original Richardson-Merrell company being serially acquired and its owner-ship transferred through six companies. While Richardson-Merrell went back to 1930 as a pharmaceutical company, after it became infamous for introducing thalidomide in the United States in the 1950s and 1960s, the company attracted Albert Sjoerdsma, MD, PhD, away from the NCI with a ten-year license to basically do what he wanted with respect to drug discovery/development. After moving the research effort to Centre de Recherche Merrell Inter-nationale in Strasbourg, France and under Sjoerdsma's leadership, Merrell Research created the first-ever rationally designed antiepileptic (Sabril®), the first-ever non-sedating antihistamine, Seldane®, and difluoromethylornithine (DFMO, Ornidyl, eflornithine), a cure for deadly African sleeping sickness that saved hundreds, maybe even thousands, of lives of Africans.

Because of that success, Merrell Research was acquired by the Dow Chemical company in 1980, when Dow Chemical decided to try their hand at pharmaceuticals and the company was renamed Merrell Dow Pharmaceuticals. In 1989, Merrell-Dow decided to grow their pharmaceutical presence and merged with Marion Laboratories as Marion Merrell Dow, Inc. Finding human pharmaceuticals more of a diversion than profit center, they sold the pharmaceutical business to Hoechst Roussel in 1995, leading to the creation of Hoechst Marion Roussel, inc. This was not the end of the company's ascent as they were then merged with Aventis in 1999, and eventually, when they were acquired by Sanofi, became Sanofi Aventis in that same year. Thus, because of all the mergers, it was very hard to find advocacy within the company for eflornithine, a drug which by that point had lost its patent protection.

In the early years, I worked with Paul J. Schecter, a physician in Merrell-Dow Pharmaceuticals who provided oral eflornithine for my clinical trials at UCSF. I do not, however, recall working with an advocate within the companies over the years that wanted to push forward for eflornithine approval for any cancer, let alone gliomas. Surprisingly, however, they continued to provide drug for my clinical trials, initially through Merrell Dow Pharmaceuticals and then by providing eflornithine to the Cancer Therapy Evaluation Program (CTEP) in the NCI for my randomized phase III study of eflornithine (DFMO) with PCV versus PCV alone. Obviously, the loss of patent protection for eflornithine reduced company interest in moving the drug forward for cancer, but it is disappointing that Orphan Drug Designation exclusivity for seven years in the U.S. and ten years in Europe was an insufficient stimulus to bring eflornithine forward to treat people with cancer at the time and for decades to come.

The path I have been on for so long feels like a circle, today returning to a drug I started to study in the early 1970s. While I believe that eflornithine may be on the cusp of becoming a drug available by prescription for mid-grade gliomas, I may be wrong, and it may not meet the stringent requirements of the FDA for approval. Science and colleagues, tenacity to succeed, a small late-stage pharmaceutical company and its investors who believed eflornithine could help people and become a commercial success, as well as some luck have brought me to this point. While I am happy for the accomplishment, I remain disappointed that it has taken 50 years to bring into the clinic the first drug for gliomas that is not a DNA-alkylating drug. While being a personal success on the one hand, this long waiting time has been concomitantly a failure of the medical research and pharmaceutical industry.

28

Concluding Thoughts and Reflections

One of the joys of writing this memoir was the journey of recollection it forced upon me and the personal enlightenment I gained. I enjoyed revisiting and luxuriating in the friendships I made and the people that helped bring me along on my life's journey.

As a young man and romantic, I saw myself as being a neurosurgeon who would make lasting contributions to the better health of the people living on our planet. I thought it natural that I would become a surgeon as I liked using my hands to repair, build, and create things, but in my final year of medical school I realized that I did not have good enough depth perception to fully utilize the binocular operating microscopes that were coming into use in operating rooms at the time. In addition, I also liked doing research and did not think, as an active neurosurgeon, I would have enough time to do the level of research I envisioned.

In retrospect, expecting that I would make "lasting contributions to the better health of the people living on our planet" I see today as a conceit. In the naivete of youth, I assumed that if I diligently sought education and training and truly applied myself, I would achieve that lofty goal. Fortunately, I was realistic enough to understand that I was unlikely to achieve this goal on my own, but optimistic for the future and what could be accomplished with vision and leadership.

As a result of my NIH years and neurology residency, I understood the importance and difficulty of finding treatments for people afflicted with unresectable CNS tumors. While my life and path to medicine was started well before my neurology residency, it was only in my last year of residency that I decided to set myself on the path that I have stayed on to this day. Did I set my course knowing where I was going or how I was going to get there? Of course not! Did I expect to be successful? The answer is yes; I was an optimist.

I believe that I understood, before starting my first faculty position at UCSF, that I had qualities and skills that I could apply to improve drug treatment of CNS tumors and I needed an environment that would be encouraging and enabling. Fortunately for me, UCSF was such an environment. There I experienced the humility that comes from being surrounded by highly productive and creative scientists and an institutional attitude of learning, teaching, willingness to forge into new research areas, and acceptance that failure is a necessary part of creative scientific success.

—⚛—

CNS tumor patients in the 1960's had few options; it was surgery, radiation, or both as chemotherapy was just starting to be introduced and far from being accepted for the treatment of high-grade gliomas. None of the treatment modalities were very effective, based on the metric of significantly longer survival or better quality of life. These treatments and their toxicities and complications were challenging to accommodate for patients as well as the surgeons, radiation oncologists, oncology purveyors, and family caregivers. Survival and quality of life for these patients was not good. When I started working in this area in the 1970s, I understood that the career path I set for myself would be scientifically, medically, and emotionally difficult for me and the adults and children entrusted in my care. Nonetheless, I went into medicine precisely to treat and care for people with diseases and practice according to the ancient Greek Hippocratic oath. The neuro-oncology practice I developed at UCSF and continued at The University of Texas MD Anderson Cancer Center, was associated with high patient mortality and a significant number of patients having poor neurological outcomes. As such, it was not always easy for those on the path with me to continue as not all those who trained with me followed the neuro-oncology path.

When I started on my path in medical research and academia, I thought if I used knowledge of regional drug pharmacokinetics and knowledge of anticancer pharmacology, I would be able to bring new drugs to the clinic to treat CNS tumor patients and thereby change the course of these diseases over time. While this would proof to be partially true, the great frustration was that much of my early laboratory and clinical research disclosed to me more about why cytotoxic therapies fail and less about how they might be made more effective. Sadly, I discovered reality early in my academic career.

How frustrating it was for me to realize that nothing in my laboratory or clinical research was going to change the trajectory for patients with infiltrative glioma and medulloblastoma tumors. In 1980, just eight years after starting my faculty position at UCSF, I wrote a paper, "Heuristic modeling of drug delivery to malignant brain tumors," that summarized everything I and two biomath-ematician colleagues, Herb Landahl and Cliff Patlak, knew at the time about the regional movement of standard molecules and anticancer drugs into brain and tumors. Internalizing this paper, I became more and more convinced that the cytotoxic drugs I was investigating in the laboratory and in clinical trials, were not going to cure or even control most CNS tumors any better going forward than they were at the time I wrote the paper. While the statement is still accurate in the global sense, the enormous increase in molecular-genetic research over the past two decades has defined subsets of patients who do very well with simple alkylating agent therapie;

for instance, overall survival is much better for subsets of glioma patients whose tumors demonstrate IDH1/2 mutations.

—ന്ന—

Shortly after publishing that 1980 manuscript, I gave up much of my research on drug regional pharmacokinetics and CNS tumor pharmacology. I still saw patients and conducted clinical trials, but my laboratory research floundered for a while until I started to see the possibility of new generations of drugs targeting specific protein tyrosine kinase signaling pathways in cancer cells. To that end, I brought together a group of scientists from the UCSF School of Medicine and School of Pharmacy as well as UC Berkeley to advance this new drug discovery approach. At the same time, the National Cancer Institute announced a new grant program to create new anticancer agents, the National Cooperative Drug Discovery Group (NCDDG) grant (Chapter 18). We were among the first to make application for this new drug discovery program and the first NCDDG approved for funding in 1983. At the time, we all thought we were on the path to changing the course of cancer treatment. We had proposed and believed we could make a peptide-based drug to bind and inactivate the catalytic site of c-Src and attain high specificity for the drugs we envisioned making. We were confident that we would be successful, and our research template could be adapted to other protein tyrosine kinases in cancer cells and the control of cancer, including CNS cancers, would be possible.

As I discussed before, one of the reasons I moved to the MDACC in 1988 and accepted the chairmanship of the Department of Neuro-Oncology was to be in a better position to expand the NCDDG research program. While my decision to move to the MDACC was admirable as it was driven by my altruism to move my family from Mill Valley (California) to Houston (Texas) and put my academic career at risk to create a new family of anticancer drugs, sometimes even well-designed research endeavors do not provide the answers you would like or answers that allow progress to be made. Earlier in my career I had also learned that sometimes good research provides answers that explain why things fail. I found this to be the case after many years studying cytotoxic drugs that worked through alkylating DNA. Unfortunately, this was also the case with our NCDDG research to develop a catalytic inhibitor of c-Src. After ten years of research to develop specific and selective inhibitors of the c-Src tyrosine kinase catalytic domain, the game-changing drug approach we advocated no longer seemed possible as we discovered that the catalytic site required a cyclic peptide to block its enzymatic function. Since cyclic peptides are not three-dimensionally stable and could not be equipped with a reactive chemical warhead in the manner we had hoped, our goal to create a unique specific drug to inhibit the catalytic site of the c-Src protein tyrosine kinase was no longer tenable. Poignantly, John McMurray, the scientist who made this discovery of the cyclic peptide substrate of the PTK of c-Src in 1993, died in 2011 of a glioblastoma, one of the tumors we hoped our new tyrosine kinase inhibitor drugs would treat.

After digesting this research setback, our tyrosine kinase re-search group did not give up on making new drug inhibitors of Src, but we adapted and hoped to achieve a partial success in our quest for specific protein tyrosine kinase inhibitors through inhibition of the ATPase enzyme site instead of the catalytic site. For the ensuing seven years we developed combinatorial chemistry and robotic synthesis in our labs at the MDACC. Nearing the end of our third 5-year NCDDG grant renewal, I realized that the only way to expand our drug synthesis program was to partner with another company or create a new pharmaceutical drug discovery and devel-opment company. After meeting with large and small pharma-ceutical companies on the East and West Coasts, it appeared that we had no option but start our own drug discovery company so

Raymond Budde, PhD, and I to co-found SIGNASE (named to reflect SIGnaling and kinASE) in Houston in 2000. Unfortunately, the company faltered over the years and failed to recruit an outside CEO and obtain second round venture capital funding before closing its doors in 2004. I sometimes wonder if part of the reason for the SIGNASE failure was the fact that I never took an administrative position in the company and Ray, who had a PhD in plant biochemistry was too inexperienced to lead the company forward without a good deal of administrative and research help.

Prior to creating SIGNASE, I remained the Chair of the Department of Neuro-Oncoogy at the MDACC and Co-Director of the Brain Tumor Center. I am very proud of my contributions to the department and the Brain Tumor Center program and my accomplishments during my tenure that led to many important and lasting contributions to MDACC programs and the thousands of patients with CNS neoplasms we treated. We created one of the first and, undoubtedly the largest truly multidisciplinary neuro-oncology program in the country. In addition, our program was enthusiastically copied by numerous other tumor-specific clinical programs at the MDACC and, in that process, made their tumor-specific clinics better. Under my leadership, our department was the nidus for neuropsychology, psychiatry, pain management, palliative care, and physiatry for the entire hospital. I created these sections within the department out of necessity to fill voids in the hospital and improve patient care. I fully expected that some of these sections would grow and become free-standing departments over time. I was very gratified that after my 1997 "retirement" as Chair of the Department four new departments were created from my Neuro-Oncology Department - the Department of Psychiatry, Department of Symptom Research, Department of Pain Medicine, and Department of Palliative Care, Rehabilitation, and Integrative Medicine.

Between 1997 and 2004 I suffered through the failure of SIGNASE and the loss of my chairmanship of the Department of

Neuro-Oncology. Recounting this period of my academic life for this book did not soften the scale of change in my life. My resilence was tested, but with suppoprt of family and friends I was able to remain optimistic and would not allow my world to crumble around me. I found other paths for new clinical and laboratory research that I found gratifying and hoped would be important for the field of neuro-oncology. Fortunately, during this time, I was also continuing laboratory and clinical research on a drug originally developed to treat sleeping sickness (trypanosomiasis brucei) called eflornithine (DFMO, α-difluoromethylornithine).

Eflornithine is an irreversible inhibitor of the enzyme, ornithine decarboxylase, and by inactivating the enzyme interrupts the synthesis of putrescine, the first polyamine in a series of three poly-amines. Polyamines are polycations and believed to be critical to the normal function of DNA. This line of research started in 1974 when I was invited to participate in polyamine research with Larry Marton, a colleague in the UCSF Brain Tumor Research Center. Within a couple of years, I was also studying the pharmacokinetics and regional biodistribution of eflornithine in brain and rodent tumors and, eventually, even in the ventricular system of beagle dogs. In total, I have conducted laboratory or clinical research with eflornithine for the past 45 years (Chapters 12, 13, 27).

Even with the ups and downs of eflornithine research over those years, I remained optimistic that eflornithine, in combination with other anticancer and signaling drugs, would find a place in the clinical anticancer armamentarium and continued my studies of the drug. After my long career in neuro-oncology, it finally appears that the tenacity of my effort and pragmatic optimism may bear fruit and may lead to eflornithine becoming the first new drug approved for the treatment of infiltrative high-grade gliomas in decades and the first drug that does not alkylate DNA as do the other drugs we use in the clinic.

Today, Orbus Therapeutics, a company co-founded in 2012 by my son, Jason Levin, and his friend and colleague, Bob Myers, is engaged in the pivotal study of eflornithine and lomustine versus single agent lomustine for recurrent/progressive anaplastic astrocytoma in eight countries in the hope of gaining approval from the FDA and the EMA (Chapter 27). At the time of this writing, I remain on edge waiting for the study to be completed and to produce the result I hope for based on my clinical experience with eflornithine. At 80 years of age, the approval of eflornithine for the treatment of anaplastic astrocytomas would be a great way to celebrate the end of my career path. So, fingers crossed.

—⁂—

"I have learnt that Life is not about the walk that we have taken
but the company, the experiences we have gathered.
I have learnt that in each and every unknown path of our journey
we get to know more of our own selves."

— Debatrayee Banerjee, author of *Whispering Leaf*

Many of us would agree with the Banerjee quote as it reflects an interpretation of the journey many of us are privileged to take in our life. I brought many people along with me on my journey, driven by a vision and passion for what I was doing. Looking back on my academic and consulting career it is interesting that what stands out to me now is not the accomplishment of attaining a laboratory or clinical research goal or a paper that was published; it is more about the people that worked with me in the laboratory and on the clinical trials as well my patients and those that shared my vision and helped me create programs, grants, academic departments, and the Society for Neuro-Oncology. On this journey I tried to support and help people I led on my life's path and career to achieve their full potential. I hold on dearly to the belief that the fun of that journey was being able to work with interesting and committed people from many walks of life and inclination.

The path, while fulfilling has not always been easy to traverse or navigate. I sometimes think being transparent and straight-forward caused problems on this journey. Some took my enthusiasm as being "too straightforward" and "in your face" for comfort. Being a "what you see is what you get guy" led to problems over the years, especially with new colleagues and trainees. To those who did not know me well, force of words and thoughts were sometimes interpreted as demeaning and repelling challenge. That has never been the intention. I always felt the force of a position provides clarity of ideas, but never intended my words to serve as the end of a conversation. I appreciate a discussion of ideas instead of a too quick acceptance of an idea. I learned at a very early age that I was not always right and have always appreciated alternative concepts and positions when they lead to a better outcome.

Another attribute that has sometimes caused problems when working with groups has been my lack of patience and a desire to move ahead quickly. If a discussion or meeting was not making any progress, I would be one of the first to suggest moving on or stopping the discussion. If I saw a solution, typically I acted on it quickly or encouraged someone else to do so. Some people I worked with did not like me making decisions so quickly as they worked more comfortably with slow deliberate processes that they could control rather than decisive actions that I initiated.

—⁂—

In this memoir, I tell my story and the experiences that guided me on my medical and scientific path in neuro-oncology. I am proud of much of what I have done and at the same time disappointed I could not have done more. I have also come to grips with the attributes that helped me on my path as well as those that might have hindered me, as a well as external forces that interrupted my path. In the end, this is a book about a boy who became a man, husband, physician, scientist, father, professor, and one who took a path in life to change the trajectory of a narrow group of cancers that affect the central nervous system. The career path I took along with my life partner, Ellen, followed a path and outcomes we could never imagine when we started on this journey together. Though it was a path laden with obstacles of the mind and the spirit, I never left the path or lost hope that one day it would end well. This was my very personal path that I hoped, if successful, would help many more patients than I could treat in a lifetime as a physician. It was also my way of leaving a legacy attesting to the fact that I walked and labored on this Earth to make it a better place.

Photos

Victor on his tricycle outside or Brownwood, Texas house in about 1943 and at the time of his second birthday party.

Victor in Explorer Scout uniform in 1957 with his awards.

Victor (second from left) in group photo of summer neurology and neurosurgery clerks at the National Hospital for Neurological Diseases, Queen Square, London in 1965.

Massachusetts General Hospital Department of Neurology 1970 group photo. Victor is in the third row and fourth from the right

Family in Framingham in 1971 during residency

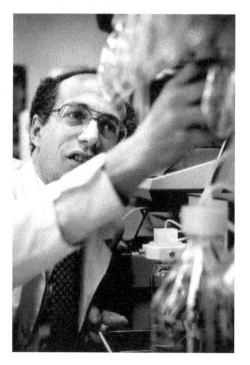
Victor running samples
on his high-pressure
liquid chromatography
machine in 1974
at UCSF.

Asilomar Brain Tumor Research and Treatment Conference in 1975 that was held at the Asilomar Conference in Monterey California. I am kneeling and fifth from the right in the first row and Charlie Wilson is standing in the third row just to the left of me.

265

Victor listening to a question after giving his first European talk in 1977 at a brain tumor meeting on the Gardone Riviera of Lake Garda, Italy

Victor in his UCSF laboratory in early 1980s, looking quite serious, typing into his Tektronix terminal with Data General minicomputer behind him.

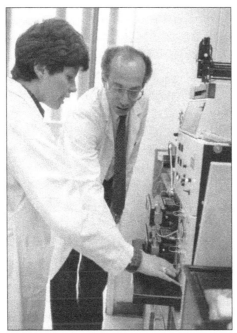

Ellen and Vicor considering which column to use for a high-pressure liquld chromatography (HPLC) assay at UCSF in 1981

Victor and Yukitaka Ushio touring in Osaka, May 1981

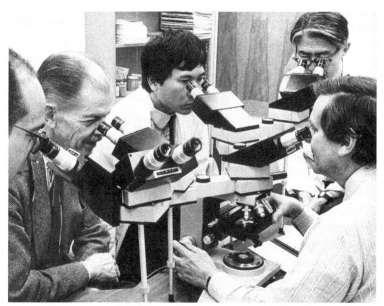

UCSF neuropath viewing of tumors about 1982. Left to right: Victor, Edwin Boldrey, Surasak Phuphanich, Takao Hoshino, and Richard Davis, our neuropathologist at the time.

Hiroshi Abe, Takao Hoshino, and Victor at the Levin Family Mill Valley home for a 1983 BTRC party

Ellen, Victor, and Yukitaka Ushio in front of the Miyajima shrine after the 3rd Japan Society for Neuro-Oncology annual meeting held at Mt. Rokko in 1984

Professor Herb Landahl and Victor at UCSF in 1987

1987 International Brain Tumor Research and Treatment Conference in Hakone, Japan (left to right: Nicolas de Tribolet, Victor, Masakatsu Nagai, Yukitaka Ushio, Masao Matsutani)

Jason, Ellen, Victor, Lisa, and Tera family photo at 4 Midhill Home in Mill Valley in 1984

Family (Victor, Ellen, Jason, and Lisa) photo in 1988 at UCSF going away party.

Jerzy Hilderbrand and Victor walking down the Matterhorn during a break from the Eighth International Conference on Brain Tumor Research and Therapy, held in Zermatt in 1989.

Ellen and Victor in back of Houston home
in 1990

Victor's surprise 50th birthday celebration organized by members
of the Department of Neuro-Oncology (MDACC) in 1991. Maryjo
Gleason, our senior research nurse, showing the pinata she made
in my image

Ellen at Victor's 50th birthday celebration at the MD Anderson

MDACC Division of Medicine 1993 retirement dinner for Irv Krakoff surrounded by some department chairs (lower row: Gabe Hortybogi, Irv Krakoff, Ki Hong; upper row: Al Deisseroth, Victor Levin, Martin Raber)

Goodbye dinner for Hideyuki Saya with MDACC lab colleagues Sadhan
Majumder, John McMurray, Gary Gallick, Ellen, Victor and Hideyuki
in 1995

Victor & Don Herzog on the 1995 Oregon Bike Ride from
Baker City to Reedsport

275

Casual post-dinner evening of the 16th Japanese Society for Neuro-Oncology meeting in 1997 at Mount Aso in Kumamoto, Japan with colleagues and their wives

Dennis Deen, Mitch Berger, and Victor at a reception during the 16th International Brain Tumor Research and Treatment Conference of 2001 in Napa, California.

Victor and Bill Shapiro were guests at the first meeting of the Asian
Society of Neuro-Oncology, Kumamoto, Japan, in 2002

Dinner at First Asian Society of Neuro-Oncology (ASNO) Meeting in
2002. Left to right: Hideyuki Saya, Toru Hayakawa, Kil Soo Choi, Victor,
Keiji Sano, William Shapiro, Yukitaka Ushio, Kintomo Takakura,
Masakatsu Nagai

Ed Shaw, President of SNO, giving Victor the SNO Gold Medal at the
Annual Meeting in 2002

Linda Greer and Victor at 2006 SNO Annual Meeting

Victor, Mitch Berger, and Ed Shaw, SNO Foundation members, in 2006

Lind Greer, Jan Esenwein, and Chas Haynes SNO Annual Meeting picture in 2006

My MDACC lab team Jacob Jochec, BS, Sonali Panchabhai, MBBS, and
Yoshinori Kajiwara, MD in our lab in 2007

Victor and Susan Chang presenting Charlie Wilson with the
SNO Lifetime Achievement Award in 2008

Victor, Jim Rutka, and Mike Prados at Japan meeting in 2008

Victor, Masao Matsutani, and Yukitaka Ushio at 2008 meeting in Japan

Jan Esenwein, Victor, and Chas Haynes at World Federation of Neuro-Oncology meeting in 2009

Laurel Westcarth, Victor, and Tara Alexander in MDACC Clinic in 2009

Vinay Puduvalli, Sujit Prabhu, and Victor in MDACC clinic in 2009

Fred Lang, Jr with Victor in MDACC Neuro-Oncology clinic in 2009

Victor with Mark Gilbert in MDACC Neuro-Oncology clinic in 2009

Victor, Geline Tamayo, Chuck Conrad, and Laurel Westcarth in MDACC
Neuro-Oncology clinic in 2009

Hideyuki Saya and Yukitaka Ushio at Victor's 2009 retirement day at MDACC

Victor making presentation to Hideyuki Saya for his special lecture in honor of 2009 MDACC retirement

Speakers at Victor's Retirement Dinner Party at the Petroleum Club of Houston. Top left to bottom: Alfred Yung and Yukitaka Ushio, Ki Hong, William Shapiro, Alexandra Flowers, Raymond Sawaya, Jun Uhm, Norman Leeds, Lauren Langford, John Mendelsohn, Jason Levin, George Bobustuc, and Yvonne Kew

Lauren Langford presenting Victor with the TIME magazine cover she made for his 2009 MD Anderson retirement party

Joking with Morris Groves at 2009 MDACC retirement party

Family and friends group picture at 2009 retirement day celebration
at MDACC

Department of Neuro-Oncology group photo at Victor's
2009 retirement party

References

References by Chapter

CHAPTER 5

1. Ausman JI, Shapiro WR, and Rall DP. Studies on the chemotherapy of experimental brain tumors: development of an experimental model. *Cancer Res.* 1970;30(9):2394-400.

2. Shapiro WR. Further studies on chemotherapy of experimental brain tumors. *Neurology.* 1970;20(4):390-1.

3. Shapiro WR, Ausman JI, and Rall DP. Studies on the chemotherapy of experimental brain tumors: evaluation of 1,3-bis(2-chloroethyl)-l-nitrosourea, cyclophosphamide, mithramycin, and methotrexate. *Cancer Res.* 1970;30(9):2401-13.

4. Levin VA, Clancy TP, and Ausman JI. Methotrexate permeability and steady-state distribution in the murine ependymoblastoma. *Trans Am Neurol Assoc.* 1969;94:294-6.

5. Levin VA, Shapiro WR, Clancy TP, and Oliverio VT. The uptake, distribution, and antitumor activity of 1-(2-chloroethyl)-3-cyclohexyl-1-nitrosourea in the murine glioma. *Cancer Res.* 1970;30(10):2451-5.

6. Levin VA, Chadwick M, and Little AD. Distribution of 5-fluorouracil-2-14C and its metabolites in a murine glioma. *J Natl Cancer Inst.* 1972;49(6):1577-84.

7. Levin VA, Clancy TP, Ausman JI, and Rall DP. Uptake and distribution of 3 H-methotrexate by the murine ependymoblastoma. *J Natl Cancer Inst.* 1972;48(4):875-83.

8. Levin VA, and Ausman JI. Relationship of peripheral venous hematocrit to brain hematocrit. *Journal of Applied Physiology.* 1969;26(4):433-7.

9. Ausman JI, Levin VA, Brown WE, Rall DP, and Fenstermacher JD. Brain-tumor chemotherapy. Pharmacological principles derived from a monkey brain-tumor model. *J Neurosurg.* 1977;46(2):155-64.

10. Fenstermacher JD, Li CL, and Levin VA. Extracellular space of the cerebral cortex of normothermic and hypothermic cats. *Exp Neurol.* 1970;27(1):101-14.

11. Fenstermacher JD, Rall DP, Patlak CS, and Levin VA. *Capillary Permeability*. Munksgard, Copenhagen; 1970:483-90.

12. Levin VA, Fenstermacher JD, and Patlak CS. Sucrose and inulin space measurements of cerebral cortex in four mammalian species. *Am J Physiol.* 1970;219(5):1528-33.

CHAPTER 6
1. Ransohoff J, Martin BF, Medrek TJ, Harris MN, Golomb FM, and Wright JC. Preliminary clinical study of mithramycin (nsc-24559) in primary tumors of the central nervous system. *Cancer Chemother Rep.* 1965;49:51-7.
2. Walker MD, Alexander E, Jr., Hunt WE, Leventhal CM, Mahaley MS, Jr., Mealey J, et al. Evaluation of mithramycin in the treatment of anaplastic gliomas. *J Neurosurg.* 1976;44(6):655-67.
3. Walker MD, Green SB, Byar DP, Alexander E, Jr., Batzdorf U, Brooks WH, et al. Randomized comparisons of radiotherapy and nitrosoureas for the treatment of malignant glioma after surgery. *N Engl J Med.* 1980;303(23):1323-9.

CHAPTER 7
1. Fenstermacher JD, Li CL, and Levin VA. Extracellular space of the cerebral cortex of normothermic and hypothermic cats. *Exp Neurol.* 1970;27(1):101-14.
2. Fenstermacher JD, Rall DP, Patlak CS, and Levin VA. *Capillary Permeability.* Munksgard, Copenhagen; 1970:483-90.
3. Levin VA, Fenstermacher JD, and Patlak CS. Sucrose and inulin space measurements of cerebral cortex in four mammalian species. *Am J Physiol.* 1970;219(5):1528-33.
4. Levin VA, Shapiro WR, Clancy TP, and Oliverio VT. The uptake, distribution, and antitumor activity of 1-(2-chloroethyl)-3-cyclohexyl-1-nitrosourea in the murine glioma. *Cancer Res.* 1970;30(10):2451-5.
5. Levin VA, Chadwick M, and Little AD. Distribution of 5-fluorouracil-2-14C and its metabolites in a murine glioma. *J Natl Cancer Inst.* 1972;49(6):1577-84.
6. Levin VA, Clancy TP, Ausman JI, and Rall DP. Uptake and distribution of 3 H-methotrexate by the murine ependymoblastoma. *J Natl Cancer Inst.* 1972;48(4):875-83.
7. Levin VA, Milhorat TH, Fenstermacher JD, Hammock MK, and Rall DP. Physiological studies on the development of obstructive hydrocephalus in the monkey. *Neurology.* 1971;21(3):238-46.
8. Milhorat TH, Hammock MK, Fenstermacher JD, and Levin VA. Cerebrospinal fluid production by the choroid plexus and brain. *Science.* 1971;173(3994):330-2.

9. Levin V, and Patlak CS. A compartmental analysis of 24 Na kinetics in rat cerebrum, sciatic nerve and cerebrospinal fluid. J Physiol. 1972;224(3):559-81.

10. Levin VA, and Ausman JI. Relationship of peripheral venous hematocrit to brain hematocrit. *Journal of Applied Physiology.* 1969;26(4):433-7.

11. Levin VA, Chelmicka-Szorc E, and Arnason BG. Peripheral nerve segmental demyelination induced by intraneural diphtheria toxin injection. Sodium Na 24 and carbon 14-labeled inulin kinetics in diphtheria toxin-injected nerve and the effect of hydrocortisone. *Arch Neurol.* 1974;30(2):163-8.

CHAPTER 9

1. Levin VA, and Kabra P. Effectiveness of the nitrosoureas as a function of their lipid solubility in the chemotherapy of experimental rat brain tumors. *Cancer Chemother Rep.* 1974;58(6):787-92.

2. Tel E, Barker M, Levin VA, and Wilson CB. Effect of combined surgery and BCNU (NSC-409962) on an animal brain tumor model. *Cancer Chemother Rep.* 1974;58(5 Pt 1):627-31.

3. Gutin PH, Wilson CB, Kumar AR, Boldrey EB, Levin V, Powell M, et al. Phase II study of procarbazine, CCNU, and vincristine combination chemotherapy in the treatment of malignant brain tumors. Cancer. 1975;35(5):1398-404.

4. Levin VA. A pharmacologic basis for brain tumor chemotherapy. *Semin Oncol.* 1975;2(1):57-61.

5. Levin VA, Crafts D, Wilson CB, Kabra P, Hansch C, Boldrey E, et al. Imidazole carboxamides: relationship of lipophilicity to activity against intracerebral murine glioma 26 and preliminary phase II clinical trial of 5-[3,3-bis(2-chloroethyl)-1-triazeno]imidazole-4-carboxamide (NSC-82196) in primary and secondary brain tumors. *Cancer Chemother Rep.* 1975;59(2 Pt 1):327-31.

6. Levin VA, Freeman-Dove M, and Landahl HD. Permeability characteristics of brain adjacent to tumors in rats. *Arch Neurol.* 1975;32(12):785-91.

7. Levin VA, and Wilson CB. Chemotherapy: the agents in current use. *Semin Oncol.* 1975;2(1):63-7.

8. Wheeler KT, Tel N, Williams ME, Sheppard S, Levin VA, and Kabra PM. Factors influencing the survival of rat brain tumor cells after *in vitro* treatment with 1,3-bis(2-chloroethyl)-1-nitrosourea. *Cancer Res.* 1975;35(6):1464-9.

9. Levin VA. Pharmacological principles of brain tumor chemotherapy. Adv Neurol. 1976;15:315-25.

10. Levin VA, Crafts DC, Wilson CB, Schultz MJ, Boldrey EB, Enot KJ, et al. BCNU (NSC-409962) and procarbazine (NSC-77213) treatment for malignant brain tumors. *Cancer Treat Rep.* 1976;60(3):243-9.

11. Levin VA, Freeman-Dove MA, and Maroten CE. Dianhydrogalactitol (NSC-132313): pharmacokinetics in normal and tumor-bearing rat brain and antitumor activity against three intracerebral rodent tumors. *J Natl Cancer Inst.* 1976;56(3):535-9.

12. Levin VA, Landahl HD, and Freeman-Dove MA. The application of brain *capillary permeability* coefficient measurements to pathological conditions and the selection of agents which cross the blood-brain barrier. *J Pharmacokinet Biopharm.* 1976;4(6):499-519.

13. Levin VA, and Wilson CB. Nitrosourea chemotherapy for primary malignant gliomas. *Cancer Treat Rep.* 1976;60(6):719-24.

14. Levin VA, and Wilson CB. In: Fewer D, Wilson CB, and Levin VA eds. Brain Tumor Chemotherapy. Springfiled, IL: Charles C. Thomas; 1976:42-74.

15. Norman D, Enzmann DR, Levin VA, Wilson CB, and Newton TH. Computed tomography in the evaluation of malignant glioma before and after therapy. *Radiology.* 1976;121(1):85-8.

16. Wilson CB, Gutin P, Boldrey EB, Drafts D, Levin VA, and Enot KJ. Single-agent chemotherapy of brain tumors. A five-year review. *Arch Neurol.* 1976;33(11):739-44.

17. Wilson CB, Wheeler K, Levin VA, Rosenblum M, and Barker M. Brain tumor chemotherapy: translation of laboratory experiments into clinical trials. *Trans Am Neurol Assoc.* 1976;101:214-6.

18. Ausman JI, Levin VA, Brown WE, Rall DP, and Fenstermacher JD. Brain-tumor chemotherapy. Pharmacological principles derived from a monkey brain-tumor model. *J Neurosurg.* 1977;46(2):155-64.

19. Hill TC, Hoffer PB, and Levin VA. Comparison of 1- and 2-hr delayed brain scans in patients undergoing chemotherapy for primary brain tumors. *J Nucl Med.* 1977;18(9):877-80.

20. Levin VA, Crafts DC, Norman DM, Hoffer PB, Spire JP, and Wilson CB. Criteria for evaluating patients undergoing chemotherapy for malignant brain tumors. *J Neurosurg.* 1977;47(3):329-35.

21. Crafts DC, Levin VA, Edwards MS, Pischer TL, and Wilson CB. Chemotherapy of recurrent medulloblastoma with combined procarbazine, CCNU, and vincristine. *J Neurosurg.* 1978;49(4):589-92.

22. Enzmann DR, Norman D, Levin V, Wilson C, and Newton TH. Computed tomography in the follow-up of medulloblastomas and ependymomas. *Radiology.* 1978;128(1):57-63.

23. Levin EM, Meyer RB, Jr., and Levin VA. Quantitative high-pressure liquid chromatographic procedure for the determination of plasma and tissue levels of 2,4-diamino-5-(3,4-dichlorophenyl)-6-methylpyrimidine (metoprine) and its application to the measurement of brain *capillary permeability* coefficients. *J Chromatogr.* 1978;156(1):181-7.

24. Levin VA, Hoffman WF, Pischer TL, Seager ML, Boldrey EB, and Wilson CB. BCNU-5-fluorouracil combination therapy for recurrent malignant brain tumors. *Cancer Treat Rep.* 1978;62(12):2071-6.

25. Levin VA, Kabra PA, and Freeman-Dove MA. Relationship of 1,3-bis(2-chloroethyl)-1-nitrosourea (BCNU) and 1-(2-chloroethyl)-3-cyclohexyl-1-nitrosourea (CCNU) pharmacokinetics of uptake, distribution, and tissue/plasma partitioning in rat organs and intracerebral tumors. *Cancer Chemother Pharmacol.* 1978;1(4):233-42.

26. Levin VA, and Wilson CB. Correlations between experimental chemotherapy in the murine glioma and effectiveness of clinical therapy regimens. *Cancer Chemother Pharmacol.* 1978;1(1):41-8.

27. Norman D, Berninger W, Boyd D, Levin VA, and Newton TH. Wiesbaden, West Germany; 1978.

28. Wheeler KT, Levin VA, and Deen DF. The concept of drug dose for *in vitro* studies with chemotherapeutic agents. *Radiat Res.* 1978;76(3):441-58.

29. Edwards MS, Levin VA, and Byrd A. Quantitative observations of the subacute effects of X irradiation on brain capillary permeability: Part II. *Int J Radiat Oncol Biol Phys.* 1979;5(9):1633-5.

30. Edwards MS, Levin VA, Seager ML, Pischer TL, and Wilson CB. Phase II evaluation of thioTEPA for treatment of central nervous system tumors. *Cancer Treat Rep.* 1979;63(8):1419-21.

31. Hoffman WF, Levin VA, and Wilson CB. Evaluation of malignant glioma patients during the postirradiation period. *J Neurosurg.* 1979;50(5):624-8.

32. Levin VA, Edwards MS, and Byrd A. Quantitative observations of the acute effects of X-irradiation on brain capillary permeability: Part I. *Int J Radiat Oncol Biol Phys.* 1979;5(9):1627-31.

33. Levin VA, Stearns J, Byrd A, Finn A, and Weinkam RJ. The effect of phenobarbital pretreatment on the antitumor activity of 1,3-bis(2-chloroethyl)-1-nitrosourea (BCNU), 1-(2-chloroethyl)-3-cyclohexyl-1-nitrosourea (CCNU) and 1-(2-chloroethyl)-3-(2,6-dioxo-3-piperidyl-1-nitrosourea (PCNU), and on the plasma pharmacokinetics and biotransformation of BCNU. *J Pharmacol Exp Ther.* 1979;208(1):1-6.
34. Levin VA, Wilson CB, Davis R, Wara W, Pischer TL, and Irwin L. Preliminary results of a phase III comparison study of BCNU, hydroxyurea and radiation to BCNU and radiation. *Int J Radiat Oncol Biol Phys.* 1979;5(9):1573-6.
35. Levin VA, Wilson CB, Davis R, Wara WM, Pischer TL, and Irwin L. A phase III comparison of BCNU, hydroxyurea, and radiation therapy to BCNU and radiation therapy for treatment of primary malignant gliomas. *J Neurosurg.* 1979;51(4):526-32.
36. Seidenfeld J, Levin VA, Devor WN, and Marton LJ. Kinetics and distribution of tritiated putrescine in the domestic cat. *Eur J Cancer.* 1979;15(11):1319-27.
37. Afra D, Norman D, and Levin VA. Cysts in malignant gliomas. Identification by computerized tomography. *J Neurosurg.* 1980;53(6):821-5.
38. Edwards MS, Levin VA, and Wilson CB. Chemotherapy of pediatric posterior fossa tumors. *Childs Brain.* 1980;7(5):252-60.
39. Edwards MS, Levin VA, and Wilson CB. Brain tumor chemotherapy: an evaluation of agents in current use for phase II and III trials. *Cancer Treat Rep.* 1980;64(12):1179-205.
40. Levin VA. Relationship of octanol/water partition coefficient and molecular weight to rat brain capillary permeability. *J Med Chem.* 1980;23(6):682-4.
41. Levin VA, and Edwards MS. In: Thomas DGT, and Grahan DI eds. *Brain Tumours.* Londaon: Butterworth; 1980:344-57.
42. Levin VA, Edwards MS, Wright DC, Seager ML, Schimberg TP, Townsend JJ, et al. Modified procarbazine, CCNU, and vincristine (PCV 3) combination chemotherapy in the treatment of malignant brain tumors. *Cancer Treat Rep.* 1980;64(2-3):237-44.
43. Levin VA, Hoffman WF, Heilbron DC, and Norman D. Prognostic significance of the pretreatment CT scan on time to progression for patients with malignant gliomas. *J Neurosurg.* 1980;52(5):642-7.

44. Levin VA, Patlak CS, and Landahl HD. Heuristic modeling of drug delivery to malignant brain tumors. *J Pharmacokinet Biopharm.* 1980;8(3):257-96.

45. Levin VA, Wright DC, Landahl HD, Patlak CS, and Csejtey J. *In situ* drug delivery. *Br J Cancer Suppl.* 1980;4:74-8.

46. Weinkam RJ, Finn A, Levin VA, and Kane JP. Lipophilic drugs and lipoproteins: partitioning effects on chloroethylnitrosourea reaction rates in serum. *J Pharmacol Exp Ther.* 1980;214(2):318-23.

47. Levin VA, Csejtey J, and Byrd DJ. Brain, CSF, and tumor pharmacokinetics of alpha-difluoromethylornithine in rats and dogs. *Cancer Chemother Pharmacol.* 1983;10(3):196-9.

48. Levin VA, Byrd D, Campbell J, Davis RL, and Borcich JK. CNS toxicity and CSF pharmacokinetics of intraventricular DFMO and MGBG in beagle dogs. *Cancer Chemother Pharmacol.* 1984;13(3):200-5.

49. Levin VA, Byrd D, Sikic BI, Etiz BB, Campbell J, Borcich JK, et al. Central nervous system toxicity and cerebrospinal fluid pharmacokinetics of intraventricularly administered bleomycin in beagles. *Cancer Res.* 1985;45(8):3810-5.

50. Levin VA, and Landahl HD. Pharmacokinetic approaches to drug distribution in the cerebrospinal fluid based on ventricular administration in beagle dogs. *J Pharmacokinet Biopharm.* 1985;13(4):387-403.

51. Levin VA, Chamberlain M, Silver P, Rodriguez L, and Prados M. Phase I/II study of intraventricular and intrathecal ACNU for leptomeningeal neoplasia. *Cancer Chemother Pharmacol.* 1989;23(5):301-7.

52. Dorwart RH, Wara WM, Norman D, and Levin VA. Complete myelographic evaluation of spinal metastases from medulloblastoma. *Radiology.* 1981;139(2):403-8.

53. Choucair AK, Levin VA, Gutin PH, Davis RL, Silver P, Edwards MS, et al. Development of multiple lesions during radiation therapy and chemotherapy in patients with gliomas. *J Neurosurg.* 1986;65(5):654-8.

54. Murovic J, Turowski K, Wilson CB, Hoshino T, and Levin V. Computerized tomography in the prognosis of malignant cerebral gliomas. *J Neurosurg.* 1986;65(6):799-806.

55. Chamberlain MC, Murovic JA, and Levin VA. Absence of contrast enhancement on CT brain scans of patients with supratentorial malignant gliomas [published erratum appears in Neurology 1988 Nov;38(11):1816]. *Neurology.* 1988;38(9):1371-4.

56. Valk PE, Budinger TF, Levin VA, Silver P, Gutin PH, and Doyle WK. PET of malignant cerebral tumors after interstitial brachytherapy. Demonstration of metabolic activity and correlation with clinical outcome. *J Neurosurg*. 1988;69(6):830-8.

57. Levin VA, Wara WM, Davis RL, Silver P, Resser KJ, Yatsko K, et al. Northern California Oncology Group protocol 6G91: response to treatment with radiation therapy and seven-drug chemotherapy in patients with glioblastoma multiforme. *Cancer Treat Rep*. 1986;70(6):739-43.

58. Phuphanich S, Levin EM, and Levin VA. Phase I study of intravenous bromodeoxyuridine used concomitantly with radiation therapy in patients with primary malignant brain tumors. *Int J Radiat Oncol Biol Phys*. 1984;10(9):1769-72.

59. Phillips TL, Levin VA, Ahn DK, Gutin PH, Davis RL, Wilson CB, et al. Evaluation of bromodeoxyuridine in glioblastoma multiforme: a Northern California Cancer Center Phase II study. *Int J Radiat Oncol Biol Phys*. 1991;21(3):709-14.

60. Deen DF. San Francisco; 2005.

CHAPTER 10

1. Sixth international conference on brain tumor research and therapy. Asheville, North Carolina, October 20-23, 1985. Abstracts. J Neurooncol. 1986;4(1):91-116.

2. Abstracts for the Eighth International Conference on Brain Tumor Research and Therapy. September 10-13, 1989, Zermatt, Switzerland. J Neurooncol. 1989;7 Suppl:S1-37.

3. Rosenblum ML, and de Tribolet N. Summary of the Eighth International conference on Brain Tumor Research and Therapy. *Neurosurgery*. 1990;26(5):886-7.

4. Deen DF, Chiarodo A, Grimm EA, Fike JR, Israel MA, Kun LE, et al. Brain Tumor Working Group Report on the 9th International Conference on Brain Tumor Research and Therapy. Organ System Program, National Cancer Institute. J Neurooncol. 1993;16(3):243-72.

5. The 10th International Conference on Brain Tumor Research and Therapy. Voss, Norway, September 6-9, 1993. Abstracts. J Neurooncol. 1993;15 Suppl:S1-32.

6. 11th International Conference on Brain Tumor Research and Therapy. Napa, California, October 31-November 3, 1995. Abstracts. J Neurooncol. 1996;28(1):31-113.

7. 12th International Conference on Brain Tumor Research and Therapy. Oxford, United Kingdom, September 20-23, 1997. Abstracts. J Neurooncol. 1997;35 Suppl 1:S5-65.

CHAPTER 11

1. Levin VA, Crafts DC, Norman DM, Hoffer PB, Spire JP, and Wilson CB. Criteria for evaluating patients undergoing chemotherapy for malignant brain tumors. *J Neurosurg.* 1977;47(3):329-35.
2. Hill TC, Hoffer PB, and Levin VA. Comparison of 1- and 2-hr delayed brain scans in patients undergoing chemotherapy for primary brain tumors. *J Nucl Med.* 1977;18(9):877-80.
3. Norman D, Enzmann DR, Levin VA, Wilson CB, and Newton TH. Computed tomography in the evaluation of malignant glioma before and after therapy. *Radiology.* 1976;121(1):85-8.
4. Enzmann DR, Norman D, Levin V, Wilson C, and Newton TH. Computed tomography in the follow-up of medulloblastomas and ependymomas. *Radiology.* 1978;128(1):57-63.
5. Levin VA, Hoffman WF, Heilbron DC, and Norman D. Prognostic significance of the pretreatment CT scan on time to progression for patients with malignant gliomas. *J Neurosurg.* 1980;52(5):642-7.
6. Choucair AK, Levin VA, Gutin PH, Davis RL, Silver P, Edwards MS, et al. Development of multiple lesions during radiation therapy and chemotherapy in patients with gliomas. *J Neurosurg.* 1986;65(5):654-8.
7. Choucair AK, Silver P, and Levin VA. Risk of intracranial hemorrhage in glioma patients receiving anticoagulant therapy for venous thromboembolism. *J Neurosurg.* 1987;66(3):357-8.
8. Hoffman WF, Levin VA, and Wilson CB. Evaluation of malignant glioma patients during the postirradiation period. *J Neurosurg.* 1979;50(5):624-8.
9. Levin VA, Crafts DC, Wilson CB, Schultz MJ, Boldrey EB, Enot KJ, et al. BCNU (NSC-409962) and procarbazine (NSC-77213) treatment for malignant brain tumors. *Cancer Treat Rep.* 1976;60(3):243-9.
10. Levin VA, Hoffman WF, Pischer TL, Seager ML, Boldrey EB, and Wilson CB. BCNU-5-fluorouracil combination therapy for recurrent malignant brain tumors. *Cancer Treat Rep.* 1978;62(12):2071-6.
11. Gutin PH, Wilson CB, Kumar AR, Boldrey EB, Levin V, Powell M, et al. Phase II study of procarbazine, CCNU, and vincristine combination chemotherapy in the treatment of malignant brain tumors. *Cancer.* 1975;35(5):1398-404.

12. Levin VA, Edwards MS, Wright DC, Seager ML, Schimberg TP, Townsend JJ, et al. Modified procarbazine, CCNU, and vincristine (PCV 3) combination chemotherapy in the treatment of malignant brain tumors. *Cancer Treat Rep.* 1980;64(2-3):237-44.

13. Levin VA, Wilson CB, Davis R, Wara W, Pischer TL, and Irwin L. Preliminary results of a phase III comparison study of BCNU, hydroxyurea and radiation to BCNU and radiation. *Int J Radiat Oncol Biol Phys.* 1979;5(9):1573-6.

CHAPTER 12

1. Marton LJ, Heby O, and Wilson CB. Increased polyamine concentrations in the cerebrospinal fluid of patients with brain tumors. *Int J Cancer.* 1974;14(6):731-5.

2. Marton LJ, Heby O, Levin VA, Lubich WP, Crafts DC, and Wilson CB. The relationship of polyamines in cerebrospinal fluid to the presence of central nervous system tumors. *Cancer Res.* 1976;36(3):973-7.

3. Marton LJ, Edwards MS, Levin VA, Lubich WP, and Wilson CB. Predictive value of cerebrospinal fluid polyamines in medulloblastoma. *Cancer Res.* 1979;39(3):993-7.

4. Fulton DS, Levin VA, Lubich WP, Wilson CB, and Marton LJ. Cerebrospinal fluid polyamines in patients with Glioblastoma multiforme and anaplastic astrocytoma. *Cancer Res.* 1980;40(9):3293-6.

5. Seidenfeld J, Deen DF, and Marton LJ. Depletion of intracellular polyamine content does not alter the survival of 9L rat brain tumour cells after X-irradiation. *Int J Radiat Biol Relat Stud Phys Chem Med.* 1980;38(2):223-9.

6. Seidenfeld J, and Marton LJ. Effects of DL-alpha-methylornithine on proliferation and polyamine content of 9L rat brain tumor cells. *Cancer Res.* 1980;40(6):1961-6.

7. Seidenfeld J, Gray JW, and Marton LJ. Depletion of 9L rat brain tumor cell polyamine content by treatment with D,L-alpha-difluoromethylornithine inhibits proliferation and the G1 to S transition. *Exp Cell Res.* 1981;131(1):209-16.

8. Oredsson SM, Deen DF, and Marton LJ. Decreased cytotoxicity of cis-diamminedichloroplatinum(II) by alpha-difluoromethylornithine depletion of polyamines in 9L rat brain tumor cells *in vitro. Cancer Res.* 1982;42(4):1296-9.

9. Tofilon PJ, Oredsson SM, Deen DF, and Marton LJ. Polyamine depletion influences drug-induced chromosomal damage. *Science*. 1982;217(4564):1044-6.

10. Hung DT, Marton LJ, Deen DF, and Shafer RH. Depletion of intracellular polyamines may alter DNA conformation in 9L rat brain tumor cells. *Science*. 1983;221(4608):368-70.

11. Oredsson SM, Deen DF, and Marton LJ. Influence of polyamine depletion caused by alpha- difluoromethylornithine, an enzyme-activated irreversible inhibitor of ornithine decarboxylase, on alkylation- and carbamoylation-induced cytotoxicity in 9L rat brain tumor cells *in vitro*. *Cancer Res*. 1983;43(10):4606-9.

12. Tofilon PJ, Deen DF, and Marton LJ. alpha-Difluoromethylornithine-induced polyamine depletion of 9L tumor cells modifies drug-induced DNA cross-link formation. *Science*. 1983;222(4628):1132-5.

13. Marton LJ, Levin VA, Hervatin SJ, Koch-Weser J, McCann PP, and Sjoerdsma A. Potentiation of the antitumor therapeutic effects of 1,3-bis(2-chloroethyl)-1-nitrosourea by alpha-difluoromethylornithine, an ornithine decarboxylase inhibitor. *Cancer Res*. 1981;41(11 Pt 1):4426-31.

14. Levin VA, Csejtey J, and Byrd DJ. Brain, CSF, and tumor pharmacokinetics of alpha-difluoromethylornithine in rats and dogs. *Cancer Chemother Pharmacol*. 1983;10(3):196-9.

15. Levin VA, Byrd D, Campbell J, Davis RL, and Borcich JK. CNS toxicity and CSF pharmacokinetics of intraventricular DFMO and MGBG in beagle dogs. *Cancer Chemother Pharmacol*. 1984;13(3):200-5.

16. Hoshino T, and Wilson CB. Cell kinetic analyses of human malignant brain tumors (gliomas). *Cancer*. 1979;44(3):956-62.

17. Hoshino T, Townsend JJ, Muraoka I, and Wilson CB. An autoradiographic study of human gliomas: growth kinetics of anaplastic astrocytoma and glioblastoma multiforme. *Brain*. 1980;103(4):967-84.

18. Hoshino T, Nagashima T, Murovic J, Levin EM, Levin VA, and Rupp SM. Cell kinetic studies of *in situ* human brain tumors with bromodeoxyuridine. *Cytometry*. 1985;6(6):627-32.

19. Levin VA, and Wilson CB. Correlations between experimental chemotherapy in the murine glioma and effectiveness of clinical therapy regimens. *Cancer Chemother Pharmacol*. 1978;1(1):41-8.

20. Rosenblum ML, Knebel KD, Vasquez DA, and Wilson CB. In vivo clonogenic tumor cell kinetics following 1,3-bis(2-chloroethyl)-1-nitrosourea brain tumor therapy. *Cancer Res.* 1976;36(10):3718-25.

21. Nomura K, Hoshino T, Knebel K, Deen DF, and Barker M. BCNU-induced perturbations in the cell cycle of 9L rat brain tumor cells. *Cancer Treat Rep.* 1978;62(5):747-54.

22. Hoshino T, Wilson CB, Rosenblum ML, and Barker M. Chemotherapeutic implications of growth fraction and cell cycle time in glioblastomas. *J Neurosurg.* 1975;43(2):127-35.

23. Doyle WK, Budinger TF, Valk PE, Levin VA, and Gutin PH. Differentiation of cerebral radiation necrosis from tumor recurrence by [18F]FDG and 82Rb positron emission tomography. *J Comput Assist Tomogr.* 1987;11(4):563-70.

24. Valk PE, Budinger TF, Levin VA, Silver P, Gutin PH, and Doyle WK. PET of malignant cerebral tumors after interstitial brachytherapy. Demonstration of metabolic activity and correlation with clinical outcome. *J Neurosurg.* 1988;69(6):830-8.

CHAPTER 13

1. Levin VA, Hoffman W, and Weinkam RJ. Pharmacokinetics of BCNU in man: a preliminary study of 20 patients. *Cancer Treat Rep.* 1978;62(9):1305-12.

2. Shiba DA, and Weinkam RJ. Quantitative analysis of procarbazine, procarbazine metabolites and chemical degradation products with application to pharmacokinetic studies. *J Chromatogr.* 1982;229(2):397-407.

3. Shiba DA, and Weinkam RJ. The in vivo cytotoxic activity of Science.procarbazine and procarbazine metabolites against L1210 ascites leukemia cells in CDF1 mice and the effects of pretreatment with procarbazine, phenobarbital, diphenylhydantoin, and methylprednisolone upon in vivo procarbazine activity. *Cancer Chemother Pharmacol.* 1983; 11(2):124-9.

4. Levin VA. Relationship of octanol/water partition coefficient and molecular weight to rat brain capillary permeability. *J Med Chem.* 1980;23(6):682-4.

5. Levin VA, Clancy TP, Ausman JI, and Rall DP. Uptake and distribution of 3 H-methotrexate by the murine ependymoblastoma. *J Natl Cancer Inst.* 1972;48(4):875-83.

6. Levin VA, Chadwick M, and Little AD. Distribution of 5-fluorouracil-2-14C and its metabolites in a murine glioma. *J Natl Cancer Inst.* 1972;49(6):1577-84.

7. Ausman JI, Levin VA, Brown WE, Rall DP, and Fenstermacher JD. Brain-tumor chemotherapy. Pharmacological principles derived from a monkey brain-tumor model. *J Neurosurg.* 1977;46(2):155-64.

8. Edwards MS, Levin VA, and Byrd A. Quantitative observations of the subacute effects of X irradiation on brain capillary permeability: Part II. *Int J Radiat Oncol Biol Phys.* 1979;5(9):1633-5.

9. Levin VA, Edwards MS, and Byrd A. Quantitative observations of the acute effects of X-irradiation on brain capillary permeability: Part I. *Int J Radiat Oncol Biol Phys.* 1979;5(9):1627-31.

10. Prados M, Rodriguez L, Chamberlain M, Silver P, and Levin V. Treatment of recurrent gliomas with 1,3-bis(2-chloroethyl)-1-nitrosourea and alpha-difluoromethylornithine. Neurosurg. 1989;24(6):806-9.

11. Weinkam RJ, and Deen DF. Quantitative dose-response relations for the cytotoxic activity of chloroethylnitrosoureas in cell culture. *Cancer Res.* 1982;42(3):1008-14.

12. Wheeler KT, Levin VA, and Deen DF. The concept of drug dose for *in vitro* studies with chemotherapeutic agents. *Radiat Res.* 1978;76(3):441-58.

13. Hoshino T, Deen DF, Williams ME, and Sano Y. Differential response to elutriated 9L cells to treatment with 1,3-bis(2-chloroethyl)-1-nitrosourea. *Cancer Res.* 1981;41(11 Pt 1):4404-7.

14. Sano Y, Deen DF, and Hoshino T. Factors that influence initiation and growth of 9L rat brain gliosarcoma multicellular spheroids. *Cancer Res.* 1982;42(4):1223-6.

15. Pertuiset BF, Rosenblum ML, Poisson M, Hauw JJ, Deen DF, and Buge A. [Kinetics of multicellular spheroids developed from a human glioblastoma, and effect of 1,3-bis (2-chloroethyl)-1-nitrosourea]. *La semaine des hopitaux : organe fonde par l'Association d'enseignement medical des hopitaux de Paris.* 1983;59(7):468-72.

16. Sano Y, Hoshino T, Bjerkvig R, and Deen DF. The relative resistance of non-cycling cells in 9L multicellular spheroids to spirohydantoin mustard. *Eur J Cancer Clin Oncol.* 1983;19(10):1451-6.

17. Gutin PH, Bernstein M, Sano Y, and Deen DF. Combination therapy with 1,3-bis(2-chloroethyl)-1-nitrosourea and low dose rate radiation in the 9L rat brain tumor and spheroid models: implications for brain tumor brachytherapy. *Neurosurgery.* 1984;15(6):781-6.

18. Sano Y, Deen DF, Oredsson SM, and Marton LJ. Effects of alpha-difluoromethylornithine on the growth of 9L rat brain tumor multicellular spheroids and their response to 1,3-bis(2-chloroethyl)-1-nitrosourea. *Cancer Res.* 1984;44(2):577-81.

19. Sano Y, Hoshino T, Barker M, and Deen DF. Response of 9L rat brain tumor multicellular spheroids to single and fractionated doses of 1,3-bis(2-chloroethyl)-1-nitrosourea. *Cancer Res.* 1984;44(2):571-6.

20. Tofilon PJ, Arundel CM, and Deen DF. Response to BCNU of spheroids grown from mixtures of drug-sensitive and drug-resistant cells. *Cancer Chemother Pharmacol.* 1987;20(2):89-95.

21. Levin VA, Stearns J, Byrd A, Finn A, and Weinkam RJ. The effect of phenobarbital pretreatment on the antitumor activity of 1,3-bis(2-chloroethyl)-1-nitrosourea (BCNU), 1-(2-chloroethyl)-3-cyclohexyl-1-nitrosourea (CCNU) and 1-(2-chloroethyl)-3-(2,6-dioxo-3-piperidyl-1-nitrosourea (PCNU), and on the plasma pharmacokinetics and biotransformation of BCNU. *J Pharmacol Exp Ther.* 1979;208(1):1-6.

22. Levin VA, Resser KJ, McGrath L, Vestnys P, Nutik S, and Wilson CB. PCNU treatment for recurrent malignant gliomas. *Cancer Treat Rep.* 1984;68(7-8):969-73.

23. Levin VA, Crafts D, Wilson CB, Kabra P, Hansch C, Boldrey E, et al. Imidazole carboxamides: relationship of lipophilicity to activity against intracerebral murine glioma 26 and preliminary phase II clinical trial of 5-[3,3-bis(2-chloroethyl)-1-triazeno]imidazole-4-carboxamide (NSC-82196) in primary and secondary brain tumors. *Cancer Chemother Rep.* 1975;59(2 Pt 1):327-31.

24. Stevens MF, and Newlands ES. From triazines and triazenes to temozolomide. *Eur J Cancer.* 1993;29A(7):1045-7.

25. Weinkam RJ, and Shiba DA. Metabolic activation of procarbazine. *Life Sci.* 1978;22(11):937-45.

CHAPTER 14

1. Levin VA, Crafts DC, Wilson CB, Schultz MJ, Boldrey EB, Enot KJ, et al. BCNU (NSC-409962) and procarbazine (NSC-77213) treatment for malignant brain tumors. *Cancer Treat Rep.* 1976;60(3):243-9.

2. Levin VA, Hoffman WF, Heilbron DC, and Norman D. Prognostic significance of the pretreatment CT scan on time to progression for patients with malignant gliomas. *J Neurosurg.* 1980;52(5):642-7.

3. Levin VA, Crafts DC, Norman DM, Hoffer PB, Spire JP, and Wilson CB. Criteria for evaluating patients undergoing chemotherapy for malignant brain tumors. *J Neurosurg*. 1977;47(3):329-35.
4. Levin VA, Wara WM, Davis RL, Silver P, Resser KJ, Yatsko K, et al. Northern California Oncology Group protocol 6G91: response to treatment with radiation therapy and seven-drug chemotherapy in patients with glioblastoma multiforme. *Cancer Treat Rep*. 1986;70(6):739-43.
5. Mulder JH, Smink T, and Van Putten LM. Schedule dependent effectiveness of CCNU and 5-fluorouracil in experimental chemotherapy. *Eur J Cancer*. 1977;13(10):1123-31.
6. Sinclair WK. The combined effect of hydroxyurea and x-rays on Chinese hamster cells *in vitro*. *Cancer Res*. 1968;28(2):198-206.
7. Weiss BG, and Tolmach LJ. Modification of x-ray-induced killing of HeLa S3 cells by inhibitors of DNA synthesis. *Biophys J*. 1967;7(6):779-95.
8. Levin VA, Wilson CB, Davis R, Wara WM, Pischer TL, and Irwin L. A phase III comparison of BCNU, hydroxyurea, and radiation therapy to BCNU and radiation therapy for treatment of primary malignant gliomas. *J Neurosurg*. 1979;51(4):526-32.
9. Urtasun RC, Feldstein ML, and Partington T. Radiation and nitroimidazoles in supratentorial high grade gliomas: A second clinical trial. *Br J Cancer*. 1982;46:101-8.
10. Urtasun RC, Band PR, Chapman JD, and Feldstein ML. Radiation plus metronidazole for glioblastoma. *N Engl J Med*. 1977;296(13):757.
11. Kumar VAR, Renaudin J, Wilson CB, Boldrey EB, Enot KJ, and Levin VA. Procarbazine hydrochloride in the treatment of brain tumors. Phase 2 study. *J Neurosurg*. 1974;40(3):365-71.
12. Levin VA, Edwards MS, Wright DC, Seager ML, Schimberg TP, Townsend JJ, et al. Modified procarbazine, CCNU, and vincristine (PCV 3) combination chemotherapy in the treatment of malignant brain tumors. *Cancer Treat Rep*. 1980;64(2-3):237-44.
13. Levin VA, Wara WM, Davis RL, Vestnys P, Resser KJ, Yatsko K, et al. Phase III comparison of BCNU and the combination of procarbazine, CCNU, and vincristine administered after radiotherapy with hydroxyurea for malignant gliomas. *J Neurosurg*. 1985;63(2):218-23.
14. Hoshino T, Nagashima T, Murovic J, Levin EM, Levin VA, and Rupp SM. Cell kinetic studies of *in situ* human brain tumors with bromodeoxyuridine. *Cytometry*. 1985;6(6):627-32.

15. Nagashima T, and Hoshino T. Rapid detection of S-phase cells by anti-bromodeoxyuridine monoclonal antibody in 9L brain tumor cells *in vitro* and *in situ*. *Acta Neuropathol (Berl)*. 1985;66(1):12-7.

16. Hoshino T, Nagashima T, Cho KG, Murovic JA, Hodes JE, Wilson CB, et al. S-phase fraction of human brain tumors *in situ* measured by uptake of bromodeoxyuridine. *Int J Cancer*. 1986;38(3):369-74.

17. Hoshino T, Nagashima T, Murovic JA, Wilson CB, Edwards MS, Gutin PH, et al. *In situ* cell kinetics studies on human neuroectodermal tumors with bromodeoxyuridine labeling. *J Neurosurg*. 1986;64(3):453-9.

18. Ho JT, Sarkar A, Kendall LE, Hoshino T, Marton LJ, and Deen DF. Effects of fractionated radiation therapy on human brain tumor multicellular spheroids. *Int J Radiat Oncol Biol Phys*. 1993;25(2):251-8.

19. Sneed PK, Matsumoto K, Stauffer PR, Fike JR, Smith V, and Gutin PH. Interstitial microwave hyperthermia in a canine brain model. *Int J Radiat Oncol Biol Phys*. 1986;12(10):1887-97.

20. Satoh T, Seilhan TM, Stauffer PR, Sneed PK, and Fike JR. Interstitial helical coil microwave antenna for experimental brain hyperthermia. *Neurosurgery*. 1988;23(5):564-9.

21. Satoh T, Stauffer PR, and Fike JR. Thermal distribution studies of helical coil microwave antennas for interstitial hyperthermia. *Int J Radiat Oncol Biol Phys*. 1988;15(5):1209-18.

22. Fike JR, Gobbel GT, Satoh T, and Stauffer PR. Normal brain response after interstitial microwave hyperthermia. *Int J Hyperthermia*. 1991;7(5):795-808.

23. Evans CG, Bodell WJ, Tokuda K, Doane-Setzer P, and Smith MT. Glutathione and related enzymes in rat brain tumor cell resistance to 1,3-bis(2-chloroethyl)-1-nitrosourea and nitrogen mustard. *Cancer Res*. 1987;47(10):2525-30.

24. Smith MT, Evans CG, Doane-Setzer P, Castro VM, Tahir MK, and Mannervik B. Denitrosation of 1,3-bis(2-chloroethyl)-1-nitrosourea by class mu glutathione transferases and its role in cellular resistance in rat brain tumor cells. *Cancer Res*. 1989;49(10):2621-5.

CHAPTER 15

1. Levin VA, and Wheeler KT. Chemotherapeutic approaches to brain tumors. Experimental observations with dianhydrogalactitol and dibromodulcitol. *Cancer Chemother Pharmacol*. 1982;8(1):125-31.

2. Wheeler KT, Levin VA, and Deen DF. The concept of drug dose for *in vitro* studies with chemotherapeutic agents. *Radiat Res.* 1978;76(3):441-58.
3. Wheeler KT, Tel N, Williams ME, Sheppard S, Levin VA, and Kabra PM. Factors influencing the survival of rat brain tumor cells after *in vitro* treatment with 1,3-bis(2-chloroethyl)-1-nitrosourea. *Cancer Res.* 1975;35(6):1464-9.
4. Pulst S-M, Levin VA, and Deen DF. *In vitro* cytotoxic effects of dibromodulcitol in 9L rat brain tumor cells. Pharm Res. 1986;3(5):302-6.
5. Levin EM, Meyer RB, Jr., and Levin VA. Quantitative high-pressure liquid chromatographic procedure for the determination of plasma and tissue levels of 2,4-diamino-5-(3,4-dichlorophenyl)-6-methylpyrimidine (metoprine) and its application to the measurement of brain capillary permeability coefficients. *J Chromatogr.* 1978;156(1):181-7.
6. Bernstein M, Gutin PH, Deen DF, Weaver KA, Levin VA, and Barcellos MH. Radiosensitization of the RIF-1 murine flank tumor by desmethylmisonidazole (Ro 05 9963) during interstitial brachytherapy. *Int J Radiat Oncol Biol Phys.* 1982;8(3-4):487-90.
7. Edwards MS, Bolger CA, Levin VA, Phillips TL, and Jewett DL. Evaluation of misonidazole peripheral neurotoxicity in rats by analysis of nerve trains evoked response. *Int J Radiat Oncol Biol Phys.* 1982;8(1):69-74.
8. Edwards MS, Gordon DG, and Levin VA. Evaluation of desmethylmisonidazole-induced neurotoxicity in the rat using brainstem auditory evoked potentials. *Int J Radiat Oncol Biol Phys.* 1984;10(8):1377-9.
9. Edwards MS, Gordon DG, Levin VA, and Phillips TL. Misonidazole neurotoxicity in rats: Part I. Evaluation of misonidazole neurotoxicity in rats by analysis of brain stem auditory and cortical evoked potentials. J Neurooncol. 1984;2(2):91-4.
10. Edwards MS, Gordon DG, Salamy A, Levin VA, and Phillips TL. Misonidazole neurotoxicity in rats: Part II. Effect of pre- and intermittent treatment with pentobarbital on misonidazole neurotoxicity in the rat. J Neurooncol. 1984;2(2):95-8.
11. Phillips TL, Wasserman TH, Johnson RJ, Levin VA, and VanRaalte G. Final report on the United States Phase I Clinical Trial of the hypoxic cell radiosensitizer, misonidazole (Ro-07-0582; NSC :261037). Cancer. 1981;48(8):1697-704.

12. Wasserman TH, Phillips TL, Johnson RJ, Gomer CJ, Lawrence GA, Sadee W, et al. Initial United States clinical and pharmacologic evaluation of misonidazole (Ro-07-0582), an hypoxic cell radiosensitizer. *Int J Radiat Oncol Biol Phys.* 1979;5(6):775-86.
13. Wara WM, Wallner KE, Levin VA, Liu HC, and Edwards MS. Retreatment of pediatric brain tumors with radiation and misonidazole. Results of a CCSG/RTOG phase I/II study. Cancer. 1986;58(8):1636-40.
14. Levin VA, Edwards MS, Wara WM, Allen J, Ortega J, and Vestnys P. 5-Fluorouracil and 1-(2-chloroethyl)-3-cyclohexyl-1-nitrosourea (CCNU) followed by hydroxyurea, misonidazole, and irradiation for brain stem gliomas: a pilot study of the Brain Tumor Research Center and the Childrens Cancer Group. *Neurosurgery.* 1984;14(6):679-81.
15. Levin VA, Wilson CB, Davis R, Wara W, Pischer TL, and Irwin L. Preliminary results of a phase III comparison study of BCNU, hydroxyurea and radiation to BCNU and radiation. *Int J Radiat Oncol Biol Phys.* 1979;5(9):1573-6.
16. Levin VA, Wilson CB, Davis R, Wara WM, Pischer TL, and Irwin L. A phase III comparison of BCNU, hydroxyurea, and radiation therapy to BCNU and radiation therapy for treatment of primary malignant gliomas. *J Neurosurg.* 1979;51(4):526-32.
17. Levin VA, Wara WM, Davis RL, Vestnys P, Resser KJ, Yatsko K, et al. Phase III comparison of BCNU and the combination of procarbazine, CCNU, and vincristine administered after radiotherapy with hydroxyurea for malignant gliomas. *J Neurosurg.* 1985;63(2):218-23.
18. Levin VA. The place of hydroxyurea in the treatment of primary brain tumors. *Semin Oncol.* 1992;19(3 Suppl 9):34-9.
19. Prados MD, Larson DA, Lamborn K, McDermott MW, Sneed PK, Wara WM, et al. Radiation therapy and hydroxyurea followed by the combination of 6-thioguanine and BCNU for the treatment of primary malignant brain tumors. *Int J Radiat Oncol Biol Phys.* 1998;40(1):57-63.
20. Phuphanich S, Levin EM, and Levin VA. Phase I study of intravenous bromodeoxyuridine used concomitantly with radiation therapy in patients with primary malignant brain tumors. *Int J Radiat Oncol Biol Phys.* 1984;10(9):1769-72.

21. Phillips TL, Levin VA, Ahn DK, Gutin PH, Davis RL, Wilson CB, et al. Evaluation of bromodeoxyuridine in glioblastoma multiforme: a Northern California Cancer Center Phase II study. *Int J Radiat Oncol Biol Phys.* 1991;21(3):709-14.

22. Levin VA, Prados MR, Wara WM, Davis RL, Gutin PH, Phillips TL, et al. Radiation therapy and bromodeoxyuridine chemotherapy followed by procarbazine, lomustine, and vincristine for the treatment of anaplastic gliomas. *Int J Radiat Oncol Biol Phys.* 1995;32(1):75-83.

23. Prados MD, Scott CB, Rotman M, Rubin P, Murray K, Sause W, et al. Influence of bromodeoxyuridine radiosensitization on malignant glioma patient survival: a retrospective comparison of survival data from the Northern California Oncology Group (NCOG) and Radiation Therapy Oncology Group trials (RTOG) for glioblastoma multiforme and anaplastic astrocytoma. *Int J Radiat Oncol Biol Phys.* 1998;40(3):653-9.

24. Groves MD, Maor MH, Meyers C, Kyritsis AP, Jaeckle KA, Yung WK, et al. A phase II trial of high-dose bromodeoxyuridine with accelerated fractionation radiotherapy followed by procarbazine, lomustine, and vincristine for glioblastoma multiforme. *Int J Radiat Oncol Biol Phys.* 1999;45(1):127-35.

25. Levin VA, Maor MH, Thall PF, Yung WK, Bruner J, Sawaya R, et al. Phase II study of accelerated fractionation radiation therapy with carboplatin followed by vincristine chemotherapy for the treatment of glioblastoma multiforme. *Int J Radiat Oncol Biol Phys.* 1995;33(2):357-64.

26. Levin VA, Yung WK, Bruner J, Kyritsis A, Leeds N, Gleason MJ, et al. Phase II study of accelerated fractionation radiation therapy with carboplatin followed by PCV chemotherapy for the treatment of anaplastic gliomas. *Int J Radiat Oncol Biol Phys.* 2002;53(1):58-66.

27. Levin VA, Rodriguez LA, Edwards MS, Wara W, Liu HC, Fulton D, et al. Treatment of medulloblastoma with procarbazine, hydroxyurea, and reduced radiation doses to whole brain and spine. *J Neurosurg.* 1988;68(3):383-7.

28. Stupp R, Hegi ME, Mason WP, van den Bent MJ, Taphoorn MJ, Janzer RC, et al. Effects of radiotherapy with concomitant and adjuvant temozolomide versus radiotherapy alone on survival in glioblastoma in a randomised phase III study: 5-year analysis of the EORTC-NCIC trial. *Lancet Oncol.* 2009;10(5):459-66.

29. Levin VA, Uhm JH, Jaeckle KA, Choucair A, Flynn PJ, Yung WKA, et al. Phase III randomized study of postradiotherapy chemotherapy with alpha-difluoromethylornithine-procarbazine, N-(2-chloroethyl)-N'-cyclohexyl-N-nitrosurea, vincristine (DFMO-PCV) versus PCV for glioblastoma multiforme. *Clin Cancer Res.* 2000;6(10):3878-84.

30. Fu KK, Lam KN, and Rayner PA. The influence of time sequence of cisplatin administration and continuous low dose rate irradiation (CLDRI) on their combined effects on a murine squamous cell carcinoma. *Int J Radiat Oncol Biol Phys.* 1985;11(12):2119-24.

31. Van Tassel P, Bruner JM, Maor MH, Leeds NE, Gleason MJ, Yung WK, et al. MR of toxic effects of accelerated fractionation radiation therapy and carboplatin chemotherapy for malignant gliomas. *AJNR Am J Neuroradiol.* 1995;16(4):715-26.

32. Gonzalez J, Kumar AJ, Conrad CA, and Levin VA. Effect of bevacizumab on radiation necrosis of the brain. *Int J Radiat Oncol Biol Phys.* 2007;67(2):323-6.

33. Levin VA, Bidaut L, Hou P, Kumar AJ, Wefel JS, Bekele BN, et al. Randomized double-blind placebo-controlled trial of bevacizumab therapy for radiation necrosis of the central nervous system. *Int J Radiat Oncol Biol Phys.* 2011;79(5):1487-95.

34. Gutin PH, Phillips TL, Wara WM, Leibel SA, Hosobuchi Y, Levin VA, et al. Brachytherapy of recurrent malignant brain tumors with removable high-activity iodine-125 sources. *J Neurosurg.* 1984;60(1):61-8.

35. Gutin PH, Leibel SA, Wara WM, Choucair A, Levin VA, Philips TL, et al. Recurrent malignant gliomas: survival following interstitial brachytherapy with high-activity iodine-125 sources [published erratum appears in J Neurosurg 1988 Jun;68(6):990]. [Review] [65 refs]. *J Neurosurg.* 1987;67(6):864-73.

36. Gutin PH, Prados MD, Phillips TL, Wara WM, Larson DA, Leibel SA, et al. External irradiation followed by an interstitial high activity iodine-125 implant "boost" in the initial treatment of malignant gliomas: NCOG study 6G-82-2. *Int J Radiat Oncol Biol Phys.* 1991;21(3):601-6.

37. Valk PE, Budinger TF, Levin VA, Silver P, Gutin PH, and Doyle WK. PET of malignant cerebral tumors after interstitial brachytherapy. Demonstration of metabolic activity and correlation with clinical outcome. *J Neurosurg.* 1988;69(6):830-8.

38. Edwards MS, Wara WM, Urtasun RC, Prados M, Levin VA, Fulton D, et al. Hyperfractionated radiation therapy for brain-stem glioma: a phase I-II trial. *J Neurosurg.* 1989;70(5):691-700.

39. Kun LE, and Constine LS. Medulloblastoma-caution regarding new treatment approaches. *Int J Radiat Oncol Biol Phys.* 1991;20:897.
40. Deutsch M, Thomas PR, Krischer J, Boyett JM, Albright L, Aronin P, et al. Results of a prospective randomized trial comparing standard dose neuraxis irradiation (3,600 cGy/20) with reduced neuraxis irradiation (2,340 cGy/13) in patients with low-stage medulloblastoma. A Combined Children's Cancer Group-Pediatric Oncology Group Study. *Pediatr Neurosurg.* 1996;24(4):167-76.

CHAPTER 16
1. Levin VA, Wilson CB, Davis R, Wara W, Pischer TL, and Irwin L. Preliminary results of a phase III comparison study of BCNU, hydroxyurea and radiation to BCNU and radiation. *Int J Radiat Oncol Biol Phys.* 1979;5(9):1573-6.
2. Levin VA, Wilson CB, Davis R, Wara WM, Pischer TL, and Irwin L. A phase III comparison of BCNU, hydroxyurea, and radiation therapy to BCNU and radiation therapy for treatment of primary malignant gliomas. *J Neurosurg.* 1979;51(4):526-32.

CHAPTER 17
1. Levin VA, Crafts DC, Norman DM, Hoffer PB, Spire JP, and Wilson CB. Criteria for evaluating patients undergoing chemotherapy for malignant brain tumors. *J Neurosurg.* 1977;47(3):329-35.
2. Norman D, Enzmann DR, Levin VA, Wilson CB, and Newton TH. Computed tomography in the evaluation of malignant glioma before and after therapy. *Radiology.* 1976;121(1):85-8.
3. Levin VA, Prados MR, Wara WM, Davis RL, Gutin PH, Phillips TL, et al. Radiation therapy and bromodeoxyuridine chemotherapy followed by procarbazine, lomustine, and vincristine for the treatment of anaplastic gliomas. *Int J Radiat Oncol Biol Phys.* 1995;32(1):75-83.
4. Chuba PJ, Aronin P, Bhambhani K, Eichenhorn M, Zamarano L, Cianci P, et al. Hyperbaric oxygen therapy for radiation-induced brain injury in children. *Cancer.* 1997;80(10):2005-12.
5. Hart GB, and Mainous EG. The treatment of radiation necrosis with hyperbaric oxygen (OHP). *Cancer.* 1976;37(6):2580-5.
6. Kohshi K, Imada H, Nomoto S, Yamaguchi R, Abe H, and Yamamoto H. Successful treatment of radiation-induced brain necrosis by hyperbaric oxygen therapy. *J Neurol Sci.* 2003;209(1-2):115-7.

7. Leber KA, Eder HG, Kovac H, Anegg U, and Pendl G. Treatment of cerebral radionecrosis by hyperbaric oxygen therapy. *Stereotact Funct Neurosurg.* 1998;70 Suppl 1:229-36.
8. Levin VA, Leibel SA, and Gutin PH. In: DeVita VT, Hellman S, and Rosenberg SA eds. *Cancer, principles & practice of oncology.* Philadelphia, PA: Lippincott Williams & Wilkins; 2001:2100-60.
9. Glantz MJ, Burger PC, Friedman AH, Radtke RA, Massey EW, and Schold SC, Jr. Treatment of radiation-induced nervous system injury with heparin and warfarin. *Neurology.* 1994;44(11):2020-7.
10. Khan RB, Krasin MJ, Kasow K, and Leung W. Cyclooxygenase-2 Inhibition to Treat Radiation-Induced Brain Necrosis and Edema. *Journal of Pediatric Hematology/Oncology.* 2004;26(4):253-5.
11. Wu J, and Levin VA. In: Chen TC ed. *Controversies in Neuro-Oncology.* Bentham 2010:117-26.
12. Gonzalez J, Kumar AJ, Conrad CA, and Levin VA. Effect of bevacizumab on radiation necrosis of the brain. *Int J Radiat Oncol Biol Phys.* 2007;67(2):323-6.
13. Levin VA, Bidaut L, Hou P, Kumar AJ, Wefel JS, Bekele BN, et al. Randomized double-blind placebo-controlled trial of bevacizumab therapy for radiation necrosis of the central nervous system. *Int J Radiat Oncol Biol Phys.* 2011;79(5):1487-95.

CHAPTER 18

1. Levin VA, Patlak CS, and Landahl HD. Heuristic modeling of drug delivery to malignant brain tumors. *J Pharmacokinet Biopharm.* 1980;8(3):257-96.

CHAPTER 20

1. Meyers CA, Weitzner MA, Valentine AD, and Levin VA. Methylphenidate therapy improves cognition, mood, and function of brain tumor patients. *J Clin Oncol.* 1998;16(7):2522-7.
2. Weitzner MA, and Meyers CA. Cognitive functioning and quality of life in malignant glioma patients: a review of the literature. *Psychooncology.* 1997;6(3):169-77.
3. Weitzner MA, Meyers CA, and Valentine AD. Methylphenidate in the treatment of neurobehavioral slowing associated with cancer and cancer treatment. *J Neuropsychiatry Clin Neurosci.* 1995;7(3):347-50.

CHAPTER 23

1. Levin VA, Jochec JL, Shantz LM, Koch PE, and Pegg AE. Tissue-based assay for ornithine decarboxylase to identify patients likely to respond to difluoromethylornithine. *J Histochem Cytochem.* 2004;52(11):1467-74.
2. Levin VA, Jochec JL, Shantz LM, and Aldape KD. Relationship between ornithine decarboxylase levels in anaplastic gliomas and progression-free survival in patients treated with DFMO-PCV chemotherapy. *Int J Cancer.* 2007;121(10):2279-83.
3. Levin VA, Ictech SE, and Hess KR. Clinical importance of eflornithine (alpha-difluoromethylornithine) for the treatment of malignant gliomas. *CNS Oncol.* 2018;7(2):CNS16.
4. Kajiwara Y, Panchabhai S, and Levin VA. A new preclinical 3-dimensional agarose colony formation assay. *Technol Cancer Res Treat.* 2008;7(4):329-34.
5. Kajiwara Y, Panchabhai S, Liu DD, Kong M, Lee JJ, and Levin VA. Melding a New 3-Dimensional Agarose Colony Assay with the E(max) Model to Determine the Effects of Drug Combinations on Cancer Cells. *Technol Cancer Res Treat.* 2009;8(2):163-76.
6. Levin VA, Panchabhai SC, Shen L, Kornblau SM, Qiu Y, and Baggerly KA. Different changes in protein and phosphoprotein levels result from serum starvation of high-grade glioma and adenocarcinoma cell lines. *J Proteome Res.* 2010;9(1):179-91.

CHAPTER 26

1. Siimes M, Seppanen P, Alhonen-Hongisto L, and Janne J. Synergistic action of two polyamine antimetabolites leads to a rapid therapeutic response in childhood leukemia. *Int J Cancer.* 1981;28(5):567-70.
2. Gastaut JA, Tell G, Schechter PJ, Maraninchi D, Mascret B, and Carcassonne Y. Treatment of acute myeloid leukemia and blastic phase of chronic myeloid leukemia with combined eflornithine (alpha difluoromethylornithine) and methylglyoxal-bis-guanyl hydrazone (methyl-GAG). *Cancer Chemother Pharmacol.* 1987;20(4):344-8.
3. Meyskens FL, Kingsley EM, Glattke T, Loescher L, and Booth A. A phase II study of alpha-difluoromethylornithine (DFMO) for the treatment of metastatic melanoma. *Invest New Drugs.* 1986;4(3):257-62.
4. Talpaz M, Plager C, Quesada J, Benjamin R, Kantarjian H, and Gutterman J. Difluoromethylornithine and leukocyte interferon: a phase I study in cancer patients. *Eur J Cancer Clin Oncol.* 1986;22(6):685-9.

5. Croghan MK, Booth A, and Meyskens FL, Jr. A phase I trial of recombinant interferon-alpha and alpha-difluoromethylornithine in metastatic melanoma. *J Biol Response Mod.* 1988;7(4):409-15.
6. Mitchell MF, Tortolero-Luna G, Lee JJ, Hittelman WN, Lotan R, Wharton JT, et al. Phase I dose de-escalation trial of alpha-difluoromethylornithine in patients with grade 3 cervical intraepithelial neoplasia. *Clin Cancer Res.* 1998;4(2):303-10.

CHAPTER 27
1. Levin VA, Chamberlain MC, Prados MD, et al. Phase I-II study of eflornithine and mitoguazone combined in the treatment of recurrent primary brain tumors. *Cancer Treat Rep.* 1987; 71(5):459-464.
2. Levin VA, Ictech SE, Hess KR. Clinical importance of eflornithine (alpha-difluoromethylornithine) for the treatment of malignant gliomas. *CNS Oncol.* 2018; 7(2):CNS16.
3. Levin VA, Prados MD, Yung WK, Gleason MJ, Ictech S, Malec M. Treatment of recurrent gliomas with eflornithine. *J Natl Cancer Inst.* 1992; 84(18):1432-1437.
4. Yam N, Levin J, Bao Z, Qian W, Levin VA. Effect of eflornithine on mutation frequency in temozolomide-treated U87MG cells. *Oncotarget.* 2020; 11(44):3933-3942.
5. Levin VA, Hess KR, Choucair AK, et al. Final report for evaluable patients treated on DM92-035, phase III randomized study of post-irradiation PCV versus DFMO-PCV, for anaplastic gliomas (AG). *Neuro Oncol.* 2012; 14(Supplement 6):vi74.
6. Levin VA, Jochec JL, Shantz LM, Aldape KD. Relationship between ornithine decarboxylase levels in anaplastic gliomas and progression-free survival in patients treated with DFMO-PCV chemotherapy. *Int J Cancer.* 2007; 121(10):2279-2283.
7. Levin VA, Uhm JH, Jaeckle KA, et al. Phase III randomized study of postradiotherapy chemotherapy with alpha-difluoromethylornithine-procarbazine, N-(2-chloroethyl)-N'-cyclohexyl-N-nitrosurea, vincristine (DFMO-PCV) versus PCV for glioblastoma multiforme. *Clin Cancer Res.* 2000; 6(10):3878-3884.
8. Levin VA, Hess KR, Choucair A, et al. Phase III randomized study of postradiotherapy chemotherapy with combination alpha-difluoromethylornithine-PCV versus PCV for anaplastic gliomas. *Clin Cancer Res.* 2003; 9(3):981-990.

Academic Awards and Honors

1977   American Cancer Society Faculty Award for 1977-1981

1982   Medal of the Tokyo Society of Medical Sciences and
Faculty of Medicine of Tokyo University, 1982

1985   Guy Odom Lecturer, Duke University

1987   Distinguished Lecturer, Hipple Cancer Research Center
and Dayton Oncology Society

1987   Stanley N. Gore Memorial Lecture, 7th International
Conference on Brain Tumor Research and Therapy

1988   Farber Foundation Award in Neuro-Oncology, Farber
Foundation

1990   David A. Frommer Memorial Lecture in Neuro-Oncology,
Harvard Medical School, Boston

1991   Fred Plum Lecturer, University of Washington School
of Medicine

1993   Masters in Oncology Series Visiting Professor, University
of Wisconsin Clinical Cancer Center

1997   Heath Memorial Award for Cancer Care, MD Anderson
        Cancer Center

1997   First Annual Takao Hoshino Lecturer in USA, Department
        of Neurological Surgery, University of California
        San Francisco

1997   First Annual Takao Hoshino Lecturer in Japan, Japan
        Neurological Society

1999   Gerry Pencer Memorial Lecture, Princess Margaret
        Cancer Centre, University of Toronto

2001   Anne C. Brooks Award, Department of Neurosurgery,
        MD Anderson Cancer Center

2001   Burkhardt Visiting Lecture Award, The Cleveland Clinic

2002   Gold Medal Award for Extraordinary Achievement,
        Society for Neuro-Oncology

2009   Lifetime Award as Professor Emeritus, Department of
        Neuro-Oncology, MD Anderson Cancer Center

Acknowledgements

There have been many people who have helped and encouraged me in, what has become, a writing process of more than fifteen years. My initial goal was to write a history of neuro-oncology. To that end, I solicited observations, experiences, and individual histories from colleagues. Since I received few responses, it became clear that I would have to do my own research and documentation. About this time, I was talking to Jo Barrett, the daughter of one of my patients. Jo, a lawyer by education, was a published author and encouraged me to start writing about experiences and encounters that I felt were important to the field of neuro-oncology and to avoid the chronology of events. I took her advice and started to write vignette after vignette based on experiences and observations. She read some of my writing and encouraged me to continue, but I soon realized that I was writing more of a memoir than an objective history of neuro-oncology. The next pivotal help I received was from Suzanne Sherman, an author, editor, and veteran publishing professional. She reviewed and edited a late book draft and suggested I forget trying to write a combined history of neuro-oncology and my memoir but focus on writing a memoir and that is how this book came to be.

Members of my family have helped and added needed information. My wife, Ellen, has encouraged me from the beginning and supported me when I would get frustrated with the slow pace of memoir writing and editing. She has always admonished me because of my lack of patience which led to her suggestion for the title of the memoir, *Patients but no Patience*. Ellen also edited the book twice and each time providing me chapter by chapter comments, suggestions, and changes that improved the book.

My son, Jason, has also been a pillar of support and has edited and advised on chapters, events, and people that he recalls from our overlapping lives in Houston and the San Francisco Bay area. My daughter, Lisa, also urged me to create more family scenes and historical context and encouraged me to use the picture for the book cover. My older sister, Laurie, carefully edited and helped with our family history in Milwaukee where we grew up and my younger sister, Deborah, supported my effort and added family anecdotes for the book.

I also leaned on Joann Aaron, a science editor and colleague at MD Anderson who I had hired for the Department of Neuro-Oncology and who had worked with me on manuscripts for scientific journals as well as the second edition of my textbook, *Cancer in the Nervous System*. In retirement, Joann gladly gave of her time and expertise to further help to improve the memoir and, in addition, provide additional insights from our years working together at the MD Anderson Cancer Center.

CPSIA information can be obtained
at www.ICGtesting.com
Printed in the USA
BVHW060515110922
646601BV00005B/20